W9-AGV-823

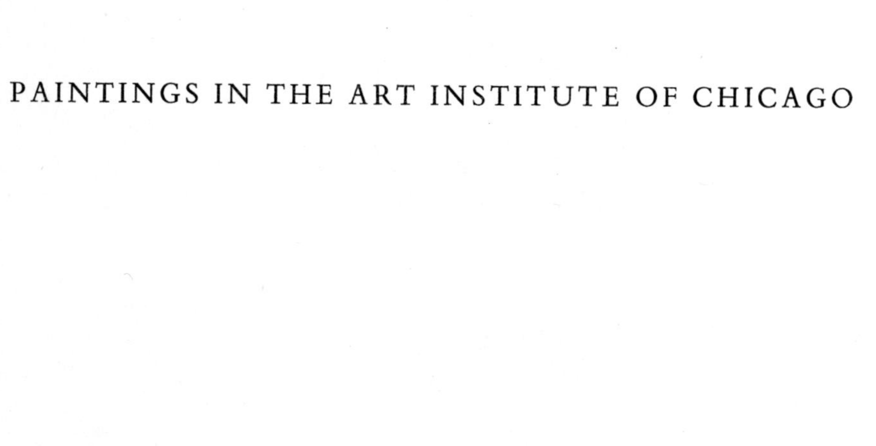

PAINTINGS IN THE ART INSTITUTE OF CHICAGO

PAINTINGS

IN THE ART INSTITUTE OF CHICAGO

A Catalogue of the Picture Collection

Printed in the Netherlands

Library of Congress Catalog Card Number: 61-6403

ILLUSTRATIONS

CATALOGUE

ADAMS, Wayman ~ *b. 1883 Muncie, Ind.*

Wayman Adams, portrait painter, studied at The John Herron Art Institute in Indianapolis, with William Merritt Chase in Florence, and Robert Henri in Spain.

JOSEPH PENNELL

Painted about 1913, signed: Wayman Adams.
Oil on canvas, 50⅛×43 in. (132.5×109.3 cm.)
Friends of American Art Collection, 18.293

Ref: International Studio *77: 89, May 1923;* Arts in Philadelphia *1: 7, May 1939*

CHARLES H. WORCESTER

Painted about 1920, signed: Wayman Adams.
Oil on canvas, 38⅛×32⅛ in. (96.9×81.6 cm.)
Charles H. and Mary F. S. Worcester Collection, 47.51

Mr. Worcester (1864–1956) served as a Trustee of the Art Institute from 1925 and was made Honorary President in 1938. He was one of the greatest benefactors of the Art Institute and gave jointly with his wife a large collection to the museum.

ADRION, Lucien ~ *b. 1889 Strasbourg*

PLACE DE L'OPERA, PARIS

Painted about 1920, signed: Adrion. Oil on panel, 23⅜×28¾ in. (59.4×73 cm.)
Gift of Joseph Winterbotham, 54.1352

ALBERS, Josef ~ *b. 1888 Bottrop, Germany*

Albers studied and then taught at the Bauhaus in Weimar and Dessau. In 1933 he was the first of the Bauhaus artists to settle in this country. Starting out as a designer for glass windows, Albers developed a style which he prefers to describe as "presentational" rather than "abstract."

HOMAGE TO THE SQUARE: LIGHT PASSAGE

Signed on the back, painted in 1956. Oil on board, 36×36 in. (91.5×91.5 cm.)
Gift of the Society for Contemporary American Art, 57.161

ALBRIGHT, Ivan Le Lorraine ~ *b. 1897 Chicago*

Albright had a wide and diverse training at Northwestern University, the School of the Art Institute, the Pennsylvania Academy of the Fine Arts, the National Academy of Design and the Ecole des Beaux-Arts in Paris.

THAT WHICH I SHOULD HAVE DONE I DID NOT DO Illus. p. 388

Painted between 1931 and 1941, signed and dated: Ivan Le Lorraine Albright, 1941.
Oil on canvas, 97 × 36 in. (246.5 × 91.5 cm.)
The Art Institute of Chicago, 55.645

HEAVY THE OAR TO HIM WHO IS TIRED, HEAVY THE COAT, HEAVY THE SEA

Painted between 1928 and 1929, signed: Ivan Le Lorraine Albright.
Oil on canvas, $53\frac{3}{8} \times 34\frac{1}{4}$ in. (135.6 × 87 cm.)
Gift of Mr. and Mrs. Earle Ludgin, 59.12

PORTRAIT OF MARY BLOCK

Signed and dated: Ivan Albright 1955–57. Oil on canvas, $39\frac{1}{8} \times 30$ in. (99.5 × 76.3 cm.)
Gift of Mr. and Mrs. Leigh B. Block, 59.7

ALEXANDER, John White ~ *b. 1856 Allegheny City, Pa. d. 1915 New York City*

After working briefly as an illustrator for *Harper's Weekly,* Alexander went to Munich in 1877 for study. He developed a fluid style which gained him great popularity as a portrait painter.

SUNLIGHT

Signed and dated: John W. Alexander '09. Oil on canvas, $83\frac{1}{4} \times 55\frac{1}{4}$ in. (203.5 × 140.4 cm.)
Friends of American Art Collection, 10.307

AMERICAN SCHOOL, 18th century

BOY WITH DOG

Painted about 1780–1800. Oil on canvas, $29\frac{7}{8} \times 24\frac{3}{4}$ in. (76 × 63 cm.)
Gift of Robert Allerton, 38.1333

BOY WITH LAMB AND BOOK

Painted about 1780–1800. Oil on canvas, $30 \times 25\frac{1}{16}$ in. (76.3 × 63.7 cm.)
Gift of Robert Allerton, 38.1334

Sons of Captain Samuel Hallett, of Hallett's Cove, Hellgate Neck, Newtown (now Astoria), Long Island, a Loyalist who moved to New Brunswick or Nova Scotia at the end of the Revolution. These two portraits of the Hallett boys were probably painted by the same hand.

MRS. NOAH SMITH AND FAMILY

Oil on canvas, $65\frac{1}{4} \times 84\frac{1}{8}$ in. (165.8 × 213.7 cm.)
Gift of Joseph Winterbotham, 54.311

Copy of a group portrait painted by Ralph Earl in Bennington, Vermont, in 1798, and now in a private collection. The children are, from left to right, Harry, Daniel, Noah, Eliza and Celia.

AMERICAN SCHOOL, 19th century

FARM SCENE WITH HOUSE AND FIGURE

Painted about 1810. Oil on panel, 23 × 36⅛ in. (58.6 × 91.8 cm.)
Gift of Robert Allerton, 46.391

This was painted by a comparatively untrained artist who, like hundreds of others, was in demand in rural areas to do tavern signs, decorative overmantels or "perspective views of gentlemen's country seats."

Ref: Prime, A. C., The Arts and Crafts in Philadelphia, Maryland and South Carolina, 1721–1785, *1929, p. 9; Ford, A.,* Pictorial Folk Art, New England to California, *1949, p. 102 (ill.)*

ELIZABETH PATTERSON

Painted about 1815. Oil on canvas, 11 × 9 in. (28 × 22.8 cm.)
Gift of Emily Crane Chadbourne, 53.8

An inscription on the back of the painting identifies the sitter as Elizabeth Patterson, the wife of Jérôme Bonaparte.

PORTRAIT OF A CAPTAIN

Painted about 1820. Oil on canvas, 22¼ × 18 in. (56.6 × 45.8 cm.)
Gift of Robert Allerton, 36.158

CORNELIUS ALLERTON

Painted about 1825. Oil on canvas, 32⅝ × 27½ in. (82.9 × 70 cm.)
Gift of Robert Allerton, 46.394

MRS. CORNELIUS ALLERTON

Painted about 1825. Oil on canvas, 33¾ × 27½ in. (85.8 × 70 cm.)
Gift of Robert Allerton, 46.395

Dr. and Mrs. Cornelius Allerton were the great-grandparents of Robert Allerton, Honorary President and Benefactor of the Art Institute and a distinguished collector.

PORTRAIT OF A YOUNG LADY

Painted about 1830. Oil on panel, 17 × 13⅛ in. (43.3 × 33.4 cm.)
Art Institute Purchase Fund, 42.294

This portrait is said to have been painted in the vicinity of Albany, New York.

PORTRAIT OF A GENTLEMAN

Painted about 1830. Oil on panel, 28⅝ × 21⅝ in. (71.2 × 55 cm.)
Gift of Robert Allerton, 46.392

This portrait, done by some local craftsman, was probably painted in Philadelphia about 1830.

PORTRAIT OF A LADY

Painted about 1830. Oil on panel, 28⅝ × 21⅞ in. (71.2 × 55 cm.)
Gift of Robert Allerton, 46.393

Companion to the *Portrait of a Gentleman* above.

LITTLE GIRL WITH PANTALETTES

Painted about 1830. Oil on canvas, 36½ × 28½ in. (92.8 × 72.5 cm.)
Gift of Colonel Leon Mandel, 45.289

The portrait is typical of the work of itinerant portrait painters who, after painting the costumes in advance, went from door to door fitting the sitters' faces above the costumes they preferred.

FRUIT AND BOTTLE

Painted about 1830–1840. Oil on canvas, 13¾ × 12⅛ in. (35 × 30.8 cm.)
Gift of Emily Crane Chadbourne, 53.11

WOMAN IN A BLUE DRESS

Painted about 1840. Oil on canvas, 12⅞ × 10 in. (32.6 × 25.5 cm.)
Gift of Emily Crane Chadbourne, 53.9

On the back of the picture is an inscription: Emma C. Emberry (?), Brooklyn, N.Y. This is presumably the name of the sitter.

GEORGE WASHINGTON ON HORSEBACK

Painted between 1840 and 1850. Oil on canvas, 72 × 54 in. (182.9 × 137.2 cm.)
Gift of Emily Crane Chadbourne, 52.996

A copy after a painting by Thomas Sully.

BOSTON COMMON

Painted about 1865. Oil on canvas, 17⅛ × 21 in. (43.6 × 53.5 cm.)
Art Institute Purchase Fund, 42.293

MR. WILLIAM M. RYSDYK AND HAMBLETONIAN

Painted after 1876. Oil on canvas, 24½ × 29½ in. (62.4 × 75 cm.)
Gift of Mrs. Rudyerd Boulton, 50.1358

J. H. Wright painted Hambletonian with his owner in 1865. This painting was lithographed for Currier & Ives by Louis Maurer, a print which was copyrighted in 1876. The present picture is a rendition of the subject probably done from the lithograph.

ANDERSON, Karl ~ *b. 1874 Oxford, Ohio*

Anderson was a student of John Vanderpoel at the School of the Art Institute and later attended the Académie Colarossi in Paris. The strongest influence on his style was French Impressionism.

THE CORAL NECKLACE

Signed and dated: Karl Anderson, 1918. Oil on canvas, 29 × 27 in. (73.7 × 68.7 cm.)
Gift of Mr. and Mrs. Charles S. Dewey, Jr., 44.212

ANDRE, Albert ~ *b. 1869 Lyon, France. d. 1954 Laudun, France*

In 1890 André began his studies with Adolphe Bouguereau and in 1894 first exhibited in the Salon des Indépendants. Strongly influenced by his friend Auguste Renoir, he closely followed the masters of Impressionism.

SQUARE DES BATIGNOLLES, PARIS

Painted 1893, signed: Albert André. Oil on canvas, 18½ × 25¾ in. (47.1 × 65.5 cm.)
Mr. and Mrs. Martin A. Ryerson Collection, 33.1108

BY THE SEA, DIEPPE

Painted 1896, signed: Alb. André. Oil on canvas, 17¾ × 20 in. (45.2 × 50.9 cm.)
Mr. and Mrs. Martin A. Ryerson Collection, 37.1015

WOMAN READING BEFORE A WINDOW

Painted 1903, signed: Alb. André. Oil on canvas, 22 × 13 in. (56 × 33 cm.)
Mr. and Mrs. Martin A. Ryerson Collection, 37.1013

ANDUZE

Painted 1910, signed: Albert André. Oil on canvas, 18½ × 24 in. (47.1 × 61.7 cm.)
Mr. and Mrs. Martin A. Ryerson Collection, 33.1103

André was visiting in Anduze in 1910 when he painted this picture.

CLAUDE MONET

Painted 1912, signed: Albert André. Oil on canvas, 51 × 38 in. (129.6 × 96.5 cm.)
The Stickney Fund, 23.149

AUTUMN MORNING

Painted 1913, signed: Albert André. Oil on canvas, 28¼ × 35⅝ in. (71.7 × 90.5 cm.)
Gift of Mrs. Bruce Borland, 53.339

AUGUSTE RENOIR

Painted 1914, signed: Albert André. Oil on canvas, 31⅞ × 25⅜ in. (81 × 64.5 cm.)
The Stickney Fund, 21.76

ANGAROLA, Anthony ~ *1893–1929 Chicago*

Angarola, a Chicago artist and pupil of Harry M. Walcott was awarded a Guggenheim Fellowship for study abroad. He was among the first Chicagoans to adopt stylized elements from Cubism.

THE MAIN TRAVEL ROAD, CAGNES, FRANCE

Painted in 1929, signed: Anthony Angarola. Oil on canvas, $24\frac{3}{4} \times 31\frac{1}{2}$ in. (63×80.2 cm.)
Gift of Yvonne and Richard Angarola, 30.121

ANISFELD, Boris ~ *b. 1879 Bieltsy, Russia*

Trained at the art academies of Odessa and Petrograd, Boris Anisfeld established his reputation as stage designer for the Imperial Russian Ballet. He taught for more than thirty years at the School of the Art Institute.

SELF PORTRAIT

Signed and dated: Boris Anisfeld, Capri, 1910. Oil on canvas, $24\frac{3}{8} \times 15\frac{5}{8}$ in. (62×39.8 cm.)
Wentworth G. Field Fund, 58.293

ARONSON, David ~ *b. 1923 Shilova, Lithuania*

Aronson studied with Karl Zerbe at the School of the Museum of Fine Arts in Boston where he learned the technique of encaustic painting.

THE LAST SUPPER

Painted 1944, signed: Aronson. Encaustic on pressed wood, 20×85 in. (50.9×215.9 cm.)
Gift of the Society for Contemporary American Art, 46.58

AUSTRIAN SCHOOL

THE CRUCIFIXION

Dated 1494. Oil on panel, $9\frac{3}{8} \times 6\frac{3}{4}$ in. (23.9×17.2 cm.)
Charles H. and Mary F. S. Worcester, Collection, 47.52

This small painting derives, perhaps, from the page of an illuminated manuscript. The painting is dated at the foot of the Cross.
Coll: Count Wilczek, Castle Kreuzenstein (near Vienna); Charles H. and Mary F. S. Worcester (1935)

Ref: Chicago. Art Institute, Catalogue of the Worcester Collection, *1938, cat. no. 31, pl. 23; Kuhn, C. L.,* Catalogue of German Paintings of the Middle Ages and Renaissance in American Collections, *1936, p. 74, cat. no. 322*

BACON, Francis ~ *b. 1910 Dublin, Ireland*

Francis Bacon had his first one-man show in 1949 in London.

HEAD SURROUNDED BY SIDES OF BEEF

Painted 1954. Oil on canvas, $50\frac{7}{8} \times 48$ in. (129.3×122 cm.)
Harriott A. Fox Fund, 56.1201

BAR, Bonaventure de ~ *1700–1729 Paris*

Little is known about this artist whose genre scenes show the strong influence of Watteau's style. In 1728 Bar was admitted to the Academy with Jean-Baptiste Chardin.

FETE CHAMPETRE

Painted about 1725. Oil on canvas, $18\frac{1}{8} \times 14\frac{1}{16}$ in. (46.2×35.7)
Gift of Mrs. Albert J. Beveridge, 53.334

The attribution to Bonaventure de Bar is tentative.
Coll: Ehrich Galleries, New York (sale, 1906); Joseph Satinover, Richmond, Va. (1921)

Ref: New York. Ehrich Galleries, Catalogue of the Ehrich Galleries Collection, *March 21, 1906, cat. no. 51;* Art News *26:5, December 10, 1921;* Art Quarterly, *Summer, 1954, pp. 184, 187*

BARTLETT, Frederic Clay ~ *b. 1873 Chicago. d. 1953 Beverly, Mass.*

Frederic Bartlett studied in Paris and Munich. When he returned to Chicago, he painted numerous mural decorations in churches, at the University Club and at the Art Institute. He was influenced by the French Impressionists and later by Van Gogh. In 1926 he gave to the Art Institute in memory of his wife *The Helen Birch Bartlett Memorial Collection* of Post-Impressionist paintings.

BLUE RAFTERS

Painted about 1919, signed: Frederic Clay Bartlett.
Oil on canvas, 28×30 in. (71.2×76.3 cm.)
Friends of American Art Collection, 19.107

The painting shows Helen Birch Bartlett at her summer home.

BARTOLOMEO DI GIOVANNI ~ *Active in Florence late 15th Century*

Bartolomeo was a pupil and collaborator of Domenico Ghirlandaio. He was also influenced by Sebastiano Mainardi and Piero di Cosimo. The only known date in Bartolomeo's life is that of the commission given to him in 1488 to paint part of an altar, *The Adoration of the Magi,* for the Hospital Church of the Innocents in Florence, on which Ghirlandaio was also working.

THE BIRTH OF SAINT JOHN THE BAPTIST

Painted about 1490. Tempera on panel, 35½×67 in. (90.2×170.2 cm.)
Mr. and Mrs. Martin A. Ryerson Collection, 37.996

Presumably this panel was the front of a chest.
Coll: Grassi, Florence (1924)

Ref: Van Marle, R., The Development of the Italian Schools of Painting, *1931, XII, p. 441 (note); XIII, p. 122 (fig. 76, p. 124 as Benedetto Ghirlandajo); Berenson, B.,* Pitture Italiane del Rinascimento, *1936, vol. 2, p. 5*

BARTON, Minette ~ *b. Minneapolis, Minn.*

THE HORSE MARKET

Signed upper right: Minetta Barton. Oil on canvas, 15½×17½ in. (39.5×44.5 cm.)
Gift of Cyrus McCormick, Jr., 28.1620

BASSANO, Jacopo ~ *1510/18–1592 Bassano, Italy*

Jacopo da Ponte, known as Bassano from his native town in the province of Venezia, was the son of Francesco da Ponte the Elder. He was trained by his father, studied briefly in Venice in the 1530's with Bonifazio Veneziano, and was strongly influenced by Titian and Tintoretto, as well as by Pordenone and Parmigianino. About 1540 he returned to Bassano.

PORTRAIT OF A BEARDED MAN Illus. p. 40

Painted about 1560. Oil on canvas, 42½×32 in. (108×81.3 cm.)
Charles H. and Mary F. S. Worcester Collection, 37.449

Ref: Chicago. Art Institute, Catalogue of the Worcester Collection, *1938, cat. no. 6A; Venice, Palazzo Ducale,* Jacopo Bassano, *1957, cat. no. 8, pp. 226–7 (ill.)*

ACTAEON AND THE NYMPHS

Painted probably between 1575 and 1600. Oil on canvas, 25×27 in. (63.6×68.7 cm.)
Charles H. and Mary F. S. Worcester Collection, 39.2239

There exist variations of this theme painted by other members of the family.

Ref: Huber and Rost, Manuel des Curieux et des Amateurs de l'Art, *1804, vol. 8, p. 146 (engraved by E. Fessard); Frölich-Bum, L.,* Burlington Magazine, *1932, p. 114; Suida, W.,* Belvedere *12: 197, 1934–1936; Chicago. Art Institute,* Bulletin *34: 94–96, 1940; Longhi, R.,* Arte Veneta, *1948, pp. 43–55; Venice. Palazzo Ducale,* Jacopo Bassano, *1957, cat. no. 60, pp. 150–151 (ill.)*

BATONI, Pompeo Girolamo ~ *b. 1708 Lucca. d. 1787 Rome*

Batoni was the leading painter of Rome in the eighteenth century, and a crucial figure in the formation of the neo-classical style. Though his fame now rests largely upon his superb portraits, he was in his time celebrated for his religious, mythological, and historical pictures.

SAINT ANDREW Illus. p. 51

Oil on canvas, 29⅛ × 24 in. (74 × 61 cm.)
Gift of the Joseph and Helen Regenstein Foundation, 60.50

Part of a set of the Lord and the Twelve Apostles, of which seven are in an English private collection, and five remained in Italy in 1960.

Coll: private collection, Forlì

BAZIOTES, William ~ *b. 1912 Pittsburgh, Pa.*

Baziotes studied at the Academy of Design in New York. He held his first one-man show in 1944.

CYCLOPS

Painted 1947, signed: Baziotes. Oil on canvas, 48 × 40 in. (122 × 101.7 cm.)
Walter M. Campana Memorial Prize, 47.468

BEAL, Gifford ~ *1879–1956 New York City*

Beal began his studies at the age of twelve with William Merritt Chase. He worked later under Henry Ward Ranger, Frank V. DuMond and George B. Bridgman.

THE PUFF OF SMOKE

Signed and dated: Gifford Beal '12. Oil on canvas, 36¼ × 48¼ in. (92.1 × 122.6 cm.)
Friends of American Art Collection, 12.1802

RECEPTION IN A PARK

Signed and dated: Gifford Beal '12. Oil on canvas, 23½ × 29½ in. (59.6 × 74 cm.)
George F. Porter Collection, 27.456

SPOTLIGHT (At the Hippodrome)

Signed and dated: Gifford Beal '15. Oil on canvas, 37⅞ × 46¾ in. (96.2 × 118.8 cm.)
Mr. and Mrs. Martin A. Ryerson Collection, 33.1182

BEAUX, Cecilia ~ *b. 1863 Philadelphia, Pa. d. 1942 Gloucester, Mass.*

Cecilia Beaux studied under William Sartain in Philadelphia, then went to the Académie Julian in Paris. She was strongly influenced by her compatriot, John Singer Sargent.

DANCING LESSON

Painted 1907, signed: Cecilia Beaux. Oil on canvas, 80×46¼ in. (203.2×117.2 cm.)
A. A. Munger Collection, 21.109

The two sisters who posed for this painting were Dorothea and Francesca, daughters of Richard Watson Gilder, editor of *Century Magazine.*

BECKMANN, Max ~ *b. 1884 Leipzig, Germany. d. 1950 New York City*

Beckmann studied at the Weimar Academy and later visited Paris and Florence. In 1925 he was appointed Professor of Painting at the Frankfurt Art School. In 1937 he left Germany to live in Amsterdam. Ten years later he came to America where he remained until his death. Here he taught painting at the School of Fine Arts, Washington University, St. Louis, at Colorado Springs and at the Brooklyn Museum School of Fine Arts.

SELF PORTRAIT Illus. p. 473

Painted and signed lower right: Beckmann, B. 37.
Oil on canvas, 75¾×35 in. (192.5×88.9 cm.)
Gift of Mr. and Mrs. Philip Ringer, 55.822

BECKWITH, James Carroll ~ *b. 1852 Hannibal, Mo. d. 1917 New York City*

Beckwith studied first at the National Academy of Design, then went to the Ecole des Beaux-Arts. He also took private lessons from Carolus-Duran and shared a studio with Sargent, who was then just beginning his studies in Paris. After returning to America, Beckwith was associated with William Merritt Chase as a teacher at the Art Students League.

THE AWAKENING

Painted about 1905, signed: Carroll Beckwith.
Oil on canvas, 35½×51¼ in. (90.2×130.3 cm.)
Gift of Chester Dale, 50.1355

BEECHEY, Sir William ~ *b. 1753 Burford, England. d. 1839 Hampstead, England*

In 1772 Beechey entered the School of the Royal Academy where he studied under Johann Zoffany. He first exhibited at the Academy in 1776; in 1793 he became painter to the Court.

PORTRAIT OF A LADY

Painted probably about 1805–1810. Oil on canvas, 72½×45 in. (184.2×114.4 cm.)
Friends of American Art Collection, 23.973

THOMAS KITE

Painted 1826. Oil on canvas, 29½ × 24½ in. (75 × 62.4 cm.)
Gift of Mrs. Franklin Rudolph, 23.145

Ref: Chicago. Art Institute, Bulletin *17: 56–58, 1924; Roberts, W.,* Sir William Beechey, R.A., *1907, p. 259*

BELLINI, Gentile (Immediate Circle of)

TWO ORIENTALS

Painted after 1480. Tempera on canvas, 26⅛ × 25 in. (66.4 × 63.6 cm.)
Charles H. and Mary F. S. Worcester Collection, 47.53

This painting of two Orientals is possibly a fragment of a larger painting, perhaps a portion of a wall decoration or a banner. It was probably painted by an artist who was strongly influenced by Gentile Bellini (1429?–1507), and who may well have been a member of his shop. Gentile, together with his brother Giovanni, became a leading figure of the 15th century Venetian School. He developed a refined and detached style of portraiture and was also the great chronicler of pageants and other events of the Venice of his day. In 1479 Gentile went to Constantinople at the invitation of Sultan Mohammed II. This picture presumably reflects this visit.
Coll: Paolo Giovio [?], Padua; Private Collection, Treviso; Carlo Foresti, Milan; Charles H. and Mary F. S. Worcester (1930)

Ref: Frankfurter, A. M., The Fine Arts *20: 14, 1933; Chicago. Art Institute,* Century of Progress Exhibition, *1934, cat. no. 43; Van Marle, R.,* The Development of the Italian Schools of Painting, *1935, XVII, pp. 154–5, fig. 87; Chicago. Art Institute,* Catalogue of the Worcester Collection, *1938, cat. no. 43; Toledo, Ohio; Museum of Art,* Four Centuries of Venetian Painting, *1940, cat. no. 5, pl. 5; Chicago. Art Institute,* Bulletin *41: 57, 1941*

BELLINI, Giovanni ~ *c. 1430–1516 Venice* (attributed to)

PORTRAIT OF A VENETIAN SENATOR

Painted about 1490. Oil on panel, transferred to canvas, 16⅞ × 13⅛ in. (42.9 × 33.4 cm.)
Max and Leola Epstein Collection, 54.280

The picture was attributed to Giovanni Bellini by Max Friedlaender and Wilhelm von Bode. Other scholars have called it a production by a follower.

BELLINI, Giovanni (School of) ~ *Venetian School, about 1480 or 1490*

MADONNA AND CHILD

Painted about 1480 or 1490. Oil on panel, 28 × 22 in. (71.2 × 56 cm.)
Charles H. and Mary F. S. Worcester Collection, 33.550

Coll: Carlo Ferrari [?], Turin; Papadopoli [?], Padua; Carlo Foresti, Milan; Charles H. and Mary F. S. Worcester (1930)

Ref: Chicago. Art Institute, A Century of Progress Exhibition, *1933, cat. no. 105; Van Marle, R.,* The Development of the Italian Schools of Painting, *1935, XV, p. 560 (note); XVII, p.p. 274–5, fig. 162; Chicago. Art Institute,* Catalogue of the Worcester Collection, *1938, cat. no. 5, pl. 9; Chicago. Art Institute,* Bulletin *41: 5, 1947*

BELLOWS, George Wesley ~ *b. 1882 Columbus, Ohio. d. 1925 New York City*

George Bellows studied painting under Robert Henri. He was progressive in his ideas, helped to organize the Armory Show in 1913, and was one of the founders of the Society of Independent Artists in 1916. He taught for a term in 1919 at the School of the Art Institute.

LOVE OF WINTER

Painted February 1914, signed: Geo. Bellows.
Oil on canvas, 32⅛ × 40 in. (81.6 × 101.7 cm.)
Friends of American Art Collection, 14.1018

This painting was done as a pendant to *A Day in June* (Detroit Institute of Arts).

MY MOTHER

Painted March 1921, signed: Geo. Bellows.
Oil on canvas, 83 × 49 in. (210.9 × 124.5 cm.)
The Frank Russell Wadsworth Memorial, 23.975

In doing this portrait of his mother, painted in Woodstock, N.Y., Bellows placed her in the setting of the Victorian parlor from their old home in Columbus, Ohio. In organizing the design he followed Jay Hambidge's theory of dynamic symmetry. An earlier version of the portrait is in the Columbus (Ohio) Gallery of Fine Arts.

BENSON, Frank Weston ~ *1862–1951 Salem, Mass.*

Benson studied at the School of the Museum of Fine Arts in Boston. After a period at the Académie Julian in Paris, he returned to Boston where he was an influential teacher for many years at the School of the Museum of Fine Arts.

RAINY DAY

Signed and dated: F. W. Benson 1906. Oil on canvas, 25 × 30 in. (63.6 × 76.3 cm.)
Friends of American Art Collection, 10.314

STILL-LIFE DECORATION

Signed and dated: F. W. Benson 22. Oil on canvas, 45 × 60 in. (114.4 × 152.5 cm.)
Wilson L. Mead Fund, 22.4449

BERMAN, Eugene ~ *b. 1889 St. Petersburg, Russia*

Berman, who studied in Paris with Edouard Vuillard and Maurice Denis, came to the United States in 1935.

BELLA VENEZIA

Signed and dated: 19 E. B. 45. Oil on canvas, 35×46 in. (88.9×116.9 cm.)
Ada S. Garrett Purchase Prize and Goodman Fund, 47.472

BERMEJO, Bartolomé ~ *Barcelona, active 1474–1495*

Bermejo, probably of Cordovan extraction, was active in Barcelona. While earlier paintings by this artist are known, his first documented work is dated 1474; he is last mentioned in 1495.

A SAINT

Painted about 1480. Oil on panel, 19×10¼ in. (48.3×26 cm.)
Mr. and Mrs. Martin A. Ryerson Collection, 47.393

This picture, once wrongly attributed to the French School, was first correctly identified by Post.
Coll: Private Collection, Treviso; Giovio, Padua

Ref: Iñiguez, D. A., Revista Española de Arte *12, anno 4: 302–3, 326, 1935; Post, C. R.,* A History of Spanish Painting, *1938, VII, part 2, p. 874*

BESNARD, Albert ~ *1849–1934 Paris*

Besnard's interest in his early youth was directed toward Ingres, but later he studied with Alexandre Cabanel and Jean Brémond. Besnard first exhibited in 1868. He was director of the Ecole des Beaux-Arts until 1932.

WOMAN'S HEAD (Repose)

Painted about 1890, signed: A. Besnard. Oil on cardboard, 19½×24 in. (49.7×61 cm.)
Potter Palmer Collection, 22.420

Ref: Chicago. World's Columbian Exposition. Official Catalogue, *1893, part X, Dept. K, cat. no. 2871; San Francisco. Panama-Pacific Exposition, 1915.* Fine Arts, French Section, *p. 98, cat. no. 254*

BY THE LAKE

Signed and dated: A. Besnard, 1923. Oil on canvas, 59×45 in. (149.9×114.4 cm.)
A. A. Munger Collection, 24.221

Ref: Mauclair, C., L'Art et les Artistes *18: 244, 1924 (ill. as* Baigneuses); *Chicago. Art Institute,* Bulletin *18: 62–63, 1924*

BETTS, Louis ~ *b. 1873 Little Rock, Ark.*

Betts was a pupil of William Merritt Chase and studied the old masters of Holland and Spain. His developed style follows with modifications the tradition of Sargent.

DR. FRANK WAKELEY GUNSAULUS

Painted about 1902, signed: Louis Betts. Oil on canvas, 65×41½ in. (165.2×105.4 cm.)
Gift of the Gunsaulus Family, 21.175

Dr. Gunsaulus, a distinguished Chicago clergyman, was so persuasive that a sermon he delivered at Plymouth Congregational Church induced Philip Armour to give $2,800,000 for the founding of Armour Institute. As a Trustee, he gave devoted service to the Art Institute and presented a notable collection of Wedgwood and Near Eastern pottery to the museum.

WILLIAM MERCHANT RICHARDSON FRENCH

Painted about 1905, signed: Louis Betts. Oil on canvas, 51×35 in. (129.6×88.9 cm.)
Gift of Mrs. William M. R. French, 08.46

Mr. French was a brother of the American sculptor, Daniel Chester French. After graduating from Harvard in 1864, he served in the Civil War. Afterward he took up engineering and landscape gardening. In 1867 he settled in Chicago and became secretary of the Chicago Academy of Design. On its founding in 1879 he was put in charge of the art collection of the Chicago Academy of Fine Arts, an organization which later became The Art Institute of Chicago.

CHARLES LAWRENCE HUTCHINSON

Painted about 1910, signed: Louis Betts. Oil on canvas, 45×36¼ in. (114.4×92.1 cm.)
Gift of Mrs. Charles L. Hutchinson, 28.659

Born in Lynn, Mass., Mr. Hutchinson came to Chicago in 1856 and entered the grain and banking business. He was one of the founders of the Art Institute and was elected its President in 1882. Besides devoting his services to the museum over a period of nearly half a century, Mr. Hutchinson became one of the museum's benefactors with a bequest of twenty paintings from his collection, among which were works by Nicolas Maes, Hals, Daubigny and Corot.

ELLA FLAGG YOUNG

Painted 1911. Oil on canvas, 75×40 in. (190.5×101.7 cm.)
Gift of Chicago Normal School Alumni, 22.4784

Ella Flagg Young was a well-known educator, served as superintendent of schools in Chicago from 1909 to 1915, and wrote several books on education.

MRS. MARTIN A. RYERSON

Signed and dated: Louis Betts 1912. Oil on canvas, 65⅜×37 in. (166.1×94 cm.)
Mr. and Mrs. Martin A. Ryerson Collection, 35.433

Caroline Hutchinson Ryerson was greatly interested in the work that her husband was doing to build up the collections and the prestige of the Art Institute, and together with her husband donated the Ryerson Library in 1901.

MARTIN ANTOINE RYERSON

Signed and dated: Louis Betts 1913. Oil on canvas, 66¼ × 38 in. (168.3 × 96.5 cm.)
Mr. and Mrs. Martin A. Ryerson Collection, 33.1183

Martin Ryerson was one of the leading figures in the early days of the Art Institute and served as a Trustee from 1890 until 1926, when he became Honorary President. He was one of America's most perceptive connoisseurs and gave to the Art Institute his entire collection, which covered a wide field from Giovanni di Paolo to Cézanne. Some of the Art Institute's greatest paintings are the result of his knowledge and generosity.

WILLIAM OWEN GOODMAN

Signed: Louis Betts, dated on back, 1913. Oil on canvas, 66⅛ × 39⅛ in. (168 × 99.5 cm.)
The William Owen and Erna Sawyer Goodman Collection, 38.1174

Mr. Goodman founded the Kenneth Sawyer Goodman Memorial Theatre of The Art Institute of Chicago in memory of his son Kenneth Sawyer Goodman (1883–1918), who died while serving in the Navy during the First World War. Kenneth had written thirty plays and was greatly interested in founding a theatre in Chicago.

THE SEA SHELL

Painted about 1928, signed: Louis Betts. Oil on canvas, 40¼ × 30⅜ in. (102.6 × 76.9 cm.)
Friends of American Art Collection, 28.815

BIERSTADT, Albert ~ *b. 1830 Solingen, Germany. d. 1920 New York City*

Born in Germany, Bierstadt was brought to New Bedford, Mass. as a baby. At twenty-one he went to Germany to study in Düsseldorf under Andreas Achenbach. He returned to America in 1858 and accompanied a military expedition to the West Coast. From sketches he made on this trip and many subsequent ones he painted in his studio a series of western panoramas.

ISLAND IN A SOUND Illus. p. 373

Painted about 1880, signed: A. Bierstadt. Oil on canvas, 29 × 43¾ in. (73.7 × 111.1 cm.)
Charles H. and Mary F. S. Worcester Collection, 45.188

This painting is developed from sketches made in the Nootka Sound, Vancouver Island.

BLAKELOCK, Ralph Albert ~ *b. 1847 New York City. d. 1919 Adirondack Mountains, N.Y.*

Blakelock trained as a physician but gave up medicine to become a painter.

THE VISION OF LIFE

Painted about 1895, signed: R. A. Blakelock. Oil on canvas, 21⅛ × 39⅜ in. (53.6 × 100 cm.)
Charles H. and Mary F. S. Worcester Collection, 47.55

BLANCHE, Jacques Emile ~ *b. 1861 Paris. c. 1942 Offranville, France*

Blanche was influenced by Manet, Whistler and Degas.

THE TRAVELER

Painted about 1890, signed: J. E. Blanche. Oil on canvas, 79¼ × 55 in. (201.3 × 139.7 cm.
Mr. and Mrs. Martin A. Ryerson Collection, 13.467

BLOCH, Albert ~ *b. 1882 St. Louis, Mo.*

Bloch studied in New York, then spent twelve years in Europe, largely in Munich where) he was closely associated with Franz Marc, Kandinsky and the Blue Rider group. From 1923 to 1947 he was Chairman of the Department of Painting of the School of Fine Arts at the University of Kansas.

THREE PIERROTS AND A HARLEQUIN

Painted 1914 in Munich, signed with monogram: A. B.
Oil on canvas, 39½ × 53⅛ in. (100.3 × 135 cm.)
Arthur Jerome Eddy Memorial Collection, 31.515

BLOOM, Hyman ~ *b. 1913 Brunaviski, Latvia*

Bloom moved to America while still a boy. In Boston, where his family settled, he, with Jack Levine, studied under Denman Ross in the Department of Fine Arts at Harvard. At the age of eighteen Bloom had already received extensive training as a draftsman but did not begin to paint until a year later.

ARCHAEOLOGICAL TREASURE

Painted about 1945. Oil on canvas, 43 × 36 in. (109.3 × 91.5 cm.)
Gift of Edgar Kaufmann, Jr., 55.825

BLUME, Peter ~ *b. 1906 Smorgon, Russia*

Blume came to the United States in 1911.

THE ROCK

Signed and dated: Peter Blume 1948. Oil on canvas, 58 × 74 in. (147.4 × 188 cm.)
Gift of Edgar Kaufmann, Jr., 56.338

BOHROD, Aaron ~ *b. 1907 Chicago*

Bohrod studied for two years at the School of the Art Institute and then at the Art Students League in New York where he was greatly impressed by the teaching of John Sloan.

WYOMING LANDSCAPE

Signed and dated: Aaron Bohrod 37. Oil on masonite, 22 × 29 in. (56 × 73.7 cm.)
Mr. and Mrs. Frank G. Logan Purchase Prize, 37.454

JOAN OF ARC AT MONTEBOURG

Painted 1944, signed: Aaron Bohrod. Oil on canvas, 24½ × 32 in. (62.4 × 81.3 cm.)
Mr. and Mrs. Frank G. Logan Purchase Prize, 45.191

Done during one of Bohrod's war assignments for *LIFE* magazine.

BOL, Ferdinand ~ *b. 1616 Dordrecht, Holland. d. 1680 Amsterdam.*

The son of a well-to-do Dordrecht family, Bol entered Rembrandt's studio soon after the master settled in Amsterdam in 1631.

PORTRAIT OF A WOMAN

Painted about 1655. Oil on canvas, 23¾ × 18⅛ in. (60.5 × 46.2 cm.)
Max and Leola Epstein Collection, 54.281

BONHEUR, Rosa ~ *b. 1822 Bordeaux, France. d. 1899 Melun, France*

CATTLE AT REST ON HILLSIDE IN THE ALPS

Signed and dated: Rosa Bonheur 1885. Oil on canvas, 21⅝ × 26⅛ in. (55 × 66.4 cm.)
A. A. Munger Collection, 01.451

BONINGTON, Richard Parkes ~ *b. 1801 Arnold, Nottinghamshire, England. d. 1828 London*

Bonington was strongly influenced by Baron Gros and by the work of his contemporary, Eugène Delacroix.

FRANCIS I AND MARGUERITE OF NAVARRE

Painted about 1825, signed: Bonington. Oil on canvas, 8¾ × 5 11/16 in. (22.3 × 14.4 cm.)
Simeon B. Williams Fund, 34.387
Coll: Sir John Fowler (sale, 1899)

BONNARD, Pierre ~ *b. 1867 Fontenay-aux-Roses. d. 1947 Paris*

Bonnard studied at the Académie Julian from 1888 to 1890. He became a member of the *Nabis,* a group influenced by Gauguin and the Symbolists, but his later development (with his friend, Vuillard) was toward a modified Impressionism known as *Intimisme.*

RED FLOWERS

Painted 1923, signed: Bonnard. Oil on canvas, 29½ × 19⅝ in. (75 × 50 cm.)
Gift of Mrs. Clive Runnells, 59.507

BONNAT, Léon ~ *b. 1833 Bayonne, France. d. 1922 Marchy-Saint-Eloi, France*
Bonnat studied with Federico Madrazo, director of the Prado in Madrid, and later with Léon Cogniet in Paris.

HENRY FIELD

Signed and dated: Ln. Bonnat, 1896. Oil on canvas, 51½×35¼ in. (130.9×89.5 cm.)
Henry Field Memorial Collection, 98.6

Mr. Field was an avid collector of paintings of the Barbizon School. His entire collection was given in his memory to the Art Institute by his widow in 1894. The present portrait was painted from a photograph after Mr. Field's death.

BONVIN, François ~ *b. 1817 Vaugirard, France. d. 1887 Saint-Germain-en-Laye, France*
Bonvin, self-taught, studied paintings by French masters in the Louvre, and was strongly influenced by French 18th century genre painting.

THE MAID

Painted about 1875, signed F. Bonvin. Oil on canvas, 17½×12⅛ in. (44.5×30.8 cm.)
Mr. and Mrs. Martin A. Ryerson Collection, 33.1110

BOSCH, Hieronymus ~ *about 1450–1516 's Hertogenbosch, Holland* (attributed to)
Little is known about the life of Hieronymus Bosch. He lived in 's Hertogenbosch, a small town in North Brabant. His early paintings and glass designs done there for the cathedral of St. John have now disappeared. Bosch, one of the most inventive of painters of all times, broke away in the early 16th century from the well-ordered tradition of Jan van Eyck, evolving a world of his own.

GARDEN OF PARADISE Illus. p. 143

Painted about 1509. Oil on panel, 10⅝×15 15/16 in. (27×40.6 cm.)
Robert A. Waller Fund, 36.239

Three scenes from the life of Adam and Eve: the Creation of Eve (foreground), the Temptation (left), and the Expulsion (right). In the center a fountain, the source of the Four Rivers of Paradise, pierces a raised plain surrounded by rocks and trees. This picture was attributed to Bosch by Max Friedlaender. In the catalogue of the Rotterdam exhibition of Bosch's work in 1936 it was called "an early Bosch before 1500." Charles de Tolnay and others do not agree with this attribution.

Ref: Rotterdam. Museum Boymans, Jeroen Bosch, Noord-Nederlandsche Primitieven, *1936, cat. no. 49, fig. 54; De Tolnay, C.,* Hieronymous Bosch, *1937, p. 104, cat. no. 52; Worcester, Mass. Art Museum,* Exhibition of Flemish Paintings, *1939, cat. no. 40 (ill.); Puyvelde, L. van,* Art News *37, pt. 1: 52, 1939 (ill.); Fraenger, W.,* Hieronymous Bosch, Grundzuege einer Auslegung, Das Tausendjaehrige Reich, *1947*

BOTKE, Jessie Arms ~ *b. 1883 Chicago*

Mrs. Botke was a pupil of Charles H. Woodbury, John C. Johansen and Albert Herter, and was commissioned to do murals in Ida Noyes Hall at the University of Chicago.

GEESE AND HOLLYHOCKS

Painted 1917, signed: Jessie Arms Botke. Oil on canvas, 28 × 35½ in. (71.2 × 90.2 cm.)
Friends of American Art Collection, 18.294

BOTTICELLI, Sandro ~ *1444–1510 Florence*

Alessandro Botticelli was probably trained by Fra Filippo Lippi, and influenced by Pollaiuolo, Verrocchio and Castagno.

MADONNA AND CHILD

Painted about 1470. Oil on panel, 33¾ × 23¼ in. (83.2 × 59.1 cm.)
Max and Leola Epstein Collection, 54.283

The present panel, which came from the Feral Collection in Paris, has been attributed to Botticelli by Adolfo and Lionello Venturi, Yukio Yashiro and Raymond van Marle.

BOTTICELLI, Sandro (attributed to)

MADONNA AND CHILD WITH ANGELS

Painted about 1490. Oil on panel, 13⅛ in. diameter (33.4 cm.) (tondo)
Max and Leola Epstein Collection, 54.282

BOUCHER, François ~ *1703–1770 Paris*

François Boucher, court painter to Louis XV, while still a pupil of François Lemoyne was commissioned to do murals for the Paris Opera in collaboration with the young Carle van Loo. In 1755 he was made Director of the Gobelins tapestry manufactory and ten years later became court painter.

BATHING NYMPH

Painted about 1740. Oil on canvas, 16¾ × 18½ in. (41.5 × 46.8 cm.)
Wilson L. Mead Fund, 31.938

BOUDIN, Eugène ~ *b. 1824 Honfleur, France. d. 1898 Paris*

Boudin was a pupil of Isabey. He was also influenced by Corot, Jongkind and Courbet.

APPROACHING STORM

Signed and dated: E. Boudin 1864. Oil on panel, 14⅜ × 22¾ in. (36.6 × 57.9 cm.)
Gift of Annie Swan Coburn to the Mr. and Mrs. Lewis L. Coburn Memorial Collection, 38.1276
Coll: Mrs. Meredith Hare (sale, New York); Chester H. Johnson (sale, 1929)

Ref: Chicago. Art Institute, Bulletin *33: 79–80, 1939*

SEASHORE

Painted in 1890's, signed: E. Boudin. Pastel on canvas, 7½ × 11¾ in. (19.1 × 29.8 cm.)
Gift of Kate L. Brewster, 50.117
Coll: Chester H. Johnson (1929); Mr. and Mrs. Walter S. Brewster, Chicago

BOUGUEREAU, William Adolphe ~ *1825–1905 La Rochelle, France*

Bouguereau went to Paris in 1846 and after four years there won the Grand Prix de Rome. He worked in Italy until his return to Paris in 1855 to participate in the great Exposition Universelle.

THE BATHERS

Signed and dated: W. Bouguereau 1884. Oil on canvas, 79 × 50¾ in. (200.7 × 128.9 cm.)
A. A. Munger Collection, 01.458

Ref: Menard, R., Portfolio *6: 44, 1875; Browne, F. C.,* Brush and Pencil *3: 2 (plate facing p. 9), 1898;* Sketch Book *5: (ill. opp. p. 30), September 1905*

BOURDON, Sébastien ~ *b. 1616 Montpellier. d. 1671 Paris*

Bourdon studied in Paris with Jean Barthélemy. In 1634, he visited Italy; in Rome, he was influenced by Poussin. Bourdon was one of the founders of the Academy, and from 1652 to 1654 was painter to the court of Queen Christina of Sweden.

CHRIST RECEIVING THE LITTLE CHILDREN

Oil on canvas, 40¼ × 52¾ in. (134 × 102.2 cm.)
Gift of Mrs. Morton Zurcher, 59.57

A smaller version of this same composition is in the Louvre.

Coll: Robert Frank, Bristol, England; Robert D. Brewster, N.Y.; S. Preston, N.Y.

Ref: Bristol (Eng.) Museum and Art Gallery, Exhibition of French Art, 1600–1800, *1938, no. 3A;* Catalogue of European and American Paintings 1500–1900, *N.Y., 1948, p. 48, no. 63; Yale University Art Gallery,* Pictures Collected by Yale Alumni, *1956, no. 7, pl. 7*

BRANCUSI, Constantin ~ *b. 1876 Rumania. d. 1957 Paris*

SKETCH OF A CHILD

Probably painted 1907–1909, signed: C. Brancusi.
Oil on board, 23⅞ × 11⅜ in. (60.8 × 28.9 cm.)
Gift of Joseph Winterbotham, 54.1353

BRANGWYN, Frank ~ *b. 1867 Bruges, Belgium. d. 1956 Ditchling, England*

Probably better known as an etcher and craftsman, Brangwyn had a varied and interesting training. He studied at the South Kensington Art School, was a pupil of William Morris, and traveled a great deal in the Orient.

ITALIAN PAINTINGS

XIIIth—XVIIIth Centuries

ILLUSTRATIONS

Opposite: Reni, Guido, Salome with the Head of the Baptist
Frank H. and Louise B. Woods Purchase Fund

Meliore Toscano, Madonna and Child Enthroned, c. 1270
Mr. & Mrs. Martin A. Ryerson Collection

Opposite: Master of the Bigallo Crucifix, c. 1240–70
A. A. Munger Collection

IC XC

Giovanni di Paolo, Saint John in the Wilderness (two scenes from a set of six), c. 1450–60

Giovanni di Paolo, Saint John in Prison
Mr. & Mrs. Martin A. Ryerson Collection

Veronese, Paolo, Creation of Eve, c. 1570. Charles H. & Mary F. S. Worcester Collection

Opposite: Crespi, Giuseppe Maria, Marriage at Cana, c. 1685. Wirt D. Walker Fund

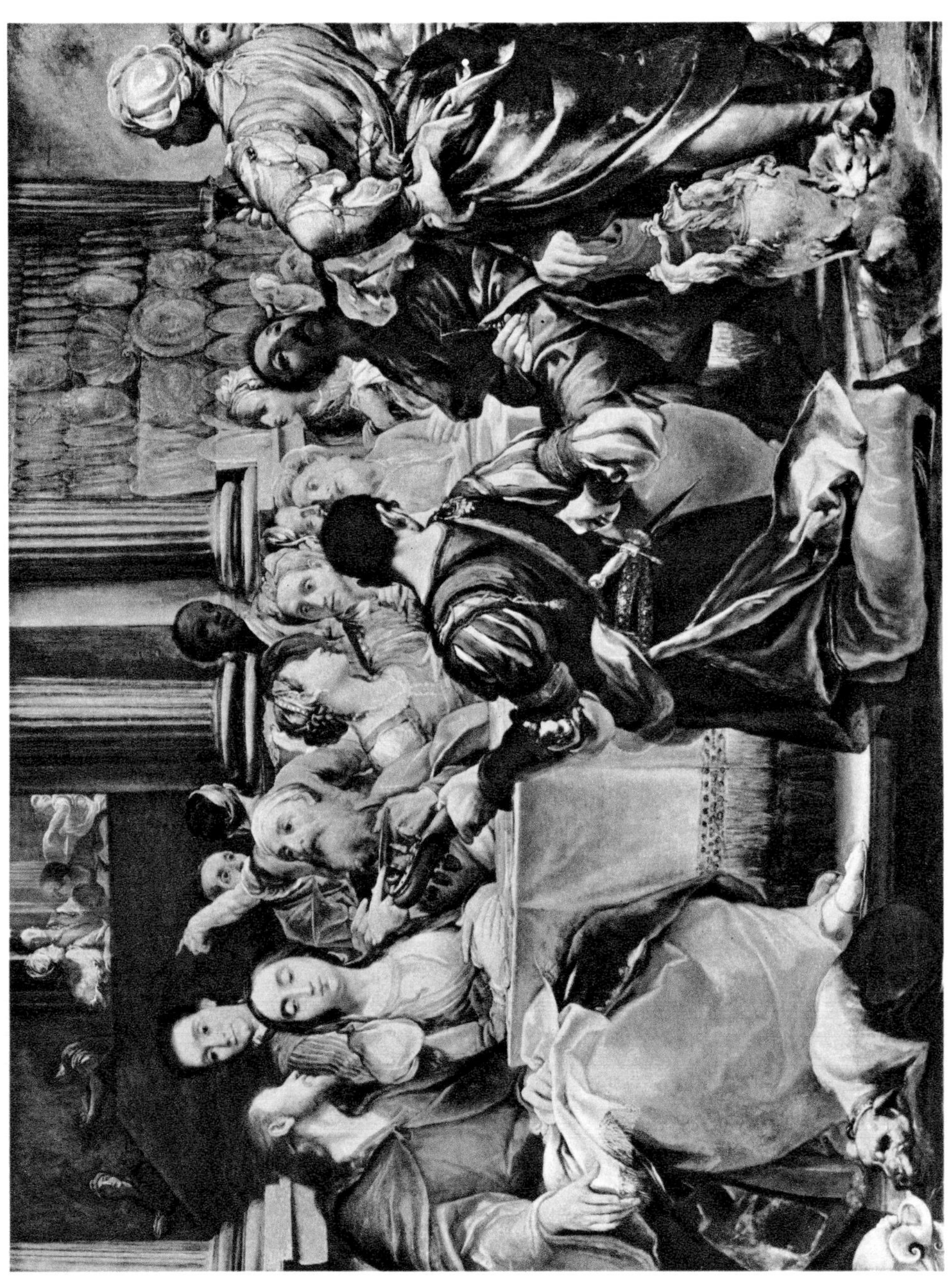

Bassano, Jacopo, Portrait of a Bearded Man, c. 1560
Charles H. and Mary F. S. Worcester Collection

Ghirlandaio, Ridolfo, Portrait of a Gentleman of Florence, c. 1550
Mr. & Mrs. Martin A. Ryerson Collection

Tintoretto, Jacopo, Tarquin and Lucretia, c. 1560. Art Institute Purchase Fund

Cambiaso, Luca, Venus and Cupid, c. 1570–75. A. A. Munger Collection

Tiepolo, Giovanni Battista, Rinaldo Enchanted by Armida (two scenes from a set of four), c. 1755

Tiepolo, Armida Abandoned by Rinaldo. Gift of James Deering

Moroni, Giovanni Battista, Ludovico Madruzzo, c. 1560
Charles H. and Mary F. S. Worcester Collection

Opposite:
Piazzetta, Giovanni Battista, Pastoral Scene, c. 1740
Charles H. and Mary F. S. Worcester Collection

Chimenti, Jacopo (Jacopo da Empoli), A Widow of the Medici Family
Frank H. and Louise B. Woods Purchase Fund

Cecco del Caravaggio, The Resurrection, c. 1600
Charles H. and Mary F. S. Worcester Collection

Batoni, Pompeo, Saint Andrew
Gift of the Joseph & Helen Regenstein Foundation

Opposite:
Strozzi, Bernardo, An Episcopal Saint, c. 1630–40. Alexander A. McKay Fund

Italian School, 17th Century, Portrait of an Officer, c. 1650
Mr. & Mrs. Martin A. Ryerson Collection

Tiepolo, Giovanni Domenico, Head of a Patriarch, c. 1750–75
Gift of Mrs. Richard E. Danielson and Mrs. Chauncey McCormick

Guardi, Francesco, The Grand Canal, Venice, c. 1745. Wirt D. Walker Fund

Opposite: Magnasco, Alessandro, The Synagogue, c. 1734-49. Gift of Annie Swan Coburn to the Mr. & Mrs. Lewis L. Coburn Memorial Collection

Opposite: Manfredi, Bartolomeo, The Chastisement of Love, c. 1605–10
Charles H. and Mary F. S. Worcester Collection

PILOTS, PORT OF PASAJES, SPAIN

Painted about 1891, signed: Frank Brangwyn. Oil on canvas, 40 × 50 in. (101.7 × 127 cm.)
The Stickney Fund, 02.116

BRAQUE, Georges ~ *b. 1882 Argenteuil, France*

Braque first exhibited publicly at the Salon des Indépendants in 1906 with the Fauves. Derain, Vlaminck, Matisse and Dufy were also members of this group. Later he turned to Cubism.

STILL LIFE WITH GRAPES

Painted 1911, signed on reverse: Braque. Oil on canvas, 13 × 16 1/16 in. (33 × 41.5 cm.)
Gift of Grant J. Pick, 58.511

This painting was done in 1911 when Picasso and Braque were working together at Ceret.

STILL LIFE Illus. p. 467

Signed and dated: G. Braque 19. Oil on canvas, 19 7/8 × 36 3/8 in. (50.7 × 92.4 cm.)
The Joseph Winterbotham Collection, 29.764

Ref: Chicago. Art Institute, Bulletin *24: 3–4 (ill.), 1930; Chicago. Art Institute,* A Century of Progress Exhibition, *1933, cat. no. 768; Gallatin, A. E.,* Georges Braque, *1943, p. 21; Chicago. Art Institute,* The Winterbotham Collection, *1947, pp. 8–9*

FRUITS AND GUITAR

Painted 1938. Oil on canvas, 31 7/8 × 39 1/2 in. (127.5 × 71.5 cm.)
Gift of Mrs. Albert D. Lasker in memory of her husband, Albert D. Lasker, 59.505

BRETON, Jules ~ *b. 1827 Courrières, France. d. 1906 Paris*

Jules Breton was trained in the classical tradition of David, and from 1849, when he first showed in the Salon, continued for half a century to be a popular figure in painting.

THE SONG OF THE LARK

Signed and dated: Jules Breton, Courrières, 1884.
Oil on canvas, 43 1/2 × 33 3/4 in. (110.6 × 85.8 cm.)
Henry Field Memorial Collection, 94.1033

Ref: Dumas, G., Catalogue illustré du Salon, *Paris, 1885, no. 369; Michel, A.,* Gazette des Beaux-Arts *31: 490, 1885;* Brush and Pencil *3: 287 (ill.) 1898; Cluit, F. E.,* Brush and Pencil *18: 108, 1906; Vachon, M.,* Jules Breton, *1919, p. 145; Van Gogh, V.,* Letters to his Brother, *1927, vol. 2, p. 488 (mention)*

BRITISH SCHOOL, 16th century

HENRY VIII, ELIZABETH, AND EDWARD VI

Inscribed: A 1597 Professors and defendors of the True Catholicke Faythe.
Oil on panel, 33¼×26 in. (84.5×66.1 cm.)
Kate S. Buckingham Bequest, 38.311

BRITISH SCHOOL, 18th century

GENTLEMAN RECEIVING A LETTER

Painted about 1730–1740. Oil on canvas, 32×40 in. (18.3×101.7 cm.)
Gift of Emily Crane Chadbourne, 25.588
Coll: Earl Cowley, Draycott House, Chippenham, England; Curie Sale, Christie, New York, 1921, cat. no. 64

Ref: Sitwell, S., Conversation Pieces, *1936, pp. 73, 104, no. 85 (ill.); Detroit. Institute of Arts,* Exhibition of English Conversation Pieces of the Eighteenth Century, *1948, cat. no. 12 (ill.)*

FAMILY GROUP WITH A DEER

Painted about 1740. Oil on canvas, 44½×39¾ in. (113.1×101 cm.)
Gift of Emily Crane Chadbourne, 51.203

FAMILY GROUP ON A TERRACE

Probably painted between 1740 and 1750. Oil on canvas, 36½×46½ in. (92.8×118.2 cm.)
Gift of Emily Crane Chadbourne, 51.204

Ref: Edwards, R., Apollo *66: 90, 91 (ill.), October 1957*

RICHARD GIPPS

Painted about 1750. Oil on canvas, 49½×39½ in. (125.8×100.3 cm.)
Gift of the Antiquarian Society, 33.798

This portrait and the mantelpiece of which it is an integral part were removed from West Harling Hall in Norfolk County, England, when the house was dismantled.
Coll: West Harling Hall in Norfolk County, England

MONAMY AND WALKER (copy after Hogarth)

Painted in the 18th century. Oil on panel, 23¼×20½ in. (59.1×52.1 cm.)
A. A. Munger Collection, 26.264

Thomas Walker, a wealthy London collector, is depicted here inspecting a seascape by the British artist, Peter Monamy (1670–1749), in the painter's studio.

BRITISH SCHOOL, 19th century

BIRTH OF BACCHUS

Painted 1810. Oil on canvas, 15×31¾ in. (38.2×80.8 cm.)
Gift of Mrs. James Ward Thorne, 37.497

PORTRAIT OF A LADY

Painted about 1825. Oil on panel, 12 × 8⅞ in. (30.5 × 22.5 cm.)
Frederick T. Haskell Collection, 40.1164

This picture was painted by an artist of the school of Lawrence.

BRITTON, Edgar ~ *b. 1901 Kearney, Nebr.*

Britton went to the State University of Iowa and to the University of Kansas. He was one of the artists on the Art Project of the Chicago WPA where he acted as mural supervisor.

BLACK BARN

Signed and dated: Edgar Britton '33. Oil on canvas, 22 9/16 × 34¾ in. (57.6 × 88.3 cm.)
Gift of Leonard Florsheim, 42.306

BROOK, Alexander ~ *b. 1898 Brooklyn, N.Y.*

Alexander Brook studied at the Art Students League under John C. Johansen, Frank V DuMond and Kenneth Hayes Miller.

THE CHILDREN'S LUNCH

Signed and dated: A. Brook 1928. Oil on canvas, 36¼ × 40¼ in. (92.1 × 102.2 cm.)
Mr. and Mrs. Frank G. Logan Purchase Prize, 29.864

TWENTIETH CENTURY RUIN

Painted 1932, signed: A. Brook. Oil on canvas, 24⅞ × 36 in. (63.3 × 91.5 cm.)
Friends of American Art Collection, 38.16

BROWERE, Albertis de Orient ~ *b. 1814 Tarrytown, N.Y. d. 1887 Catskill, N.Y.*

Browere worked for a time with his father, who had gained a great reputation for his life masks of notable people.

MOUNTAIN LANDSCAPE AND THE FALLS OF SAN JOAQUIN

Painted about 1855. Oil on canvas, 25⅛ × 30⅛ in. (63.9 × 76.5 cm.)
Gift of Mrs. John H. Harmon and Mrs. Everett L. Millard in memory of their mother, Mrs. Charles T. Boynton, 41.823

BRUEGHEL, Jan ~ *1601–1678 Antwerp*

STILL LIFE: FLOWERS

Painted ca. 1630–1640. Oil on panel, 26 × 16 in. (66.1 × 40.8 cm.)
Gift of Arthur Keating, 48.570

STILL LIFE: FLOWERS

Painted ca. 1630–1640. Oil on panel, 26½ × 18¼ in. (67.4 × 46.5 cm.)
Gift of Arthur Keating, 48.571

BRUNAIS, Augustin ~ *active about 1763–1779*

Brunais, who was of French origin, spent some time in London (1777–1779), where he changed his first name to Austin. He exhibited in London in 1763 and became known through a series of prints on which his name is occasionally spelled Brunias. Some of his most interesting work was done in the West Indies.

A VIEW OF THE RIVER OF ROSEAU IN THE ISLAND OF DOMINICA

Painted about 1779. Oil on canvas, 33¼ × 62⅛ in. (84.5 × 157.9 cm.)
Gift of Emily Crane Chadbourne, 53.14

In 1779 Brunais exhibited at the Royal Academy in London a painting called *A View of the River of Roseau in the Island of Dominica.* He also did several prints, one of which, *The Negro Dance in the Island of Dominica,* shows three figures identical to some in the present painting. A photograph of the Bath Estate on the Island of Dominica, B. W. I., depicts the same range of mountains seen in the background of the painting, thus identifying the locality and indicating that this picture may well be the one exhibited in 1779. If so, it may have belonged to Sir William Young (died 1788), first Governor of Dominica.

BRUSH, George de Forest ~ *b. 1855 Shelbyville, Tenn. d. 1941 Hanover, N. H.*

Brush was a student at the National Academy of Design and then went to Paris to work under Jean Léon Gérôme. In the eighties he returned to this country, going west to Wyoming and Montana to do paintings of Indian life.

A FAMILY GROUP

Signed and dated: George de Forest Brush 1907.
Oil on canvas, 31¼ × 39½ in. (79.3 × 100.3 cm.)
Gift of Philip D. Armour, 08.7

The artist posed his own family for this group. Mrs. Brush (Mittie Whelpley of Boston) is shown with her only son Gerome (died 1954), and her youngest daughter, Thea (Mrs. T. H. Cabot, Jr.).

BRUYN, Bartel the Elder ~ *1493–1555 Cologne, Germany*

Until about 1530, Bruyn the Elder was under the influence of the Dutch painters, Jan Joest and Joos van Cleve. He later became interested in the Italian Renaissance as transmitted through Jan van Scorel.

MADONNA, SAINTS AND DONOR

Painted about 1525 or 1530. Oil on panel, 30⅞ × 22¾ in. (78.4 × 57.9 cm.)
Mr. and Mrs. Martin A. Ryerson Collection, 33.1063

The knightly Saint Gereon (a Roman officer martyred in Cologne about 304 A.D.) presents the Virgin and Child and St. Anne to the Donor, a canon regular of the Augustinian Order.
Coll: Neven, Cologne, 1879 (no. 2); Eduard F. Weber, Hamburg (sale Berlin 1912, cat. no. 64, pl. 29); Marczell von Nemes Collection, Budapest (sale, Paris 1913, no. 23); Mr. and Mrs. Martin A. Ryerson, Chicago, 1913

Ref: Düsseldorf, Germany, Exhibition of History of Art *[?], 1904, cat. no. 468; Shaefer, K.,* Kölner Malerei, *1923, no. 33 (pl. V); Chicago. Art Institute,* A Century of Progress Exhibition, *1933, cat. no. 6; Rich, D. C.,* American-German Review *1: no. 4, pp. 35–8, June 1935 (ill. p. 36); Kuhn, C. L.,* Catalogue of German Paintings of the Middle Ages and Renaissance in American Collections, *1936, cat. no. 18 (pl. V)*

BRUYN, Bartel the Younger ~ *1530–1610 Cologne, Germany*

Little is known about this painter except that he received his training from his father and that he was long associated with Cologne. He is noted for his crisp, clean-cut portraits with enamel-like flesh tones.

PORTRAIT OF A WOMAN WITH A PRAYERBOOK Illus. p. 149

Painted about 1560. Oil on panel, 18¼ × 13⅛ in. (46.5 × 33.4 cm.)
Charles H. and Mary F. S. Worcester Collection, 40.934

Ref: New York. Kleinberger Galleries, Catalogue of a Loan Exhibition of German Primitives, *1928, cat. no. 54 (ill.); Washburn Freund, F. E.,* Belvedere *8: 285, 1929; Chicago. Art Institute,* A Century of Progress Exhibition, *1933, cat. no. 7; Chicago. Art Institute,* Bulletin *27: 113, 1933;* American-German Review *1, no. 4, pl. opp. p. 3, June 1935; Kuhn, C. L.,* Catalogue of German Paintings of the Middle Ages and Renaissance in American Collections, *1936, p. 29, no. 43; Chicago. Art Institute,* Catalogue of the Worcester Collection, *1938, cat. no. 42 (pl. 30); Chicago. Art Institute,* Bulletin *35: 33–4 (ill.), 1941*

BURCH, Hendrik van der ~ *b. about 1614 Frankenthal, Germany. d. after 1678 Amsterdam*

Van der Burch studied under his father and developed a style which showing certain elements close to Vermeer was even more closely related to the work of Pieter de Hooch. In 1636 the great English art collector, Thomas Howard, second Earl of Arundel, met van der Burch, sent him to Italy for a year's study, then made him custodian of his collection. Later the artist returned to Holland, became a member of the painters' guild at Delft, and also worked in Leyden and Amsterdam.

THE TERRACE

Painted about 1660. Oil on canvas, 41⅜ × 33¾ in. (105.1 × 85.8 cm.)
Robert A. Waller Fund, 48.81
Coll: M. Fouquet, Amsterdam (before 1805); Prince Radziwill, Neiberow, 1803; Prince Sigismund Radziwill, Paris, 1866; Prince Georg Nichlaivich de Leuchtenberg, St. Petersburg; Leonard Gaw, Glasgow, 1935; Rhode Island School of Design, Providence, 1937

Ref: Valentiner, W. R., Pieter de Hooch, *c. 1929, p. 251 (ill.); Chicago. Art Institute,* Bulletin *63: 32–3, 1949; Cologne. Wallraf-Richartz Museum,* Park und Garten in der Malerei, *1957, cat. no. 8, ill. pl. 5*

BURG, Copeland Charles ~ *b. 1895 Livingston, Mont.*

Burg went to the University of Washington and then came to Chicago where for many years he was a newspaperman and critic. He took up painting as an avocation and, except for a few private lessons, is entirely self-taught.

FLOWERS AND FRUIT

Painted about 1938, signed: Copeland Burg. Oil on board, 24½ × 16¼ in. (62.4 × 41.1 cm.)
Anonymous Donor, 40.924

BURRI, Alberto ~ *b. 1915 Città di Castello, Italy*

Burri studied medicine in Perugia and began to paint when he was a prisoner of war in Texas. After the war he settled in Rome.

COLLAGE

Painted ca. 1952 [?] Oil and collage on canvas, 22¼ × 33¼ in. (56.6 × 84.5 cm.)
Gift of Dr. and Mrs. Harry O. Maryan, 55.824

BURROUGHS, Bryson ~ *b. 1869 Hyde Park, Mass. d. 1934 New York City*

Burroughs studied at the Art Students League in New York; then from 1890 to 1895 he attended the Ecole des Beaux-Arts. He was strongly influenced by the greyed color and stylized forms of Puvis de Chavannes. In 1909 he was made Curator of Painting at the Metropolitan Museum.

THE FISHERMAN

Signed and dated: Bryson Burroughs 1915. Oil on canvas, 24 × 36 in. (61 × 91.5 cm)
Friends of American Art Collection, 19.936

BUTINONE, Bernardino ~ *b. before 1436 Treviglio, Italy. d. after 1507*

Working in Treviglio and Milan, Butinone often collaborated with his fellow countryman, Bernardino Zenale. He was influenced by Vincenzo Foppa and also by Mantegna.

FLIGHT INTO EGYPT

Painted about 1480–1485. Tempera on panel, $10\frac{3}{16} \times 8\frac{11}{16}$ in. (26×22 cm.)
Mr. and Mrs. Martin A. Ryerson Collection, 33.1003

DESCENT FROM THE CROSS

Painted about 1480–1485. Tempera on panel, $10\frac{1}{4} \times 8\frac{1}{16}$ in. (26×20.6 cm.)
Mr. and Mrs. Martin A. Ryerson Collection, 33.1004

These two panels formed part of an altarpiece of the life of Christ; more panels of a similar type are now scattered in various other collections.
Coll: Comte de Malherbe Collection, Paris; Ryerson, Chicago, 1927

Ref: Chicago. Art Institute, Bulletin *21: 86–8, 1927; Siple, E. S.,* Burlington Magazine *51: 240–1, 1927 (pl. 1); Salmi, M.,* Dedalo *10: 347–51, 1929 (ill.); Venturi, L.,* Pitture Italiane in America, *1931 (pl. 326); Berenson, B.,* Italian Pictures of the Renaissance, *1932, p. 121; Chicago. Art Institute,* A Century of Progress Exhibition, *1933, cat. no. 82, 83;* Ibid., *1934, cat. no. 25, 26; Zeri, F.,* Burlington Magazine *97: 74–7, March 1955*

BUTLER, Edward Burgess ~ *b. 1853 Lewiston, Me. d. 1928 Pasadena, Calif.*

Edward Burgess Butler was a prominent Chicago business executive who served as a Governing Life Member and Trustee of the Art Institute from 1887 until his death. He contributed to the museum's endowment and presented a large collection of paintings by George Inness. Mr. Butler studied painting with Frank Peyraud.

CLEARING UP, LONG ISLAND SOUND

Signed and dated: Edward B. Butler, 1917. Oil on canvas, 25×30 in. (63.6×76.3 cm.)
Edward B. Butler Collection, 19.189

CAMBIASO, Luca (Luchetto da Genova) ~ *b. 1527 Moneglia, Italy. d. 1585 Madrid*

Luca Cambiaso, son of Giovanni, a provincial painter, was born in a small town near Genoa. His father started him at an early age copying the drawings of Mantegna, with the result that Luca at fifteen was not only a brilliant draftsman but also a capable painter. He remained in Genoa for many years executing a prodigious number of frescoes and easel paintings. Like most Italian artists of the period, he visited Florence and Rome, where he greatly admired the works of Raphael and Michelangelo. Luca was much influenced by Pierino del Vaga, the Florentine who assisted Raphael in Rome and later worked in the Doria Palace in Genoa. The Venetian influences in Luca's work are due to Pordenone, who also worked in Genoa. In 1575 Luca went to Rome and in 1583 Philip II called him to Spain where before his death he worked on the dome of San Lorenzo el Real at the Escorial.

VENUS AND CUPID Illus. p. 43

Painted between 1570–1575. Oil on canvas, $42\frac{3}{8} \times 37\frac{3}{4}$ in. (107.7×95.9 cm.)
A. A. Munger Collection, 42.290

Coll: William Paton, (Christie Sale, February 1783); Sir Abraham Hume; Earl of Brownlow; unidentified Italian Collection; William Suida

Ref: Torriano, P., Illustrazione Italiana, *Year IV, 1927, pp. 522–3 (ill.); Labò, M.,* Mostra centenaria di Luca Cambiaso, *Genoa, 1927, cat. no. 8 (ill.); Venturi, A.,* Storia dell'Arte Italiana, *9, 1934, pt. 7, p. 854; Chicago. Art Institute,* Bulletin *37: 2–3, 1943 (cover ill.); Indianapolis, Indiana. John Herron Art Institute,* Pontormo to Greco, The Age of Mannerism... *1954, cat. no. 49 (ill.); Genova. Palazzo dell'Academia,* Luca Cambiaso, *1956, cat. no. 37 (ill.); Podestà, A.,* Emporium *24, December 1956, p. fol. 243 (ill.); Suida-Manning, B. and Suida, W.,* Luca Cambiaso, la vita e le opere, *1958, cat. p. 159, fig. 338, pl. 205*

CAMERON, Edgar Spier ~ *b. 1862 Ottawa, Ill. d. 1944 Chicago*

Cameron began his studies in Chicago, then went to New York to work with Thomas W. Dewing and William Merritt Chase. He continued his training in Paris from 1884 to 1886. He won his first recognition in Chicago with his murals at the World's Columbian Exposition of 1893.

CABARET BRETON

Painted 1916, signed: E. Cameron. Oil on canvas, $34\frac{1}{2} \times 40\frac{1}{2}$ in. (87×102.2 cm.)
Friends of American Art Collection, 17.63

CANALETTO (Antonio Canal) ~ *1697–1768 Venice*

To distinguish the painter from his father Bernardo Canal, the son was called "Il Canaletto." He studied with his father and Luca Carlevaris and about 1719 went to Rome, where he met a number of Northern painters, such as Gaspar van Wittel. Upon his return to Venice, probably in 1720, Canaletto devoted all his time to painting *vedute*, largely destined to be sold to foreign visitors, especially English travelers. Canaletto lived in England between 1747 and 1754; there he painted many views of London and English country seats.

THE TERRACE

Painted about 1745. Oil on canvas, $19\frac{5}{16} \times 23$ in. (49.2×58.6 cm.)
Gift of Mrs. Clive Runnells, 57.48

The terrace adjacent to a courtyard resembles closely a view represented in a drawing in the Print Room of the Staatliche Museen, Berlin. The drawing is signed by Canaletto and labeled "Padua." There also exists an etching by Canaletto in a series on the same subject, published between 1740 and 1743.

PORTICO WITH LANTERN

Painted about 1745. Oil on canvas, $19\frac{3}{8} \times 23$ in. (49.4×58.6 cm.)
Gift of Mrs. Clive Runnells, 57.49

This scene is a companion piece to the above painting. It represents an imaginary view with elements from classic antiquity and details taken from contemporary architecture of Padua or Venice.
Coll: Italico Brass, Venice; Gentile de Giuseppe, Paris

Ref: Ferrari, G., Les Deux Canaletto, *1915, pl. 50 (our no. 2, called Belloto here); Oulmont, C.,* Les Arts, *1917, pp. 18–9, fig. 16; Von Hadeln, D.,* The Drawings of Antonio Canal, called Canaletto, *1929, pl. 52 (drawing for* The Terrace); *Pallucchini, R., and G. F. Guarnati,* Les eaux-fortes de Canaletto, *1945, p. 34, fig. 18 (ill.); Chicago. Art Institute,* Quarterly *51, no. 3: 43 (ill. of* Portico with a Lantern)

CANALS Y LLAMBI, Ricardo ~ *b. 1876 Barcelona*

Canals was trained at the School of Fine Arts in Barcelona and later lived for several years in Paris where he came under the influence of Eugène Carrière and Renoir.

CIGAR MAKING IN SEVILLE

Painted 1899, signed: Canals. Oil on canvas, 24×20 in. (61×50.9 cm.)
Mr. and Mrs. Martin A. Ryerson Collection, 33.1113

CAPON, Georges Emile ~ *b. 1890 Paris*

Capon, a self-taught artist, has exhibited at the Salon d'Automne and the Salon des Tuileries since 1919.

THE BALL OF EBONY

Signed and dated: Capon —25—. Oil on canvas, 32¾×25 in. (83.2×63.6 cm.)
Gift of Mr. and Mrs. Carter H. Harrison, 36.5

LA JAVA

Signed and dated: Capon —25—. Oil on canvas, 28¾×24½ in. (73×62.4 cm.)
Gift of Mr. and Mrs. Carter H. Harrison, 37.377

THE SCOTCH GOWN

Painted 1926, signed: Capon. Oil on canvas, 35¾×23¼ in. (91×59.1 cm.)
Gift of Mr. and Mrs. Carter H. Harrison, 35.301

SPANISH BEGGAR BOYS

Signed and dated: Seville 28 Capon. Oil on canvas, 32×39¼ in. (81.3×99.8 cm.)
Gift of Mr. and Mrs. Carter H. Harrison, 37.378

WOMAN WITH TULIPS

Painted 1928, signed: Capon. Oil on canvas, 38¾×31½ in. (98.5×80.2 cm.)
Gift of Mr. and Mrs. Carter H. Harrison, 36.6

WOMAN READING

Painted 1930, signed: Capon. Oil on canvas, $28\frac{11}{16} \times 23\frac{5}{8}$ in. (73×60.1 cm.)
Gift of Mr. and Mrs. Carter H. Harrison, 35.302

CAPPELLE, Jan van de ~ *1624/25–1679 Amsterdam*

The son of a wealthy dyer whose flourishing business he continued, Jan van de Cappelle remained a self-taught artist who painted only in his leisure time.

THE CALM: MARINE

Signed and dated: J. v. Cappelle 1651. Oil on canvas, $22 \times 27\frac{3}{4}$ in. (56×70.6 cm.)
Mr. and Mrs. Martin A. Ryerson Collection, 33.1068 (HdG 110)
Coll: J. Louis Miéville Collection, London, 1878; Prince P. Demidoff, San Donato, Florence (sale March 15, 1880, no. 1071)

Ref: London. Royal Academy, Winter Exhibition, *1878, cat. no. 107; San Donato Sale,* Catalogue des objets d'art et d'ameublement, tableaux, *1880, cat. no. 1071 (ill.); Toledo, Ohio. Museum of Art,* Catalogue of the Inaugural Exhibition, 1912, *cat. no. 214 (reprod. opp. p. 99)*

CARLES, Arthur B. ~ *b. 1882 Philadelphia, Pa. d. 1952 Chestnut Hill, Pa.*

On graduating from the Pennsylvania Academy, Carles received a scholarship for study abroad. He returned to teach at the Academy from 1917 to 1925.

ARRANGEMENT

Painted about 1927–1928, signed Carles. Oil on canvas, $46\frac{3}{4} \times 40\frac{1}{8}$ in. (118.8×102 cm.)
Mr. and Mrs. Frank G. Logan Purchase Prize, 28.1185

CARLSEN, Soren Emil ~ *b. 1853 Copenhagen. d. 1932 New York*

Emil Carlsen studied at the Danish Royal Academy. At the age of nineteen he came to America.

NANTASKET BEACH

Signed and dated: Nantasket Beach S. Em. C. 76 26/6.
Oil on canvas, $15\frac{1}{4} \times 26\frac{1}{4}$ in. (38.8×66.7 cm.)
Friends of American Art Collection, 40.1087

STILL LIFE

Painted about 1906–1907. Oil on canvas, 24×20 in. (61×50.9 cm.)
B. F. Ferguson Fund, 08.90

CONNECTICUT HILLSIDE

Painted about 1920, signed: Emil Carlsen. Oil on canvas, $29\frac{1}{4} \times 27\frac{3}{8}$ in. (74.3×69.6 cm.)
Walter H. Schulze Memorial Collection, 30.350

THE MIRACULOUS DRAUGHT

Signed and dated: Emil Carlsen 1921. Oil on canvas, $39\frac{1}{2} \times 45\frac{3}{8}$ in. (100.3 × 115.3 cm.)
Walter H. Schulze Memorial Collection, 24.905

CARPIONI, Giulio ~ *b. 1611 Venice. d. 1674 Verona, Italy*

A pupil of Alessandro Varotari, Carpioni was active in Vicenza, Verona and Venice.

THE SACRIFICE OF A VIRGIN

Painted about 1650. Oil on canvas, 22 × 28 in. (56 × 71.2 cm.)
Charles H. and Mary F. S. Worcester Collection, 32.203

The subject of this painting, traditionally called *The Sacrifice of Polyxena,* might also represent Iphigenia in Aulis. This is probably a sketch.

Ref: Chicago. Art Institute, Catalogue of the Worcester Collection, *1938, cat. no. 16; Venice, Ca' Pesaro,* La Pittura del Seicento a Venezia, *1959, cat. no. 126*

CARRIERE, Eugène ~ *b. 1849 Gournay, France. d. 1906 Paris*

Carrière, a pupil of Alexandre Cabanel, developed a style characterized by luminosity and finely modulated tones.

PORTRAIT OF A LADY WITH A DOG

Signed and dated: Eugène Carrière, 1885. Oil on canvas, $46\frac{1}{8} \times 35\frac{1}{4}$ in. (117.2 × 89.5 cm.)
Mr. and Mrs. Martin A. Ryerson Collection, 33.1115

PORTRAIT OF A BOY

Signed and dated: Eugène Carrière, 1886. Oil on canvas, $68 \times 47\frac{1}{2}$ in. (172.8 × 120.6 cm.)
Gift of Mrs. Chauncey McCormick, 56.341

CASSATT, Mary ~ *b. 1844 Allegheny City, Pa. d. 1926 Mesnil-Théribus, France*

Mary Cassatt, after attending the Pennsylvania Academy, went abroad in 1866 for an intensive study of the old masters. She gained her greatest inspiration from eight months spent with works of Correggio at Parma. In Madrid and Antwerp she studied Rubens and in Holland, Frans Hals. She then settled in Paris and from 1872 for five successive years was accepted at the Salon. At the invitation of Degas she joined the Impressionists in 1877 and exhibited four times with this group. She worked extensively in drypoint and aquatint. Aside from her importance as an artist, Mary Cassatt is to a large degree responsible for the early interest in America in French Impressionism. She acted as art adviser to her friends, the Havemeyers, the Whittemores, Mrs. J. Montgomery Sears and James Stillman.

WOMAN READING IN A GARDEN

Painted 1880, signed: Mary Cassatt. Oil on canvas, 35½×25⅝ in. (89.2×65.2 cm.)
Gift of Mrs. Albert J. Beveridge in memory of her mother Delia Spencer Field, 38.18

The model was Mary Cassatt's sister, Lydia, who frequently posed for her. The setting is probably in the garden at Marly where the Cassatt family took a villa for the summer of 1880.

Ref: Chicago. Art Institute, Bulletin *32: 57–8, 1938 (ill.); Breuning, E.,* Mary Cassatt, *1944, p. 20 (ill.)*

PORTRAIT OF A YOUNG GIRL

Painted about 1880, signed: Mary Cassatt. Oil on canvas, 24⅛×20⅛ in. (62.4×51.2 cm.)
Gift of Kate L. Brewster, 50.119

MOTHER AND CHILD

Painted 1888, signed: Mary Cassatt. Pastel on paper, 33×29 in. (89.3×73.7 cm.)
Potter Palmer Collection, 22.421

Ref: Chicago. Art Institute, Handbook, *1925, p. 129, no. 803; Breuning, E.,* Mary Cassatt, *1944, p. 21 (ill.)*

YOUNG WOMAN SEWING

Painted about 1890. Oil on canvas, 24×19¾ in. (61×50.4 cm.)
Charles H. and Mary F. S. Worcester Collection, 47.61
Coll: Mme Mathilde X; A. M. Reitlinger, Paris, 1927

ON THE WATER

Painted early 1890's. Oil on canvas. 23¾×28¾ in. (60.5×73 cm.)
Charles H. and Mary F. S. Worcester Collection, 47.60

THE BATH (La Toilette) Illus. p. 369

Painted about 1891, signed: Mary Cassatt. Oil on canvas, 39½×26 in. (100.3×66.1 cm.)
Robert A. Waller Fund, 10.2
Coll: Durand-Ruel, New York, 1910

Ref: Ségard, Mary Cassatt, *1894, pp. 52, 53 (ill.); New York. Durand-Ruel,* Exposition . . . Mary Cassatt, *April 1895, cat. no. 21; Cincinnati. Museum of Art,* 7th Annual Exhibition of American Art, *1900, cat. no. 13 (ill.); Chicago. Art Institute,* Bulletin *3: 61, 1910; Chicago. Art Institute,* Catalogue of a Memorial Collection of the Works of Mary Cassatt, *1926–1927, cat. no. 29 (ill.); Pittsburgh. Carnegie Institute,* Mary Cassatt Memorial Exhibition, *1928, cat. no. 33; Valerio, E.,* Mary Cassatt, *1930 (ill. pl. 5); Watson, F.,* Mary Cassatt, *1932, pl. 42; Chicago. Art Institute,* A Century of Progress Exhibition, *1933, cat. no. 439; Chicago. Art Institute,* Bulletin *27: 118, 1933; Chicago. Art Institute,* A Century of Progress Exhibition, *1934, cat. no. 440; Brooklyn Museum,* Leaders of American Impressionism, *1937, cat. no. 22; New York. Museum of Modern Art,* Art in Our Time,

1939, cat. no. 48 (ill.); Santa Barbara, California. Museum of Art, Painting Today and Yesterday in the United States, *1941, cat. no. 23 (ill.); Breuning, E.,* Mary Cassatt, *1944, p. 39 (ill.); Baltimore. Museum of Art,* Mary Cassatt, *1941–1942, cat. no. 25 (ill.); New York. Wildenstein & Co.,* Mary Cassatt, *1947, cat. no. 25 (ill.); Des Moines. Art Center,* 19th and 20th Century European and American Art, *1948, cat. no. 16; Springfield, Mass. Museum of Art,* Exhibition, *1948; New York. Wildenstein & Co.,* Landmarks of American Art, *1953, cat. no. 38 (ill.); Chicago. Art Institute,* Sargent, Whistler, and Mary Cassatt, *1954, cat. no. 19 (ill.)*

MOTHER AND CHILD

Painted about 1900, signed: Mary Cassatt. Oil on canvas, 39⅝ × 32⅛ in. (100.6 × 81.6 cm.)
Gift of Alexander Stewart, 56.760

MOTHER AND LITTLE GIRL

Painted about 1905, signed: Mary Cassatt. Pastel on paper, 23¾ × 29 in. (60.5 × 73.7 cm.)
Charles H. and Mary F. S. Worcester Collection, 47.59

CAZIN, Jean Charles ~ *b. 1841 Samer, France. d. 1901 Le Lavandou, France*

Cazin started his career as a drawing master in Tours.

TOBIAS AND THE ANGEL

Signed and dated: J. C. Cazin 1878. Oil on canvas, 23 × 33⅛ in. (58.6 × 84.2 cm.)
Henry Field Memorial Collection, 94.1036

Ref: Thieme-Becker, Künstler-Lexikon, *6, 1912, p. 246*

THEOCRITUS

Painted about 1885–1890, signed: J. C. Cazin.
Oil on canvas, 28⅞ × 22 9/16 in. (73.4 × 59.6 cm.)
Potter Palmer Collection, 22.401

Ref: Gazette des Beaux-Arts, *Per. 3, vol. 26, 1901 (reprod. opp. p. 52); Chicago. Art Institute,* Bulletin *15: 145, 1921; Gibson, F.,* Six French Artists of the 19th Century, *1925, p. 52; Chicago. Art Institute,* A Century of Progress Exhibition, *1934, cat. no. 158*

LANDSCAPE

Painted about 1890–1895, signed: J. C. Cazin.
Oil on canvas, 12¾ × 16⅛ in. (32.3 × 41.1 cm.)
Henry Field Memorial Collection, 94.1037

OCTOBER DAY

Painted about 1890–1895, signed: J. C. Cazin. Oil on canvas, 15⅛ × 18¼ in. (38.5 × 46.5 cm.)
Henry Field Memorial Collection, 94.1039

"CECCO DEL CARAVAGGIO" ~ *Italian, active first quarter of 17th century*

THE RESURRECTION Illus. p. 49

Painted about 1600. Oil on canvas, 133½ × 78½ in. (339.1 × 199.5 cm.)
Charles H. and Mary F. S. Worcester Collection, 34.390

The attribution is R. Longhi's to a member of the Caravaggesque circle of the first quarter of the 17th century. Other canvases assigned by Longhi to this painter include the Berlin *Temple-Cleansing,* the so-called *Narcissus* in a Bolognese private collection, and the Fitzwilliam *Flautist.* The picture has also been attributed to L. Finsonius (1500–1617), a Caravaggesque painter born in Bruges, who worked in Southern France.
Coll: Palazzo Barberini, Rome [?]

Ref: Dannenberg, A., Vassar Journal of Undergraduate Studies *10: 62–9, 1936; Longhi, R.,* Proporzioni, *1943, p. 52, no. 60 (pl. 60)*

CEZANNE, Paul ~ *1839–1906 Aix-en-Provence, France*

Cézanne studied at the Académie Suisse in Paris. Much influenced in his early years by Pissarro, he worked with this artist at Pontoise during the summer of 1872. After Cézanne joined the Impressionists, he exhibited with them in 1874 and 1877. Because there was no public interest in his work, he painted in seclusion, mostly in Aix-en-Provence, until the dealer Vollard became his agent and arranged a large exhibition of his paintings in 1895. Probably the most influential artist of the 19th century and the outstanding forerunner of modern painting, his importance was not generally recognized until after his death.

AUVERS: VILLAGE PANORAMA

Painted between 1873 and 1875. Oil on canvas, 25⅝ × 32 in. (65.2 × 81.3 cm.)
Mr. and Mrs. Lewis L. Coburn Memorial Collection, 33.422 (Venturi 150)
Coll: Dr. Georges Viau, Paris; Choquet Collection, Paris (sale, 1899); Alfred Strotin, Paris (sale, 1921); Annie S. Coburn Collection

Ref: London. Grafton Gallery, Exhibition of Works by French Impressionists, *1905; Chicago. Art Institute,* Catalogue of the Coburn Collection, *1932, p. 10, cat. no. 1 (ill. p. 36); Chicago. Art Institute,* A Century of Progress Exhibition, *1933, cat. no. 304; Chicago. Art Institute,* Bulletin *27: 70, 1933; Venturi, L.,* Cézanne, *1, 2, 1936, no. 150 (ill.); Paris. Orangerie,* Van Gogh et les Peintres d'Auvers-sur-Oise, *1954–1955, cat. no. 12, pl. 7 (ill.); Cooper, D.,* Burlington Magazine *97: 103, April 1955, fig. 8 (ill.) (notes)*

THE PLATE OF APPLES

Painted about 1877, signed: P. Cézanne. Oil on canvas, 18⅛ × 21¾ in. (46.2 × 55.4 cm.)
Gift of Kate L. Brewster, 49.512 (Venturi 210)
Coll: Collection Schoen, Berlin; Walter S. Brewster Collection

Ref: D'Ors, E., Paul Cézanne, *1930 (ill. pl. 23); Chicago. Art Institute,* Bulletin *44, no. 3: 51, 1950*

HOUSE ON THE RIVER

Painted probably between 1885–1890. Oil on canvas, $20\frac{1}{8} \times 24$ in. (51.2×61 cm.)
The Joseph Winterbotham Collection, 54.304

APPLES ON A TABLECLOTH

Painted between 1886–1890. Oil on canvas, $15\frac{1}{8} \times 18\frac{1}{4}$ in. (38.5×46.5 cm.)
The Joseph Winterbotham Collection, 53.333 (Venturi 510)

THE GULF OF MARSEILLES, SEEN FROM L'ESTAQUE Illus. p. 291

Painted between 1886 and 1890. Oil on canvas, $31\frac{3}{4} \times 39\frac{1}{4}$ in. (80.8×99.8 cm.)
Mr. and Mrs. Martin A. Ryerson Collection, 33.1116 (Venturi 493)

L'Estaque, on the outskirts of Marseilles, fifteen miles from Aix, was one of Cézanne's favorite spots. Here he often stayed in his mother's house or in a rented cottage. This canvas is the last of a group devoted to the same subject, one of which is in the Louvre, and another in the Metropolitan Museum. In a sketchbook by Cézanne belonging to the Art Institute, similar views of the Gulf of Marseilles appear.
Coll: Hoogendyck Collection, Amsterdam; Joseph Hessel, Paris (sale, June 1920)

Ref: Jourdain, F., Cézanne, *1914 (pl. 42);* L'Amour de l'Art *1: 263, 1920 (ill.); New York. Museum of Modern Art,* First Loan Exhibition . . . , *1929, cat. no. 18 (ill.); Chicago. Art Institute,* Bulletin *24: 114–7, 1930; Chicago. Art Institute,* A Century of Progress Exhibition, *1933, cat. no. 309, p. 61;* Ibid., *1934, cat. no. 293; Logan, J. H.,* Sanity in Art, *1937 (ill. p. 105); Mackenzie, H. F.,* Masterpieces of Painting, XIX Century, *1946, pp. 26–7 (ill.); Dorival, B.,* Cézanne, *1948, p. 76*

THE VASE OF TULIPS Illus. p. 327

Painted between 1890 and 1894. Oil on canvas, $23\frac{1}{2} \times 16\frac{5}{8}$ in. (59.6×42.3 cm.)
Mr. and Mrs. Lewis L. Coburn Memorial Collection, 33.432 (Venturi 617)
Coll: Choquet Collection, Paris (sale, 1899, no. 124); Durand-Ruel, Paris (no. 8154); Mrs. Annie S. Coburn

Ref: Klingsor, T. L., Masters of Modern Art, *1924, pl. 20; Chicago. Art Institute,* Catalogue of the Coburn Collection, *1932, p. 10, no. 3; Chicago. Art Institute,* Bulletin *26: 70–1, 1932 (ill. p. 64); Chicago. Art Institute,* A Century of Progress Exhibition, *1933, cat. no. 310 (pl. 62);* Ibid., *1934, cat. no. 294*

THE BASKET OF APPLES

Painted between 1890 and 1894, signed: P. Cézanne.
Oil on canvas, $25\frac{3}{4} \times 32$ in. (65.5×81.3 cm.)
Helen Birch Bartlett Memorial Collection, 26.252 (Venturi 600)
Coll: Joseph Hessel Collection, Paris (sale, 1913)

Ref: Bernard, E., Kunst und Kuenstler *6: 521, 1908 (ill.); Hind, C. L.,* The Post-Impressionists, *1911, p. 74 (ill.); Weisbach, W.,* Impressionismus, *1911, 2, p. 162 (ill.);* Les Arts *11: VII, 1912 (ill. only); Vollard, A.,* Cézanne, *1914, p. 102 (pl. 33);* The Fine

Arts Journal *35: 74, May 1917 (ill. only); Coquiot, C.,* Paul Cézanne, *1919, p. 246; Meier-Graefe,* Cézanne und sein Kreis, *1922, p. 185 (ill.);* L'Amour de l'Art *5, no. 2: 41, 1924 (ill. only);* The Art News *24: 29, June 12, 1926 (Supplement); Chicago. Art Institute,* Annual Report, *1926 (ill.); Chicago. Art Institute,* Bulletin *20: 61–4, 1926 (ill. p. 61); Watson, F.,* The Arts *9: 304, 1926 (ill.); Zabel, M. D.,* Art and Archæology *25: 227, 233, 234, 1928 (ill.); Bertram, A.,* The World's Masters—Cézanne, *1929 (pl. 22); Cambridge. Fogg Art Museum,* Exhibition of French Painting of the XIX Century, *1929, cat. no. 6 (pl. XXIV); Chicago. Art Institute,* A Century of Progress Exhibition, *1933, cat. no. 305;* Ibid., *1934, cat. no. 290; Philadelphia. Museum of Art,* Cézanne, *1934, cat. no. 17; Jewell, E. A.,* Paul Cézanne, *1944, p. 21 (ill.); Chicago. Art Institute,* Catalogue of the Helen Birch Bartlett Collection, *1946, pp. 6–7 (ill.)*

MADAME CEZANNE IN A YELLOW ARMCHAIR Illus. p. 326

Painted between 1890 and 1894. Oil on canvas, 31⅞×25½ in. (81×64.8 cm.)

Wilson L. Mead Fund, 48.54 (Venturi 572)

Coll: Ambroise Vollard, Paris; Bernheim-Jeune, Paris (after 1906); Alphonse Kann, Paris; Thannhauser, Berlin

Ref: Paul Cézanne, Mappe, *Munich, 1912, pl. 6;* Emporium, *December 1913, p. 422 (ill.); Vollard, A.,* Paul Cézanne, *1914, pl. 46; Meier-Graefe, J.,* Cézanne und sein Kreis, *1922, p. 200; Pfister, K.,* Gestalt, Werk, Mythos, *1927, pl. 74;* The Arts *13: 34, 107, 1928 (ill.); New York. Wildenstein Galleries,* Paul Cézanne, *January 1928, cat. no. 19; Paris. Paul Rosenberg,* Exposition des Grands Maîtres du 19e siècle, *1939, cat. no. 7; Javorskaia, N.,* Cézanne, *1935, pl. 16; Huyghe, R.,* Cézanne (Sommaire de l'exposition au Musée de l'Orangerie), *XVII, May 1936, p. 177, fig. 61 (ill.); Paris. Musée de l'Orangerie,* Cézanne, *1936, cat. no. 75; Paris, Paul Rosenberg,* Cézanne, *1939, cat. no. 26 (ill.); Cogniat, R.,* Cézanne, *1939, p. 73 (ill.);* Art News *47: 34–5, November 1948; New York. Paul Rosenberg & Co.,* Masterpieces Recalled, Loan Exhibition, *1957, cat. no. 19*

THE BATHERS

Painted between 1900 and 1905. Oil on canvas, 20 3/16×24¼ in. (51×61.7 cm.)

The Amy McCormick Memorial Collection, 42.457 (Venturi 722)

Coll: Zoubaloff, Paris; Hessel Collection, Paris

Ref: New York. Paul Rosenberg & Co., Loan Exhibition of Paintings by Paul Cézanne, *January 1928, cat. no. 8; New York. Museum of Modern Art,* Summer Exhibition, Retrospective, *1930, cat. no. 15; Chicago. Art Institute,* A Century of Progress Exhibition, *1933, cat. no. 306;* Ibid., *1934, cat. no. 291; Chicago. Art Institute,* Bulletin *34: 60, 1934 (ill.); Jewell, E. A.,* Paul Cézanne, *1944, p. 34 (ill.); Edinburgh. Royal Scottish Academy,* An Exhibition of Paintings by Cézanne, *1954, cat. no. 60*

CHAGALL, Marc ~ *b. 1887 Vitebsk, Russia*

Chagall's imaginative visions, culled from a Russian-Jewish background, are not based on folk legends or fairy tales as is often claimed, but evolve from memories of his childhood and past. His youth was spent in the Russian village of Vitebsk. His later residence in France (1910–1914 and since 1924) explains his identification with the international School of Paris. During the last war he came to the United States and lived in New York.

NAISSANCE

Signed and dated: M. Chagall Paris 1911; inscribed: Naissance.
Oil on canvas, 44¼×76⅛ in. (112.4×193.4 cm.)
Gift of Mr. and Mrs. Maurice E. Culberg, 52.3
Coll: Mr. and Mrs. M. E. Culberg

Ref: Sturm Bilderbuecher, I—Marc Chagall, *1923, p. 14; With, K.,* Marc Chagall (Junge Kunst, *35), 1923 (ill. pl. 2); Venturi, L.,* Marc Chagall, *1945, pp. 21–7; Sweeney, J. J.,* Marc Chagall, *1946, p. 16*

THE PRAYING JEW (THE RABBI OF VITEBSK) Illus. p. 469

Painted 1914, signed: Marc Chagall. Oil on canvas, 46×35 in. (116.9×88.9 cm.)
The Joseph Winterbotham Collection, 37.188
Coll: P. M. Sweeney Collection, New York

Ref: George, W., Marc Chagall, *1928, p. 43, no. 31 (ill.); Chicago. Art Institute,* A Century of Progress Exhibition, *1933, cat. no. 725 (pl. 74);* Art Digest *7: 25, May 15, 1933 (ill.); Huyghe, R.,* L'Amour d'Art *15, no. 2: 319, 1934 (ill.); Dallas, Texas,* Centennial Exhibition, *1936, p. 42, cat. no. 21; Toledo, Ohio. Museum of Art,* Contemporary Movements in European Painting, *1938, cat. no. 13 (ill.); New York. Museum of Modern Art,* 20th Century Portraits, *1942, cat. no. 58; Venturi, L.,* Marc Chagall, *1945; Sweeney, J. J.,* Marc Chagall, *1946, p. 35 (ill.);* Emporium *103–4: 208, 1946 (ill.); Chicago. Art Institute,* Marc Chagall, *1946, cat. no. 18 (ill.); Chicago. Art Institute,* Catalogue of the Winterbotham Collection, *1947, p. 9–10 (ill.); Paris. Musée National d'Art Moderne,* Chagall, *1947, cat. no. 19; Frankfurter, A. M.,* Art News *45: 24–5, 1948 (ill.); London. Tate Gallery,* Marc Chagall, *1948, cat. no. 18 (pl. 8); Zürich. Kunsthaus,* Marc Chagall, *1950–1951, cat. no. 19; Baltimore. Museum of Art,* Man in His Years, *1954, cat. no. 69 (ill.)*

THE CIRCUS RIDER

Painted about 1927, signed: Chagall. Oil on canvas, 9¼×7½ in. (23.5×19.1 cm.)
Gift of Mrs. Gilbert W. Chapman, 49.516

One of a series of circus scenes which Chagall painted in the late 1920's in Paris.

Ref: Chagall, M., Ma Vie, *c. 1913, p. 7; Lozowick, L.,* Theatre Arts Monthly *13: 595–8, August 1921*

WHITE CRUCIFIXION

Signed and dated: Marc Chagall 1938. Oil on canvas, 61×55 in. (155×139.7 cm.)
Gift of Alfred S. Alschuler, 46.925
Coll: Marc Chagall, 1938; Pierre Matisse, New York, 1944

Ref: Maritain, R., Marc Chagall, *c. 1943, pp. 28–30; Dayton, Ohio. Art Institute,* Liturgical Arts *12: 64, May 1944; Weisstein, A.,* The Kenyon Review, *Winter 1954, pp. 38–48 (ill.)*

THE JUGGLER

Signed and dated: Marc Chagall, 1943. Oil on canvas, 43¼×31⅛ in. (109×79 cm.)
Gift of Mrs. Gilbert W. Chapman, 52.1005

Ref: Sweeney, J. J., Marc Chagall, *1946, cat. no. 53, p. 63*

CHAPIN, Francis ~ *b. 1899 Bristol, Ohio*

Chapin graduated from Washington and Jefferson College in 1921, then spent six years at the School of the Art Institute, where he won a traveling fellowship. He has had great influence in the Chicago area as a teacher.

THE PINK HOUSE

Painted about 1933, signed: Francis Chapin. Oil on canvas, 30×25⅛ in. (76.3×63.9 cm.)
Mr. and Mrs. Frank G. Logan Purchase Prize, 33.26

SKETCH OF A NUDE

Painted about 1935. Oil on composition board, 13⅝×17⅛ in. (34.7×43.6 cm.)
Charles H. and Mary F. S. Worcester Collection, 35.169

LITTLE RIVER

Painted Saugatuck, Mich., before 1938, signed: Francis Chapin.
Oil on canvas, 28⅛×40 in. (71.5×103.9 cm.)
Gift of the Society for Contemporary American Art, 41.8

CHAPIN, James ~ *b. 1887 West Orange, N.J.*

Chapin studied at the Art Students League and Cooper Union in New York, then went to the Royal Academy in Antwerp.

THE OLD FARM HAND

Signed and dated: James Chapin 26. Oil on canvas, 28½×23⅝ in. (72.5×60.1 cm.)
Mr. and Mrs. Frank G. Logan Purchase Prize, 27.1434

CHARDIN, Jean-Baptiste Siméon ~ *1699–1779 Paris*

Chardin was a pupil of Pierre Jacques Cazes and of Noël Nicholas Coypel. An important early influence in his career came through his sharing a studio with Aved, who had studied in Holland and who passed on to Chardin an enthusiasm for still life.

THE WHITE TABLECLOTH Illus. p. 229

Painted about 1737. Oil on canvas, 37⅞×48¾ in. (95.9×123.8 cm.)
Gift of Annie Swan Coburn to the Mr. and Mrs. Lewis L. Coburn Memorial Collection, 44.699
(Wildenstein 1057)

This picture, done as a *devant la cheminée* or fire-board to close the opening of a fireplace when not in use, had rounded contours at the top to conform to the opening of a Louis XV mantel.

Coll: Alexandre Gabriel Décamps, Paris, 1851; Laperlier Collection, Paris; Léon Michel-Lévy, Paris (sale, 1925); David-Weill, Paris, 1937

Ref: Paris. Exposition de la Caisse de Secours des Artistes, *1860, cat. no. 351; Tourneux, M.,* Gazette des Beaux-Arts *38, p. 3: 89–102, August 1907 (ill. p. 97); Paris. Gallery Georges Petit,* L'Exposition Chardin-Fragonard, *1907, cat. no. 53; Guiffrey, J.,* Catalogue Raisonné de l'Oeuvre . . . de J.-B. Siméon Chardin, *1908, p. 82, cat. no. 165; Wildenstein, G.,* Chardin, *c. 1933, p. 235, cat. no. 1057 (pl. 106); Frankfurter, A. M.,* Art News *36: 13, November 6, 1937 (ill.); New York. Wildenstein & Co.,* David-Weill Pictures, *1937, cat. no. 3;* Art News *41: 15, December 15, 1942 (ill.); Chicago. Art Institute,* Bulletin *39: 49–53, 1945 (ill.); Minneapolis. Institute of Arts,* French 18th Century Painters, *1954; Saint-Jal, G. de Lastic,* Connaissance *39: 31, May 15, 1955*

CHARLEMONT, Hugo ~ *b. 1850 Jamnitz, Austria. d. 1939 Vienna*

Charlemont studied in Vienna, visited Holland, and later studied with Hans Makart, who greatly influenced his work.

THE ROYAL LIBRARY

Signed and dated: Hugo Charlemont 1883. Oil on panel, 12⅜ × 16⅜ in. (31.5 × 41.7 cm.)
A. A. Munger Collection, 01.434

CHARMY, Emilie ~ *b. about 1880 Saint-Etienne, France*

Mme Charmy, a self-taught artist (but influenced by Matisse and Van Dongen) made use in her paintings of brilliant color and the heavily-outlined forms admired by the Fauves.

L'ESTAQUE

Painted about 1910, signed: E. Charmy. Oil on canvas, 22½ × 29 in. (57.3 × 73.7 cm.)
Arthur Jerome Eddy Memorial Collection, 31.518
Coll: Arthur Jerome Eddy

Ref: New York. Armory Show, *1913, cat. no. 170; Eddy, A. J.,* Cubists and Post-Impressionism, *1914 (ill.); Chicago. Art Institute,* Catalogue of the Eddy Collection, *1922, cat. no. 14;* Ibid., *1931/2, cat. no. 2*

CHASE, William Merritt ~ *b. 1849 Williamsburg, Ind. d. 1916 New York City*

Chase was not only one of the leading figures in American painting at the turn of the century but was also one of its most influential teachers. His chief training was in Munich where he went in 1872 to study with Carl von Piloty. Chase was a brilliant student and had already achieved considerable recognition before returning to New York in 1878.

WOMAN WITH A BASKET

Signed and dated: Chase 1875. Oil on canvas, 44×34 in. (111.9×86.4 cm.)
Friends of American Art Collection, 46.56

An unfinished painting.

Coll: Frank Duveneck; Cincinnati Museum

Ref: Cincinnati, Ohio. Museum, Catalogue of the Permanent Collection of Paintings, *1913, cat. no. 363*

ALICE

Painted probably 1892, signed: Wm. M. Chase.
Oil on canvas, 67⅝×49⅜ in. (171.8×125.5 cm.)
Gift of Ernest A. Hamill, 93.107
Coll: Ernest A. Hamill, 1893

Ref: Munich. Glaspalast, 6th Internationale Kunstausstellung, *1892, p. 94 (ill.); Chicago. Art Institute,* Columbian Exposition, *1893, cat. no. 769;* Art World *2: 198, 1895 (ill.);* Brush and Pencil, *1898, p. 259; Sherwood, J. B.,* Childhood in Art, *1912, p. 67 (ill.); Toledo, Ohio. Museum of Art,* Inaugural Exhibition, *1912, cat. no. 18 (ill.); Roof, K. M.,* The Life and Art of William Merritt Chase, *1917, pp. 165, 166 (ill.); Chicago. Art Institute,* First Exhibition of Works of Former Students, *1918, cat. no. 96 (ill.); Bryant, L. M.,* American Pictures and their Painters, *1920, pp. 114–?, fig. 75 (ill.);* Arts and Decoration *15, July 1921 (cover ill.);* The Mentor *12: 33, October 1924 (ill.); Buffalo. Albright Art Gallery,* 72nd Annual Exhibition of Paintings by American Artists, *1928, cat. no. 26; Chicago. Art Institute,* A Century of Progress Exhibition, *1933, cat. no. 440; Indianapolis. John Herron Art Institute,* Chase Centennial Exhibition, *1949, cat. no. 31 (ill.); Philadelphia. Pennsylvania Academy of the Fine Arts,* Exhibition, *1955*

NORTH RIVER SHAD

Painted about 1910, signed: Wm. M. Chase. Oil on canvas, 29×36⅛ in. (73.7×91.8 cm.)
Friends of American Art Collection, 14.56

Ref: Chicago. Art Institute, Friends of American Art Yearbook, *1913–1914, p. 24 (ill.); Chicago. Art Institute,* Bulletin *7: 65, 1914; Dallas, Texas. Art Association,* Third Annual Exhibition of American Art, *1922, cat. no. 29; San Francisco. California Palace of the Legion of Honor,* Loan Exhibition, Friends of American Art Collection, *1926, cat. no. 3; Dallas, Texas. Museum of Fine Arts,* Centennial Exposition, *1936, p. 49, cat. no. 23; Philadelphia. Pennsylvania Academy of the Fine Arts,* Exhibition, *1955*

CHASSERIAU, Théodore ~ *b. 1819 Samana, San Domingo. d. 1856 Paris*

At the age of twelve Chassériau began a three-year period of study with Ingres. In 1836, when he was sixteen, he showed his first picture at the Salon.

SARACENS AND CRUSADERS

Painted between 1846 and 1850, [signature Eug. D. lacroix is spurious.]
Oil on canvas, 23¼ × 30¾ in. (59.1 × 78.1 cm.)
Simeon B. Williams Fund, 32.1180
Coll: Mme de Brasch, Paris; Sen. H. Gruenewald, Baden-Baden, Germany; Roosevelt Collection, Baden-Baden

Ref: Chicago. Art Institute, A Century of Progress Exhibition, *1933, cat. no. 247;* Ibid., *1934, cat. no. 193; Detroit Institute of Arts,* From David to Courbet, *1950, cat. no. 41*

CHIMENTI, Jacopo, called Jacopo da Empoli ~ *b. c. 1554. d. 1640 Florence* (attributed to)

A YOUNG WIDOW OF THE MEDICI FAMILY Illus. p. 48

Oil on canvas, 87 × 48¼ in.
Frank H. and Louise B. Woods Purchase Fund, 60.1

CHURCH, Frederick Edwin ~ *b. 1826 Hartford, Conn. d. 1900 New York City*

Although Church studied briefly with Benjamin Coe in Hartford, his chief inspiration came from Thomas Cole. He became interested in Humboldt's records of South America and made two trips himself to Ecuador and Colombia.

VIEW OF COTOPAXI

Signed and dated: F. E. Church 57. Oil on canvas, 24½ × 36½ in. (62.4 × 92.8 cm.)
Gift of Jennette Hamlin in memory of Mr. and Mrs. Louis Dana Webster, 19.753

CIKOVSKY, Nicolai ~ *b. 1894 Pinsk, Poland*

Cikovsky was trained at the Moscow Art Academy in Russia and came to America in 1923. He is a lithographer as well as a painter and has had a distinguished career as a teacher.

PIGEONS

Painted 1931, signed: N. Cikovsky. Oil on canvas, 30 × 42 in. (76.3 × 106.7 cm.)
Mr. and Mrs. Frank G. Logan Purchase Prize, 32.1183

CLAESZ, Pieter ~ *b. 1597/98 Steinfurt, Germany. d. 1661 Haarlem, Holland*

Although nothing is known of his early training Claesz was an artist of great technical competence who took delight in tables elaborately set with linen, pewter, glass and food.

STILL LIFE Illus. p. 186

Painted about 1630, signed: PC. Oil on panel, 18⅞ × 30¼ in. (48 × 76.9 cm.)
Simeon B. Williams Fund, 35.300

CLARK, Alson Skinner ~ *b. 1876 Chicago. d. 1949 Pasadena, Calif.*

After studying at the School of the Art Institute, Clark continued his work with William Merritt Chase in New York and in Paris with Whistler.

COFFEE HOUSE

Painted about 1905–1906, signed: A. S. Clark. Oil on canvas, 38 × 30 in. (96.5 × 76.3 cm.)
Gift of Mr. and Mrs. Alson S. Clark, 15.256

CLARKSON, Ralph Elmer ~ *b. 1861 Amesbury, Mass. d. 1942 Chicago*

Trained at the School of the Museum of Fine Arts, Boston, and the Académie Julian in Paris, Clarkson settled in Chicago in 1895.

NEWTON HENRY CARPENTER

Painted about 1900, signed: Ralph Clarkson. Oil on canvas, 50¼ × 38¼ in. (127.7 × 97.2 cm.)
Gift of Mrs. Newton II. Carpenter, 32.1150

Mr. Carpenter served variously as instructor, secretary, director *pro tem* and business manager of the Chicago Academy of Design and the Art Institute from 1877 to 1918.

NOUVART DZERON, A DAUGHTER OF ARMENIA

Signed and dated: Ralph Clarkson, 1912. Oil on canvas, 80 × 40 in. (203.2 × 101.7 cm.)
Friends of American Art Collection, 12.1803

CLAYS, Paul Jean ~ *b. 1819 Bruges, Belgium. d. 1900 Brussels*

SHIPPING

Painted ca. 1860–1880 [?] Oil on canvas, 22 × 30½ in. (56 × 77.5 cm.)
Gift of John C. Black, 21.112

CLEVE, Joos van ~ *b. about 1485 near Cleve [?] Belgium. d. 1540/41 Antwerp*

The artist once called Master of the Death of the Virgin has been identified with Joos van Cleve. He entered the Antwerp Painters Guild in 1511, and was influenced by Dürer, Leonardo and Memling. Sometime between 1528 and 1535 he made a trip to Paris and was commissioned to paint the portraits of Francis I, the queen, and others.

HOLY FAMILY

Painted about 1520, signed with initial. Oil on panel, 19 × 14⅜ in. (48.3 × 36.6 cm.)
Mr. and Mrs. Martin A. Ryerson Collection, 33.1038 (Friedlaender 66 1)

There are about seventeen versions of this same subject by Joos, all varying in minor details.

Coll: Galerie Manzi (Marczell von Nemes sale, Paris), June 1913, no. 18; Martin A. Ryerson Collection, 1913

Ref: Marczell von Nemes de Budapest, Galerie Manzi, Catalogue des tableaux anciens, *1913, cat. no. 18; Chicago. Art Institute,* Bulletin *7: 38, 1914; New York. Kleinberger Galleries,* Flemish Primitives, *1929, cat. no. 56 (ill.); Friedlaender, M. J.,* Die Altniederlaendische Malerei, *9, 1931, p. 138, no. 66 1; Chicago. Art Institute,* A Century of Progress Exhibition, *1933, cat. no. 36;* Ibid , *1934, cat. no. 117*

CLOUET, François ~ *b. 1522 Tours, France. d. 1572 Paris*

François Clouet, the foremost French portrait painter of the 16th century, was strongly influenced by Hans Holbein the Younger. He studied in the workshop of his father, Jean Clouet, succeeding Lim as court painter to Francis I. Only a few paintings bear the signature of François Clouet, but many portraits, some of which were identified by labeled drawings, have been attributed to him.

PORTRAIT OF A COURT LADY

Painted about 1570. Oil on panel, 14×10⅝ in. (35.7×27 cm.)
Gift of Mrs. William S. Timken, 51.317

CODDE, Pieter ~ *1599–1678 Amsterdam*

Codde was probably a pupil of Frans Hals. He is known to have completed a group portrait of the Amsterdam Guard that Hals left unfinished at the time of his death.

THE ASSEMBLY

Painted about 1630 or 1640. Oil on panel, 22¼×35¾ in. (56.6×90.8 cm.)
Mr. and Mrs. Martin A. Ryerson Collection, 33.1069

COEN, Eleanor ~ *b. 1916 Normal, Ill.*

Eleanor Coen studied at the School of the Art Institute. Upon graduation in 1941, she won a fellowship with which she traveled and worked in Mexico.

GROWING CITY

Painted 1956, signed: E. Coen. Oil on canvas, 42×50 in. (106.7×127 cm.)
Mr. and Mrs. Frank G. Logan Purchase Prize, 57.631

COLE, Thomas ~ *b. 1801 Bolton-le-Moors, England. d. 1848 Catskill, N.Y.*

Cole who may be regarded as the founder of the Hudson River School of romantic landscape painting, began his career as an itinerant painter. In 1825 he came to New York and soon after settled up the Hudson at Catskill, where he lived in the midst of rugged mountain scenery. He also painted the White Mountains and made two trips to Europe.

LANDSCAPE

Signed and dated (signature indistinct) 1839. Oil on canvas, 22⅝ × 18⅝ in. (57.6 × 47.4 cm.)
Nickerson Collection, 00.558

COLE, Thomas (follower of)

NIAGARA FALLS

Painted in late 1840's. Oil on panel, 18⅞ × 23⅞ in. (48 × 60.8 cm.)
Friends of American Art Collection, 46.396

COLMAN, Samuel ~ *b. 1832 Portland, Me. d. 1920 New York City*

Colman, the landscape painter, a follower of the Hudson River School, was a pupil of Asher B. Durand. During his extensive travels in Europe Colman became strongly influenced by Turner and Andreas Achenbach. He was one of the founders of the Society of American Artists in 1878, a splinter group from the National Academy.

OLD TOWER AT AVIGNON

Painted about 1892, signed: Sam Colman. Oil on canvas, 7⅝ × 8⅞ in. (19.4 × 22.5 cm.)
Mr. and Mrs. Martin A. Ryerson Collection, 33.1187

GENESEE MEADOWS

Painted about 1892, signed: Sam Colman. Oil on canvas, 12 × 22¼ in. (30.5 × 56.6 cm.)
Nickerson Collection, 00.559

CONNELLY, Brian ~ *b. 1926 Roseburg, Ohio*

Connelly studied at the University of Oregon and at Parsons School of Design.

ATTRACTION

Signed and dated: Brian 1950. Oil and tempera on panel, 20 × 24¼ in. (50.9 × 61.7 cm.)
Wentworth Greene Field Memorial Fund, 51.56

CONSTABLE, John ~ *b. 1776 East Bergholt, England. d. 1837 London*

The son of a well-to-do miller, Constable followed his father's trade in his early youth; but encouraged by friends, he entered the Royal Academy School in 1799. Thirty years later he was elected a member of the Royal Academy. Constable never left England, concentrating his interests on the country scenes in his home region in Norfolk. He inaugurated a new era and, though he had no direct followers, influenced French painters, particularly Delacroix. Constable's paintings, especially the *Hay Wain*, caused a sensation when exhibited in the Paris Salon of 1824. A generation later his work exerted influence on Monet and Pissarro.

STOKE-BY-NAYLAND Illus. p. 237

Painted 1836. Oil on canvas, 49½ × 66⅜ in. (125.8 × 168.8 cm.)
Mr. and Mrs. W. W. Kimball Collection, 22.4453

"... a summer morning, July or August, at eight or nine o'clock, after a slight shower during the night, to enhance the dews in the shadowed part of the picture, under 'Hedgerow elms and hillocks green.' Then the plough, cart, horse, gate, cows, donkey, etc., are all good paintable material for the foreground, and the size of the canvas sufficient to try one's strength, and keep one at full collar." These were Constable's words to his friend, William Purton, February 6, 1836, about the picture he intended to paint of Stoke-by-Nayland. There are a number of preparatory sketches for the picture, all varying slightly in composition.

Coll: Nield Sale, 1879

Ref: Chicago. Art Institute, Annual Report, *1922 (ill.); Chicago. Art Institute,* Bulletin *20: 51–3, 1926 (ill.); Collins Baker, C. R.,* British Painting, *1930, p. 160 (pl. 106); Chicago. Art Institute,* A Century of Progress Exhibition, *1933, cat. no. 190 (pl. 41);* Ibid., *1934, cat. no. 136; Leslie, C. R.,* Memoirs of the Life of John Constable, *1937, p. 337; Chicago. Art Institute,* Masterpieces of English Painting, *1946, cat. no. 44 (pl. 25); New York. Museum of Modern Art,* Masters of British Painting, *1800–1950, 1956, cat. no. 27, (pl. p. 33)*

COPLEY, John Singleton ~ *b. 1738 Boston, Mass. d. 1815 London*

Copley, a precocious artist, began his career in his early teens under the tutelage of his step-father, Peter Pelham, the engraver. He was no doubt familiar with the work of John Smibert, John Greenwood, Joseph Blackburn and Robert Feke, all of whom had been working in Boston. In 1766 his *Boy with a Squirrel* was shown with great success at the Royal Academy in London. Copley moved permanently to London in 1774.

DANIEL HUBBARD

Signed and dated: John S. Copley pinxt 1764. Oil on canvas, 50⅜ × 39¾ in. (128 × 101 cm.)
Art Institute Purchase Fund, 47.27
Coll: Mary Hubbard; Miss M. H. Whitwell; Henry D. Tudor, Cambridge, Mass.

Ref: Perkins, A. T., John Singleton Copley, *1873, p. 75;* Masters in Art, *V, 1904, p. 498; Bayley, F. W.,* John Singleton Copley, *1915, p. 150; Parker, B. M., and A. B. Wheeler,* John Singleton Copley, *1938, pp. 115–6;* Connoisseur *122: 123–4, December 1948 (ill.); Chicago. Art Institute,* Bulletin *42: 16, 17, December 1948 (ill.); Chicago. Art Institute,* From Colony to Nation, *1949, cat. no. 32; Colorado Springs. Fine Arts Center,* Likeness of America, *1680–1820, 1949, cat. no. 13; Chicago. Art Institute,* Quarterly *45, no. 3: 42–50, 1959 (ill. p. 43)*

MRS. DANIEL HUBBARD (Mary Greene) Illus. p. 371

Painted about 1764. Oil on canvas, 50¼ × 39⅞ in. (127.7 × 101.3 cm.)
Art Institute Purchase Fund, 47.28

Copley used as a basis for the pose an English mezzotint by John Faber, Jr. after Thomas Hudson's *Mary, Viscountess Andover.*

Coll: Mary Hubbard; Miss M. H. Whitwell; Henry D. Tudor, Cambridge, Mass.

Ref: Perkins, A. T., op. cit., *p. 75;* Masters of Art, *V, 1904, pp. 498–9 (ill. p. 469); Bayley, F. W.,* op. cit., *p. 150;* Country Life in America *65: 638, December 1933 (ill.); Parker, B. M. and A. B. Wheeler,* op. cit., *p. 116 (pl. 41);* Art in America *30: 30, 33, 1942; Chicago. Art Institute,* Bulletin *42: 16, 17, 1948 (ill.); Flexner, J. T.,* John Singleton Copley, *1948, p. 32;* Connoisseur *122: 123–4, December 1948 (ill.); Chicago. Art Institute,* From Colony to Nation, *1949, cat. no. 33; Colorado Springs. Fine Arts Center,* Likeness of America, *1680–1820, 1949, cat. no. 14; Chicago. Art Institute,* Quarterly *45, no. 3: 43, 1959 (ill.)*

PORTRAIT OF ANNA BARRETT HILL (Mrs. Henry Hill)

Painted about 1765–1770. Pastel, panel backing, 21¾ × 16¼ in. (55.4 × 41.5 cm.)
Anonymous Gift, 59.511

Ref: Parker, B. N. and Wheeler, A. B., op. cit., *p. 226; Bolton, T.,* Early American Portrait Draftsmen in Crayons, *1923, p. 20, no. 30; Bayley, F. W.,* op. cit., *p. 143; Perkins, A. T.,* op. cit., *p. 72*

JOSEPH GERRISH

Painted about 1770. Oil on canvas, 30½ × 25 in. (77.5 × 63.6 cm.)
Gift of the Estate of Adela Barrett, 57.564

Son of Captain John and Sarah (Hobbes) Gerrish, Joseph was born and brought up in Boston. In 1744 he was commissioned in the 3rd Massachusetts Regiment and served at the siege of Louisburg in 1754. After his release from the army, Gerrish settled in Halifax, where he was listed in 1758 as a member of the Nova Scotia Council and Store Keeper of the Navy Yard.

Coll: Barrett Family; Major Samuel E. Barrett; Mrs. Samuel E. Barrett, Chicago

Ref: Eaton, A. W. H., Old Boston Families, *no. 2, 1913, p. 12; Bayley, F. W.,* op. cit., *p. 115; Parker, B. M., and A. B. Wheeler,* op. cit., *pp. 80–1 (ill. pl. 99)*

ROBERT HYDE, SQUIRE OF HYDE

Signed and dated: J. S. Copley Pinx.1778. Oil on canvas, 29¾ × 24¾ in. (75.6 × 63 cm.)
Friends of American Art Collection, 43.1002

BRASS CROSBY

Painted about 1780, signature indistinct. Oil on canvas, 88½ × 54½ in. (224.8 × 138.5 cm.)
A. A. Munger Collection, 22.2196
Coll: Archibald Ramsden Collection; Ehrich Galleries, New York

Ref: Chicago. Art Institute, Annual Report, *1922 (ill.);* Magazine of Art *13: 498, 1922 (ill.);* Art News *20: 1, May 1922 (ill.); Chicago. Art Institute,* Bulletin *16: 65–7, 1922 (ill.); Chicago. Art Institute,* A Century of Progress Exhibition, *1933, cat. no. 41;* Ibid., *1934, cat. no. 368*

CORBINO, Jon ~ *b. 1905 Vittoria, Italy*

Corbino came to the United States in 1913 and studied at the School of the Pennsylvania Academy of the Fine Arts. He also attended the Art Students League.

ROCKPORT BEACH

Painted 1937, signed: Jon Corbino. Oil on canvas, 24⅞ × 30 in. (63.3 × 76.3 cm.)
Hi Simons Memorial, 46.45

CORNEILLE DE LYON (Corneille de la Haye) ~ *active 1533/4–1574 Lyon, France*

Corneille de Lyon, who came to Lyon from The Hague sometime before 1534, brought from Holland the concept of the small-sized portrait. In 1551 Corneille de Lyon was appointed painter to the French court.

PORTRAIT OF A MAN

Painted about 1550–1560. Oil on panel, 9½ × 7½ in. (24.2 × 19.1 cm.)
Gift of Everett D. Graff, 53.466

LOUISE HALLEWYN DE CIPIERRE

Painted about 1560. Oil on panel, 8 × 6¾ in. (20.3 × 17.2 cm.)
Mr. and Mrs. Martin A. Ryerson Collection, 33.1061

Louise de Hallewyn was a member of the house of Piennes and lady-in-waiting to Catherine de Medici. Her wedding was celebrated at the court of Blois in 1560, when she was married to Philibert de Marcilly, Seigneur de Cipierre, governor of two provinces under the youthful Charles IX.

Coll: Senator Colin Collection, Paris; Kleinberger Galleries, Paris; Kleinberger Galleries, New York; Martin A. Ryerson Collection, Chicago

Ref: Dimier, L., Histoire de la Peinture de Portrait en France au XVIe Siècle, *II, 1925, p. 71, no. 33; Chicago. Art Institute,* A Century of Progress Exhibition, *1933, cat. no. 11;* Ibid., *1934, cat. no. 10*

CORNELISZ VAN AMSTERDAM, Jacob (also called van Oostsanen) ~ *b. about 1470 Oostsanen, Holland. d. 1533 Amsterdam*

Cornelisz van Amsterdam was the most important painter in Amsterdam during the transitional period between the Middle Ages and the dawning Renaissance. He utilized earlier compositions, engravings and the work of his contemporaries to form his style.

VIRGIN AND ST. JOHN

Painted about 1510. Oil and tempera on panel, $13\frac{5}{16} \times 10\frac{3}{4}$ in. (34×27.3 cm.)
Mr. and Mrs. Martin A. Ryerson Collection, 37.1011 (Friedlaender 256)
Coll: Duke de Blacos, Paris

Ref: Steinbart, K., Kunstchronik und Kunstmarkt *34, pt. 2: 606, 1923; Steinbart, K.,* Marburger Jahrbuch *5: 256, 1929; Chicago. Art Institute,* A Century of Progress Exhibition, *1933, cat. no. 39; Friedlaender, M. J.,* Altniederlaendische Malerei, *XII, 1935, no. 275*

ADORATION OF THE MAGI

Painted about 1520. Oil and tempera on panel, $17\frac{9}{16} \times 21\frac{9}{16}$ in. (44.6×55.8 cm.)
Wilson L. Mead Fund, 35.381 (Friedlaender 275)
Coll: Dr. H. Tietje, Amsterdam, 1929; C. Castiglione, Vienna; V. Ferstel Collection, Vienna

Ref: Pantheon *4: 340, 1929; Steinbart, K.,* Marburger Jahrbuch *5: 234–6, 1929 (ill.); Cohen, W.,* Pantheon *5: 106, 108, 1930 (ill.); Friedlaender, M. J.,* Altniederlaendische Malerei, *XII, 1935, p. 195, no. 256 (pl. 52); Hoogewerff, G. J.,* De Noord-Nederlandsche Schilderkunst, *III, 1938, p. 119*

COROT, Jean-Baptiste Camille ~ *1796–1875 Paris*

Born in 1796, Corot was educated in the neoclassic tradition. He went to Rome in 1825 to follow in the footsteps of Poussin. Without belonging to any school, Corot was a personality of importance in the development of modern art.

VIEW OF GENOA

Stamped: Vente Corot, inscribed and dated: Gènes 1834.
Oil on paper, mounted on canvas, $11\frac{5}{8} \times 16\frac{3}{8}$ in. (29.5×41.7 cm.)
Mr. and Mrs. Martin A. Ryerson Collection, 37.1017 (Robaut 301)
Coll: Vente Corot (no. 68); Collection Brame, Paris; May Collection, "Vente Corot," (June 4, 1890, cat. no. 20)

MONTE PINCIO, ROME Illus. p. 240

Painted between 1840 and 1850, signed: Corot.
Oil on canvas, $10\frac{5}{8} \times 16$ in. (27×40.8 cm.)
Gift of Annie Swan Coburn to the Mr. and Mrs. Lewis L. Coburn Memorial Collection, 42.466

Although some have thought that this was done during Corot's first stay in Rome (1825–1828), it may be a later repetition, done between 1840 and 1850, with some genre figures introduced. The painting may also be by another hand.
Coll: G. Tempelaere, Paris; Mme Henry Marcel, Paris, 1936; A. Weil, New York

Ref: Rewald, J., Art News *41, pt. 2: 11, 1942*

BATHING NYMPHS AND CHILD

Painted between 1855 and 1860, signed: Corot.
Oil on canvas, 32½ × 39½ in. (82.6 × 100.3 cm.)
Mr. and Mrs. W. W. Kimball Collection, 22.4454 (Robaut 1113)

Ref: Paris. Ecole des Beaux-Arts, Corot Memorial Exhibition, *1875, cat. no. 1875; Paris. Palais Gallièra,* Centennial Exhibition, *1895, cat. no. 34; Chicago. Art Institute,* Bulletin *14: 69, 77, 1920 (ill.);* Ibid., *18: 100, 101, 1924 (ill.); Chicago. Art Institute,* A Century of Progress Exhibition, *1934, cat. no. 165*

SOUVENIR OF ITALY

Painted between 1855 and 1860, signed: Corot.
Oil on canvas, 32½ × 26⅛ in. (82.6 × 66.4 cm.)
Potter Palmer Collection, 22.408 (Robaut 1148)
Coll: M. Délins, Reims, 1868; Mrs. Potter Palmer Collection, Chicago, 1922

Ref: Chicago. Art Institute, Bulletin *18: 100, 1924 (ill.); Chicago. Art Institute,* A Century of Progress Exhibition, *1934, cat. no. 161*

JUST BEFORE SUNRISE

Painted between 1865 and 1870, signed: Corot. Oil on canvas, 13 × 21⅝ in. (33 × 55 cm.)
Henry Field Memorial Collection, 94.1041

INTERRUPTED READING Illus. p. 241

Painted about 1865 or 1870, signed: Corot. Oil on canvas, 36½ × 25¾ in. (92.8 × 65.5 cm.)
Potter Palmer Collection, 22.410 (Robaut 1431)
Coll: Larochenoire, Paris; Alexandre Dumas (sale, February 1882, no. 15; May 1892, no. 24); Mrs. Potter Palmer

Ref: Paris. Ecole des Beaux-Arts, Exhibition, *1875, cat. no. 93; Jaccaci, A. F.,* Art in America *2: 6–11, 1913–1914 (ill.); Chicago. Art Institute,* Bulletin *18: 102, 1924; Meier-Graefe, J.,* Kunst und Kuenstler *28: 50, 51, 1929 (ill.); Cambridge, Mass. Fogg Museum of Art,* Exhibition of French Paintings of the 19th and 20th Centuries, *1929, cat. no. 12; Meier-Graefe, J.,* Corot, *1930, pl. 107; New York. Museum of Modern Art,* Corot-Daumier, *1930, cat. no. 29 (ill.); Chicago. Art Institute,* A Century of Progress Exhibition, *1933, cat. no. 231 (pl. 52);* Ibid., *1934, cat. no. 164; New York. M. Knoedler & Co.,* J. B. C. Corot, *1934, cat. no. 20 (ill.); Bazin, G.,* L'Amour de l'Art *17, no. 11: 64, February 1936, (fig. 70); Watt, A.,* Apollo *23: 225, April 1936; Paris. Musée de l'Orangerie,* Corot. *1936, cat. no. 82 (pl. 21);* Home Collection of Great Art Masterpieces, *I, 1950 (ill. opp. p. 110); Philadelphia. Museum of Art,* Corot, *1950, cat. no. 49 (pl. 49); Fosca, F.,* Corot, *1958, p. 138*

WOUNDED EURYDICE

Painted between 1868 and 1870, signed: Corot. Oil on canvas, 22 × 16¼ in. (56 × 41.5 cm.)
Henry Field Memorial Collection, 94.1042 (Robaut 2001)

SPANISH PAINTINGS

XIVth—XIXth Centuries

ILLUSTRATIONS

Opposite: El Greco, Assumption of the Virgin, 1577
Gift of Nancy Atwood Sprague in memory of Albert Arnold Sprague

El Greco, Assumption of the Virgin—Detail

El Greco, Assumption of the Virgin—Detail

Spanish School, Ayala Altar, 1393. Gift of Charles Deering—Detail

Ayala Altar—Detail

Velázquez, Queen Isabella of Spain, c. 1632. Max & Leola Epstein Collection

Martorell, Bernardo, Saint George and the Dragon, c. 1435-40
Gift of Mrs. Richard E. Danielson & Mrs. Chauncey McCormick

El Greco, Feast in the House of Simon, c. 1610–14. The Joseph Winterbotham Collection

Above: Zurbarán, Franciso de, Bowl with Fruit and Flowers, c. 1633–44. Wirt D. Walker Fund

Velázquez, Saint John, c. 1619/20. Gift of Mrs. Richard E. Danielson

Velázquez, The Servant, c. 1618–22. Robert A. Waller Fund

Opposite: Zurbarán, San Roman, 1638
Gift of Mrs. Richard E. Danielson
and Mrs. Chauncey McCormick

El Greco, Saint Francis, c. 1590–1604. Robert A. Waller Fund

BEATVS RO
MANVS ORA
BAT DICENS
ODEST BENEDI
ORA PRO NOBI
BEATE ROMA
NE VT DIGNI
EFFICIAMVR
CHRISTI

Goya, Francisco de, The Hanged Monk, c. 1810. Robert A. Waller Fund

Opposite:
Goya, Francisco de, Capture of the Bandit Maragato, c. 1806/7
(two scenes from a set of six)
Mr. & Mrs. Martin A. Ryerson Collection

Opposite: Zurbarán, Francisco de, Crucifix, 1627
Robert A. Waller Fund

Coll: A. Sensier, Paris; O. Edwards, 1878, Paris, [Amateur ?] Sale, February 1881; Tavernier, Paris; Henry Field, 1893

Ref: Paris. Durand-Ruel, Sales Catalogue, *1878, cat. no. 59;* Art in America *2: 6–11, 1913–1914; Chicago. Art Institute,* Bulletin *18: 100, 1924 (ill.); New York. M. Knoedler & Co.,* Exhibition, *1929; Chicago. Art Institute,* A Century of Progress Exhibition, *1933, cat. no. 235;* Ibid., *1934, cat. no. 172*

ARLEUX-PALLUEL, THE BRIDGE OF TRYSTS

Painted 1871 or 1872, signed: Corot. Oil on canvas, 23¾×28¾ in. (60.5×73 cm.)
Potter Palmer Collection, 22.407 (Robaut 2210)

Ref: Chicago. Art Institute, Annual Report, *1921 (ill.); Chicago. Art Institute,* A Century of Progress Exhibition, *1933, cat. no. 230;* Ibid., *1934, cat. no. 159; New York. Wildenstein & Co.,* The Serene World of Corot, *1942, cat. no. 69 (ill.)*

COSTIGAN, John Edward ~ *b. 1888 Orangeburg, N.Y.*

Costigan, a self-taught artist, received his first recognition in 1922 when he won a prize at the Art Institute.

SHEEP AT THE BROOK

Signed and dated: J. E. Costigan, 1922. Oil on canvas, 33½×39 in. (85.2×99.2 cm.)
Charles S. Peterson Purchase Prize, 22.4451

A SUMMER DAY

Painted 1926, signed: J. E. Costigan. Oil on canvas, 49¾×60 in. (126.4×152.5 cm.)
Mr. and Mrs. Frank G. Logan Purchase Prize, 27.1433

COTER, Colijn de ~ *After 1450– about 1510 Brussels*

Influenced by Rogier van der Weyden and the Master of Flémalle, Colijn de Coter was perhaps the most outstanding painter of his time in Brussels.

MADONNA AND CHILD WITH ANGELS

Painted about 1500. Oil on panel, 59⅞×34 15/16 in. (152.1×88.6 cm.)
Mr. and Mrs. Martin A. Ryerson Collection, 33.1039 (Friedlaender 99)
Coll: P. and D. Colnaghi & Co., London; M. Knoedler & Co. (October 1912)

Ref: Friedlaender, M. J., Jahrbuch der Preussischen Kunstsammlungen *29: 229–231, 1908 (ill.); Chicago. Art Institute,* Bulletin *6: 36–7, 1913 (ill.); Conway, M. W.,* The Van Eycks and their Followers, *1921, p. 264 (pl. 12, fig. 2); Hensler, E.,* Jahrbuch der Preussischen Kunstsammlungen *45: 117–20, 1924 (ill. p. 119); Friedlaender, M. J.,* Altniederlaendische Malerei, *IV, 1925, p. 147, no. 99 (pl. 72); Fierens-Gevaert and P. Fierens,* Histoire de la Peinture Flamande, *III, 1929, p. 92; Chicago. Art Institute,* A Century of Progress Exhibition, *1934, cat. no. 118; Chicago. Art Institute,* Bulletin *36: 97, 1942 (ill. only)*

COTTET, Charles ~ *b. 1863 Puy, France. d. 1925 Paris*

Cottet studied with Puvis de Chavannes and was somewhat influenced by Gauguin. He traveled widely, worked in Egypt, Italy and Switzerland but lived for many years in Brittany.

PORTRAIT OF A WOMAN

Painted about 1900, signed: Ch. Cottet. Oil on canvas, $22\frac{3}{4} \times 19$ in. (57.9×48.3 cm.)
Gift of Henry J. Willing, 21.82

COURBET, Gustave ~ *b. 1819 Ornans, France. d. 1877 La Tour de Peilz, Switzerland*

Ornans, near the Swiss border, was Courbet's birthplace, and during most of his life he often returned there to paint the scenery. For a time Courbet attended the casual and informal Atelier Suisse in Paris and haunted the Louvre, where he copied Spanish and Dutch pictures, especially Rembrandt. For the most part he worked on his own, struggling hard to find means of expressing his concepts of reality.

THE BROOK OF LES PUITS-NOIR

Painted about 1855, signed: G. Courbet. Oil on canvas, $18\frac{1}{4} \times 21\frac{7}{8}$ in. (46.5×55.7 cm.)
Mr. and Mrs. Martin A. Ryerson Collection, 33.1117

This is a smaller and earlier painting of a scene similar to the one described on page 108.

Coll: Vente Courbet, 1876; J. P. Magaroz sale

Ref: Leger, C., Courbet, *1929, p. 57; Chicago. Art Institute,* A Century of Progress Exhibition, *1934, cat. no. 175*

MERE GREGOIRE

Illus. p. 242

Painted 1855, signed with initials. Oil on canvas, $50\frac{3}{4} \times 38\frac{1}{4}$ in. (128.9×97.2 cm.)
Wilson L. Mead Fund, 30.78

In this portrait of Mme Andler, the Swiss wife of the proprietor of the Brasserie Andler, the artist shows her behind the counter where she made change for the customers and occasionally offered a flower to a favorite.

Coll: Prince de Wagram; Princesse de la Tour d'Auvergne

Ref: Paris, Courbet Exhibition, *1867, cat. no. 96; Leningrad,* Exhibition of French Painting, *1911; Elder, M.,* A Giverny chez Claude Monet, *1924, p. 28; Leger, C.,* Courbet, *1929, p. 41; Chicago. Art Institute,* Bulletin *24: 42–3, 1930 (ill. cover);* Creative Arts *6, 1930 (pl. opp. p. 16);* Parnassus *2, no. 5: 36, 1930 (ill.);* Art Digest *4: 5, April 1930 (ill.); Chicago. Art Institute,* A Century of Progress Exhibition, *1933, cat. no. 237 (pl. 51);* Ibid., *1934, cat. no. 176; Rich, D. C.,* Formes *33: 381–3, 1933 (ill.); Hartford, Wadsworth Athanaeum,* 43 Portraits, *1937, cat. no. 37 (ill.); Toledo, Ohio.* The Spirit of Modern France, *1946, cat. no. 26 (ill.)*

LANDSCAPE

Signed and dated: G. Courbet '67. Oil on canvas, 21×31⅞ in. (53.5×81 cm.)
Gift of Joseph Winterbotham, 54.306

THE BROOK OF LES PUITS-NOIR Illus. p. 239

Signed and dated: G. Courbet '68. Oil on canvas, 43¾×54¼ in. (111.1×137.8 cm.)
Gift of Mr. and Mrs. Morris Kaplan, 56.762

A painting of a similar scene is in the Ryerson Collection of the Art Institute, but the *Ruisseau Couvert* in the Louvre, dated 1865, is closer in time and treatment.

AN ALPINE SCENE

Signed and dated: 74 G. Courbet. Oil on canvas, 23⅝×28¾ in. (60.1×73 cm.)
A. A. Munger Collection, 01.456
This was one of Courbet's last pictures after he had fled to Switzerland.

Ref: Duret, T., Courbet, *1918, p. 149; Meier-Graefe, J.,* Courbet, *1921, p. 49; St. Louis. City Art Museum,* Loan Exhibition of French Paintings, *1931, cat. no. 7; Chicago. Art Institute,* A Century of Progress Exhibition, *1933, cat. no. 236;* Ibid., *1934, cat. no. 174; Baltimore. Museum of Art,* An Exhibition of Paintings by Courbet, *1938, cat. no. 18; Chicago. The Arts Club,* Courbet, *1941, cat. no. 1; Leger, C.,* Courbet et son temps, *1948, p. 170, ill. fig. 45;* Sele Arte, *anno 2, no. 12, May–June 1954, ill. foll. p. 40; Cooper, D.,* Burlington Magazine *96: 322, 1954; Venice,* XXVII Biennale di Venezia, *1954; Lyon. Musée,* Courbet, *1954, cat. no. 55; Pallucchini, R.,* Burlington Magazine *97: 86, March 1955; Paris. Petit Palais,* G. Courbet, *1955, cat. no. 95 (ill. pl. 68); New York. Rosenberg & Co.,* Loan Exhibition of Gustave Courbet, *January–February 1956, cat. no. 18 (ill.)*

COUTURE, Thomas ~ *b. 1815 Senlis, France. d. 1879 Villiers-le-Bel, France*

Couture, who studied with Baron Gros and Paul Delaroche, began exhibiting in the Salon of 1840. He was popular as a teacher, and among his pupils were Manet, Diaz, Puvis de Chavannes, the German painter Anselm Feuerbach, William Morris Hunt and John La Farge.

THE BIRD-CATCHER

Painted about 1870, signed: T. C. Oil on canvas, 16×23½ in. (40.8×59.6 cm.)
Gift of Annie Swan Coburn to the Mr. and Mrs. Lewis L. Coburn Memorial Collection, 42.49
A larger version of the picture is in the collection of the museum in Dresden.
Coll: Blodgett; André Seligmann

Ref: Bertauts-Couture, Etudes d'Art *11–2: 203, 1955–1956*

CRADOCK, Marmaduke ~ *b. about 1660 Somerton, England. d. 1717 London*

BIRDS IN LANDSCAPE

Painted about 1700. Oil on canvas, 41½×39⅝ in. (105.4×100.6 cm.)
Gift of Robert Allerton, 32.960

CRANACH, Lucas the Elder ~ *b. 1472 Kronach, Germany. d. 1553 Weimar, Germany*

Lucas was a pupil of his father Hans Cranach, and was greatly influenced by Dürer's woodcuts. He first worked in Vienna, but in 1504 he was called to the court of the Elector of Saxony at Wittemberg where he became a close friend of Martin Luther. His early woodcuts and paintings done in Vienna give evidence of the independence with which he rid himself of conventional impediments of the Gothic style. Cranach painted nudes (Eve, Venus, etc.), religious subjects of the Reformation (especially Crucifixions), and portraits.

HEDWIG OF BRANDENBURG-ANSBACH

Signed and dated: winged serpent 1529. Oil on panel, 23½ × 16⅜ in. (59.6 × 41.7 cm.)
Gift of Kate S. Buckingham, 38.310 (Friedlaender-Rosenberg 263)

This is a portrait of the second wife of the Margrave of Brandenburg-Ansbach, George the Pious, whose portrait, forming a pendant to this, is now in the John G. Johnson Collection in Philadelphia.

Coll: Buchner; Alexis Schoenlank, Cologne; J. Vigouroux, New York

Ref: Paris. Sedelmeyer Gallery, Catalogue of the Sixth Series of 100 Paintings by Old Masters, *1900, cat. no. 7 (ill.); Reinach, S.,* Répertoire de peintures du moyen-âge et de la renaissance, *II, 1905, p. 377 (ill. no. 2); Valentiner, W. R.,* Catalogue of the Johnson Collection, *III, 1914, cat. no. 739 (the pendant to our picture)*

ADAM TEMPTED BY EVE (a)

EVE TEMPTED BY THE SERPENT (b) Illus. p. 151

Painted about 1530. (a) Oil on panel, 42¼ × 14¼ in. (107.4 × 36.3 cm.)
(b) Oil on panel, 42⅜ × 14⅜ in. (107.7 × 36.6 cm.)
Charles H. and Mary F. S. Worcester Collection, 35.294, 35.295

Many versions of this theme are known to have come from Cranach's workshop, but this is acknowledged to be one of the finest.

Coll: Private collection, Stockholm

Ref: Chicago. Art Institute, Annual Report, *1935 (ill.); Chicago. Art Institute,* Bulletin *30: 45–50, 1936 (ill.); Chicago. Art Institute,* Catalogue of the Worcester Collection, *1937, cat. no. 33 (pl. 25)*

THE CRUCIFIXION Illus. p. 150

Signed and dated: winged serpent 1533 [38?]
Oil on panel, 47 11/16 × 32½ in. (120.9 × 82.6 cm.)
Charles H. and Mary F. S. Worcester Collection, 47.62 (Friedlaender-Rosenberg 302)

The fact that Cranach has omitted other episodes usually associated with the Crucifixion reflects the atmosphere of the Protestant center of Wittemberg. This composition is based on a woodcut by Dürer.

Coll: Sir R. Fairfax Cartwright

Ref: Mather, F. J., The Arts *14: 309, 310, 1928 (ill.); Chicago. Art Institute,* Bulletin *23: 6–7, 1929 (ill.); Friedlaender, M. J., and J. Rosenberg,* Die Gemälde von Lucas Cranach, *1932, p. 85, cat. no. 302 (pl. 302); Chicago. Art Institute,* A Century of Progress Exhibition, *1933, cat. no. 13 (pl. 1);* Ibid., *1934, cat. no. 11; Kuhn, C. L.,* A Catalogue of German Paintings of the Middle Ages and Renaissance, *1936, pp. 38, 40, cat. no. 108; Chicago. Art Institute,* A Catalogue of the Worcester Collection, *1937, cat. no. 34 (pl. 26)*

PORTRAIT OF A BEARDED MAN

Signed and dated: winged serpent 1538, inscribed: *Annodo: M.D. XXXVIII, EATATI SUAE XXXV.* Oil on panel, 19½×13⅞ in. (49.7×35.3 cm.)
Charles H. and Mary F. S. Worcester Collection, 45.274 (Friedlaender-Rosenberg 334a)

Because of the close liaison in Cranach's workshop between his son and himself, it is not always possible to distinguish definitely between the works of the father and those of the son, Lucas Cranach the Younger. This portrait may have been executed by the latter.

Coll: Cloister Lamback, Germany; Galerie Alte Kunst, Munich

Ref: Friedlaender, M. J., and J. Rosenberg, Die Gemälde von Lucas Cranach, *1932, cat. no. 334a; Kuhn, C. L.,* A Catalogue of German Paintings of the Middle Ages and Renaissance in American Collections, *1936, p. 44, cat. no. 146 (pl. 26); Chicago. Art Institute,* Catalogue of the Worcester Collection, *1937, cat. no. 35 (pl. 27)*

CRESPI, Giuseppe Maria (called Lo Spagnolo) ~ *1665–1747 Bologna, Italy*

Crespi studied in Bologna with some of the local masters, until a wealthy patron provided him with means to travel and study in Venice and towns of northern Italy. He was deeply impressed by the great Venetians. In Bologna Crespi was in constant contact with the work of the Carracci and Guercino. Crespi gained great fame as a muralist and painter of religious and mythological scenes, and was commissioned to do pictures of Prince Eugène of Savoy and the Grand Duke Ferdinand of Tuscany.

THE MARRIAGE AT CANA Illus. p. 39

Painted about 1685. Oil on canvas, 74×97¾ in. (188×248.4 cm.)
Wirt D. Walker Fund, 56.129

WOMAN LOOKING FOR FLEAS

Painted about 1710. Oil on canvas, 19½×15⅜ in. (49.7×38.1 cm.)
Charles H. and Mary F. S. Worcester Collection, 47.63
Coll: Private collection, Naples; Arnold Seligmann, Rey & Co.

Ref: Lasareff, V., Art in America *17: 7, 1928; McComb, A.,* Baroque Painters of Italy, *1934, p. 94 (ill.); Howe, T. C., Jr.,* Pacific Art Review *1, no. 2: 2–3, 1941 (ill.); San Francisco. California Palace of the Legion of Honor,* Italian Baroque Painting, *1941, cat. no. 28*

CRIVELLI, Carlo ~ *1430–1435– about 1495 Venice*

Crivelli, a Venetian, was influenced by the Paduan School under Francesco Squarcione and reluctantly adopted the newer styles developed by Mantegna and Bellini.

THE CRUCIFIXION

Painted about 1490. Tempera on panel, 29⅝×21¾ in. (75.3×55.4 cm.)
Wirt D. Walker Fund, 29.862
Coll: Alexander Barker, London, 1874; De Beurnonville (sale, Paris 1881, no. 632); Joseph Spiridon (sale, Berlin 1929, no. 15)

Ref: Drey, F., Carlo Crivelli, *1927, pp. 89, 90, 147 (pl. 74); Chicago. Art Institute,* Annual Report, *1929, p. 17 (ill.); Chicago. Art Institute,* Bulletin *23: 145–7, 1929 (ill. p. 141);* Kunst und Kuenstler *27: 331, 1929 (ill.); Rich, D. C.,* Art News *28, pt. 1: 3, 6, December 7, 1929 (ill.); Berenson, B.,* Italian Pictures of the Renaissance, *1932, p. 161; Chicago. Art Institute,* A Century of Progress Exhibition, *1933, cat. no. 115;* Ibid., *1934, cat. no. 27; van Marle, R.,* The Development of the Italian Schools of Painting, *XVIII, 1936, pp. 59–60 (ill.)*

CURRAN, Charles Courtney ~ *b. 1861 Hartford, Ky. d. 1942 New York City*

Curran studied at the Cincinnati School of Design and later spent five years in New York at the National Academy of Design and the Art Students League. In 1885 he continued his studies in Paris at the Académie Julian. In 1900 he was Assistant Director of the American section of the Paris Exposition. He settled in New York, was made an Academician in 1904 and for twenty years was Secretary of the Academy.

ACADEMIE JULIAN

Signed and dated: Chas. C. Curran '88. Oil on canvas, 8½×11½ in. (21.7×29.2 cm.)
Gift of Kate L. Brewster, 50.1514
Coll: James Ellsworth, Chicago

Ref: Curran, C. C., Palette and Bench *1: 52–7, 1908, 2: 68–71, 1909*

CURRIER, J. Frank ~ *1843–1909 Boston, Mass.*

Although Currier had worked in Boston with Samuel Gerry and William Morris Hunt, his formative years were spent in Munich where he came under the strong influence of Wilhelm Leibl.

THE PAINTING CLASS (Americans in Dachau)

Painted about 1878. Oil on panel, 11¼×15$\frac{15}{16}$ in. (28.6×40.4 cm.)
Samuel P. Avery Fund, 33.857
Coll: Franz Langheinrich, Munich; Prof. C. Marr

CURRY, John Steuart ~ *b. 1897 Dunavant, Kan. d. 1946 Madison, Wisc.*

Curry, Thomas Hart Benton, and Grant Wood became known in the 1930's as the painters of the "American Scene." Trained at the School of the Art Institute and at the Art Students League in New York, Curry returned to his native Kansas where he found the themes and types appearing in his work.

HOGS KILLING RATTLESNAKE

Painted 1930, signed: John Steuart Curry. Oil on canvas, $30\frac{3}{8} \times 38\frac{5}{16}$ in. (77.2×97.5 cm.)
Gift of Mrs. Charles F. Glore, 47.392

Ref: The Arts *18: 54, October 1931;* Index of 20th Century Artists *4: 340, November 1936; Schneckebier, L. E.,* John Steuart Curry's Pageant of America, *1943, pp. 61, 62 (fig. 161)*

CUYP, Jacob Gerritz (attributed to)

DUTCH GIRL

Painted about 1655. Oil on canvas, $30\frac{1}{2} \times 25\frac{1}{4}$ in. (76.9×64.2 cm.)
Max and Leola Epstein Collection, 54.284

Jacob Gerritz Cuyp (1594– c. 1651), a pupil of Abraham Bloemaert, was well known for his portraits, battle scenes and landscapes with cattle. He was the father of the better-known Aelbert Cuyp.

Coll: Sir Worth Lethbridge, Sandhill Hale, near Taunton; Ehrich Galleries, New York, 1921

DAGNAN-BOUVERET, Pascal Adolphe Jean ~ *b. 1852 Paris. d. 1929 Quincey, France*

Dagnan-Bouveret was trained in the tradition of Gérôme.

WOMAN FROM BRITTANY

Signed and dated: P. A. J. Dagnan-B. 1886. Oil on canvas, $14\frac{1}{2} \times 11$ in. (36.9×28 cm.)
Potter Palmer Collection, 22.442

DALI, Salvador ~ *b. 1904 Figueras, Spain*

During his youth in Spain, Dali studied art in a private academy in Figueras and later in Madrid. It was not until 1928 that he made a brief excursion to Paris.

INVENTIONS OF THE MONSTERS

Painted 1937. Oil on canvas, $20\frac{1}{8} \times 30\frac{7}{8}$ in. (51.2×78.4 cm.)
The Joseph Winterbotham Collection, 43.798

Painted in 1937, *Inventions of the Monsters* is composed of fantastic images irrationally combined with portraits of the artist and his wife Gala. When Dali learned that the Art Institute had purchased his painting, he wired the following explanation: "Am pleased and honored by your acquisition. According to Nostradamus the apparition of monsters presages the outbreak of war. This canvas was painted in the Semmering mountains near Vienna a few months before the Anschluss and has a prophetic character. Horse women equal maternal river monsters. Flaming giraffe equals cosmic masculine apocalyptic monster. Cat angel equals divine heterosexual monster. Hourglass equals metaphysical monster. Gala and Dali equal sentimental monster. The little blue dog alone is not a true monster. Sincerely, Salvador Dali."

Coll: James T. Soby, Farmington, Conn.

Ref: Soby, J. T., Salvador Dali, *1941, p. 62 (ill.); Chicago. Art Institute,* Catalogue of the Winterbotham Collection, *1947, p. 13 (ill.)*

MAE WEST

Painted about 1934, signed: Salvador Dali. Gouache on paper, 11⅛ × 7 in. (28.3 × 17.8 cm.)
Gift of Mrs. Gilbert W. Chapman, 49.517

DANNAT, William Turner ~ *b. 1853 New York City. d. 1929 Monte Carlo*

Dannat's principal teachers were Carolus-Duran and Mihaly Munkacszy. In the late 1880's he settled in Paris, where his style was influenced by Japanese art.

STUDY OF AN ARAGONESE SMUGGLER

Painted in 1881, signed: W. T. Dannat. Oil on canvas, 32⅛ × 23½ in. (81.6 × 59.6 cm.)
Gift of the Artist, 87.231

DAUBIGNY, Charles François ~ *1817–1878 Paris*

Daubigny, a pupil of his father Edmé-François Daubigny, was educated in the classic tradition. He later turned to the new realism of the Barbizon School, with which he associated himself in the early forties. Success came soon after his first exhibition in 1838.

THE MARSH

Signed and dated: Daubigny 1871. Oil on panel, 13½ × 22⅞ in. (34.4 × 58.2 cm.)
Henry Field Memorial Collection, 94.1044

Ref: Henriet, F., C. Daubigny, *1875, p. 3*

LANDSCAPE WITH HOUSES

Painted between 1870 and 1878, signed: Daubigny.
Oil on canvas, 10¾ × 15⅞ in. (27.3 × 40.4 cm.)
Henry Field Memorial Collection, 94.1045

HOUSE OF MERE BAZOT

Signed and dated: Daubigny 1874. Oil on canvas, 36 × 73 in. (91.5 × 185.4 cm.)
Potter Palmer Collection, 22.405

Ref: Henriet, F., op. cit., *pp. 28, 183*

VILLAGE STREET (sketch)

Signed and dated: Daubigny 18?4. Oil on canvas, 9¼ × 14 in. (23.5 × 35.7 cm.)
Charles H. and Mary F. S. Worcester Sketch Collection Fund, 57.71

DAUMIER, Honoré ~ *b. 1808 Marseilles. d. 1879 Valmondois, France*

Daumier studied with Alexandre Lenoir and at the Académie Suisse. Charles Ramelet taught him lithography. Between 1830 and 1863, Daumier made caricatures for *La Caricature, Le Charivari* and *L'Association Mensuelle Lithographique.* Noted for his many lithographs, which number about four thousand, he had time for only a few paintings.

TWO LAWYERS

Painted about 1845 [?]. Oil on canvas, 5¼ × 5¾ in. (13.3 × 14.6 cm.)
Mr. and Mrs. Lewis L. Coburn Memorial Collection, 33.425
Coll: Emile Courbet, Paris; Countess Greffulhes, Paris; Mme de la Beraudière, Paris; Etienne Bignou, Paris; Mrs. Annie S. Coburn

Ref: Fuchs, E., Der Maler Daumier, *1927 (pl. 25a);* Daumier raconté par lui-même et par ses amis, *1945, p. 70; Adhemar, J.,* Honoré Daumier, *1954, p. 142*

THE PRINT COLLECTOR — Illus. p. 233

Probably painted about 1857–1863, signed: H. Daumier.
Oil on panel, 16⅝ × 13 in. (42.3 × 33 cm.)
Gift of the estate of Marshall Field, 57.305
Coll: (probably in Corot sale, Paris 1875, no. 663); Georges Viau, Paris; Henri Vever, Paris; Mme Jacques Doucet

Ref: Paris, Exposition Internationale Universelle, *1900, cat. no. 182; Klossowski, E.,* Honoré Daumier, *1923, cat. no. 373 (pl. 138); Amsterdam.* Exposition Rétrospective d'Art Français, *1926, cat. no. 32; Fuchs, E.,* Der Maler Daumier, *1927, (pl. 10); Focillon, H.,* Gazette des Beaux-Arts *2, per. 6: 81, July/December 1929 (ill.); New York. Museum of Modern Art,* Exposition Corot-Daumier, *1930, cat. no. 90 (ill.); Paris. Musée de l'Orangerie,* Daumier, *1934, cat. no. 21 (ill.);* Daumier raconté par lui-même et par ses amis, *1945, p. 276, no. 21*

DAVEY, Randall ~ *b. 1887 East Orange, N.J.*

Davey studied architecture at Cornell University. He began painting under Robert Henri and also studied abroad.

A YOUNG LADY (Mildred Cowing, Mrs. Wilder Haines)

Painted in 1912, signed: Randall Davey. Oil on canvas, 34 × 26 in. (86.4 × 66.1 cm.)
Friends of American Art Collection, 15.564

FLOWERS

Painted about 1913, signed: Randall Davey. Oil on canvas, 32×26 in. (81.3×66.1 cm.)
Friends of American Art Collection, 15.251

JOHN GALSWORTHY

Signed and dated: Randall Davey, 1926. Oil on canvas, 32⅛×26⅛ in. (81.6×66.4 cm.)
Gift of Mr. and Mrs. Cyrus McCormick, Jr., 26.399

DAVID, Gerard ~ *b. 1450–1460 Oudewater, Holland. d. 1523 Bruges, Belgium*

Although David was Dutch by birth, he settled in Bruges. Like many of the early Flemish and Dutch artists, David must have received considerable training as an illuminator. His early style suggests a close association with Geertgen tot Sint Jans, probably during the time of apprenticeship to Aelbert van Ouwater of Haarlem. In Bruges, where he was admitted to the painter's guild in 1484, David felt the impact of Jan van Eyck, Rogier van der Weyden and Memling.

LAMENTATION AT THE FOOT OF THE CROSS Illus. p. 146

Painted about 1511, inscribed: Reghe. Oil on panel, 21½×24½ in. (54.7×62.4 cm.)
Mr. and Mrs. Martin A. Ryerson Collection, 33.1040

This painting, cropped now at the right and on top, was in all probability part of a large altarpiece, constructed of several panels in one wooden frame. The altar was later broken up and the panels thus separated. A similar composition is in the Philadelphia Museum of Art (Johnson Collection).

Coll: Cardinal Despuig, Palma di Majorca; Countess Renée de Béarn, Paris; W. Gay, Paris; Marczell von Nemes, Budapest (sale at Manzi, Paris, 1913, cat. no. 17, ill.)

Ref: Justi, K., Zeitschrift für Bildende Kunst *21: 137, 1886; Benoit, C.,* Chronique des Arts, *1903, p. 105; Bodenhausen, E.,* Gerhard David und Seine Schule, *1905, p. 168, no. 31; Bodenhausen, E., and Valentiner,* Zeitschrift für Bildende Kunst, *N.F. 22: 184, 1911;* Marczell von Nemes Collection, *Budapest (sale at Manzi, Paris), 1913, I, no. 17;* L'Art et les Artistes *17, 1913 (supplément); Conway, M.,* The Van Eycks and their Followers, *1921, p. 286; Friedlaender, M. J.,* Van Eyck bis Breughel, *1921, p. 191; Friedlaender, M. J.,* Altniederlaendische Malerei, *VI, 1928, pp. 150, 151, cat. no. 195*

DAVIES, Arthur Bowen ~ *b. 1862 Utica, N.Y. d. 1928 Florence*

In 1893 Arthur B. Davies won a fellowship that enabled him to study in Italy. Renaissance painting, particularly the work of Giorgione and Piero di Cosimo, exerted a strong influence on his development. Davies was one of the chief organizers of the Armory Show in 1913. He also became a member of The Eight.

DIRGE IN SPRING

Painted in 1900, signed: A. B. Davies. Oil on canvas, 8½×20 in. (21.7×50.9 cm.)
Mr. and Mrs. Martin A. Ryerson Collection, 37.1036

FULL-ORBED MOON

Painted in 1901, signed: A. B. Davies. Oil on canvas, 23 × 15¾ in. (58.6 × 40.1 cm.)
Mr. and Mrs. Martin A. Ryerson Collection, 33.1191

EVENING AMONG THE RUINS

Painted in 1902. Oil on canvas, 11 × 16 in. (28 × 40.8 cm.)
George F. Porter Collection, 27.530

OUR RIVER HUDSON

Painted in 1903, signed: A. B. Davies. Oil on canvas, 23½ × 28 in. (59.6 × 71.2 cm.)
Mr. and Mrs. Martin A. Ryerson Collection, 37.1038

SUMMER AND THE MOTHER-HEARTED

Painted about 1903, signed: A. B. Davies. Oil on canvas, 28 × 23 in. (71.2 × 58.6 cm.)
Gift of Emily Crane Chadbourne, 26.1029

LAKE AND ISLAND, SIERRA NEVADAS

Painted in 1905, signed: A. B. Davies. Oil on canvas, 17½ × 39 in. (44.5 × 99.2 cm.)
Mr. and Mrs. Martin A. Ryerson Collection, 33.1194

LEDA AND THE DIOSCURI

Painted in 1905, signed: A. B. Davies. Oil on canvas, 25¼ × 36⅜ in. (64.2 × 92.4 cm.)
Gift of Emily Crane Chadbourne, 26.1028

SEMELE—THE FIREFLY

Painted in 1907, signed: A. B. Davies. Oil on canvas, 7½ × 14¾ in. (19.1 × 37.5 cm.)
Mr. and Mrs. Martin A. Ryerson Collection, 33.1199

HELEN, THE DAWN FLOWER

Painted about 1907, signed: A. B. Davies. Oil on canvas, 23¾ × 11¾ in. (60.5 × 29.8 cm.)
Mr. and Mrs. Martin A. Ryerson Collection, 33.1192

LISTENING VALLEYS HEAR

Painted about 1907, signed: A. B. Davies. Oil on canvas 14½ × 7½ in. (36.9 × 19.1 cm.)
Mr. and Mrs. Martin A. Ryerson Collection, 33.1195

MAYA, MIRROR OF ILLUSIONS

Painted about 1910. Oil on canvas, 26 × 40 in. (66.1 × 101.7 cm.)
Friends of American Art Collection, 10.318

SILVER SPRINGS

Painted in 1910, signed: A. B. Davies. Oil on canvas, 17 × 39½ in. (43.3 × 100.3 cm.)
Mr. and Mrs. Martin A. Ryerson Collection, 37.1037

TWO VOICES: HARMONY AND DISCORD

Painted about 1910, signed: A. B. Davies. Oil on canvas, 17⅜ × 39½ in. (44.2 × 100.3 cm.)
Mr. and Mrs. Martin A. Ryerson Collection, 33.1200

AN ANTIQUE ORISON

Painted about 1914, signed: A. B. Davies. Oil on canvas, 25½ × 40 in. (64.8 × 101.7 cm.)
Gift of Emily Crane Chadbourne, 18.312

SACRAMENTAL TREE

Painted in 1915, signed: A. B. Davies. Oil on canvas, 26 × 42 in. (66.1 × 106.7 cm.)
Mr. and Mrs. Martin A. Ryerson Collection, 33.1198

CHORAL SEA

Painted in 1915, signed: A. B. Davies. Oil on canvas, 17 × 39⅜ in. (43.3 × 100 cm.)
Mr. and Mrs. Martin A. Ryerson Collection, 33.1189

GOLDEN SEA GARDEN

Painted about 1915, signed: A. B. Davies. Oil on canvas, 16⅜ × 21⅜ in. (41.7 × 54.4 cm.)
George F. Porter Collection, 27.305

LANDSCAPE

Oil on canvas, 12 × 14 in. (30.5 × 35.7 cm.)
Gift of Mrs. Arthur T. Aldis, 43.1187

DAVIS, Charles Harold ~ *b. 1856 Amesbury, Mass. d. 1933 Mystic, Conn.*

Davis studied at the School of the Museum of Fine Arts in Boston and attended the Académie Julian in Paris.

THE NORTHWEST WIND

Painted 1914, signed: C. H. Davis. Oil on canvas, 49½ × 39½ in. (125.8 × 100.3 cm.)
Walter H. Schulze Memorial Collection, 24.907

DAVIS, Stuart ~ *b. 1894 Philadelphia*

Though Davis studied with Robert Henri, it was not so much his training as the overwhelming experience of the Armory Show in 1913 that gave direction to his development. The post-Cubist work of Picasso and particularly Léger influenced Davis greatly. After a trip to Paris in 1928–29, Davis taught at the Art Students League and executed a number of murals under the WPA program.

READY-TO-WEAR Illus. p. 392

Painted 1955, signed: Stuart Davis. Oil on canvas, 56¼ × 42 in. (143 × 106.7 cm.)
Gift of Mr. and Mrs. Sigmund W. Kunstadter and Goodman Fund, 56.137

DEARTH, Henry Golden ~ *b. 1864 Bristol, Rhode Island. d. 1918 New York City*

Dearth was trained at the Ecole des Beaux-Arts in Paris and studied with Aimé Morot.

VIRGIN AND CHILD

Painted about 1913, signed: H. Dearth. Oil on canvas, 45½ × 32 in. (115 × 81.3 cm.)
Friends of American Art Collection, 14.359

DECAMPS, Alexandre-Gabriel ~ *b. 1803 Paris. d. 1860 Fontainebleau, France*

Decamps studied with Abel de Pujol, who had been a pupil of Jacques Louis David. Traveling to the Near East in 1829, Decamps became one of the first European painters to be inspired by Oriental life.

COURTYARD

Painted about 1855. Oil on canvas, 19¼ × 15 in. (49 × 38.2 cm.)
Henry Field Memorial Collection, 94.1046

Ref: Silvestre, T., Histoire des Artistes Vivants, *1857, p. 186; Delacroix, E.,* Journal, *III, c. 1932, pp. 277–8*

STUDY OF PIGS

Painted about 1850–1860. Oil on paper, mounted on canvas, 10⅞ × 13¾ in. (27.6 × 35 cm.)
Henry Field Memorial Collection, 94.1047

DE CHIRICO, Giorgio ~ *b. 1888 Volo, Greece*

Though De Chirico was born in Greece, his antecedents are Italian; his work bears testimony to both countries.

THE PHILOSOPHER'S CONQUEST Illus. p. 471

Painted 1914, signed: G. de Chirico. Oil on canvas, 49½ × 39¼ in. (125.8 × 100.3 cm.)
The Joseph Winterbotham Collection, 39.405

Ref: Soby, J. T., The Early Chirico, *1941, pp. 38–40 (pl. 26)*

CLASSICAL FIGURES

Probably painted between 1925 and 1928, signed upper left: G. de Chirico.
Oil on panel, 25½ × 21¼ in. (64.8 × 54.1 cm.)
Gift of Joseph Winterbotham, 54.305

NUDE

Painted around 1928–1929, signed upper right: G. de Chirico.
Oil on canvas, 21¾ × 18 in. (55.4 × 45.8 cm.)
Gift of Joseph Winterbotham, 54.1354

DEGAS ~ *1834–1917 Paris*

Degas founded no school, had virtually no pupils, and was one of the great creative figures of the 19th century. Beginning his training under Louis Lamothe in 1855, he was an avid student of classical art and the old masters. The greatest single influence on his development was Ingres. Inspired by him, Degas trained himself with severe discipline to achieve an unsurpassed facility of line. He was one of the chief organizers of the famous Impressionist exhibitions and showed his work in seven, held from 1874 to 1886. His art, though closely related to the Impressionist movement, revealed basic differences; whereas the Impressionist painters dissolved all forms in light and atmosphere, Degas was primarily concerned with line and motion. He found inspiration in Japanese prints and in the perspectives disclosed by the camera. A superb portrait painter, mainly in his early years, Degas later found his favorite subjects among ballet dancers and on the race track. In his nude figures and bathers he demonstrated all phases of the body in motion, each final composition being preceded by countless sketches and drawings. To aid him in achieving a perfect grasp of the human figure in action, he often made small models in wax.

MME LISLE AND MME LOUBENS

Painted about 1869–1870, signed with red stamp "Degas"
Oil on canvas, $33\frac{1}{4} \times 38\frac{1}{16}$ in. (85 × 96.5 cm.)
Gift of Annie Laurie Ryerson in memory of Joseph Turner Ryerson, 53.335 (Lemoisne no. 265)

The two women have been identified by sketches in the Metropolitan Museum. Mme Loubens is said to have been the owner of a boarding house.

Coll: Atelier Degas, Paris; Georges Petit, Paris (sale, Atelier Degas, Paris, 1918, cat. no. 105); Detroit Institute of Arts, 1921

Ref: Paris. Catalogue des tableaux et dessins par Edgar Degas et provenant de son atelier, le vente à Georges Petit, *1918, p. 57, cat. no. 105 (ill.); Detroit. Institute of Arts,* Bulletin *2: 71, May 1921; Detroit. Institute of Arts,* Bulletin *3: 39, January 1922; Detroit. Institute of Arts,* The More Important Paintings and Sculpture, *1927, p. 147 (ill.); Detroit. Institute of Arts,* Catalogue of Paintings, *1930, cat. no. 55 (ill.)*

UNCLE AND NIECE Illus. p. 287

Painted about 1876. Oil on canvas, $39\frac{1}{4} \times 47$ in. (99.8 × 119.4 cm.)
Mr. and Mrs. Lewis L. Coburn Memorial Collection, 33.429 (Lemoisne no. 394)

Shown here is the artist's bachelor uncle, Henri De Gas and his niece, Lucy De Gas.

Coll: Mme Bazzi, Naples; Bellelli-Cicerale, Naples

Ref: Kunst und Kuenstler *25: 40, 1926–1927 (ill.); Manson, J. B.,* Life and Works of Edgar Degas, *1927, p. 48 (pl. 5); Hausenstein, W.,* Pantheon *7: 162, 1931; Guérin, M.,* Musées de France *4: 106, 1932; Nirdlinger, V.,* Parnassus *4: 12–15, 1932; Walker, J.,* Gazette des Beaux-Arts *10, per. 6: 179, 182, September 1933 (ill.); Vollard, A.,* Degas, *c. 1937, no. 34 (ill.); Graber, H.,* Edgar Degas, *1942 (ill.)*

CAFE SINGER

Painted about 1878, signed: Degas. Oil on canvas, 20⅞ × 16¼ in. (53.1 × 41.5 cm.)
Gift of Clara Lynch, 55.738 (Lemoisne no. 477)

The singer is Mlle Desgranges, who married the pianist Ritter.

Coll: de Bonnières, Paris; Lynch, Chicago

Ref: Lafond, P., Degas et son oeuvre, *II, 1919 (ill.); Grappe, G.,* L'Art et le Beau, *3me Année, 1: 36, 1920 (ill.); Maier-Graefe, A. L.,* Degas, *1920, pl. 55 (ill.); Jamot, P.,* Degas, *1924, pl. 55 (ill.);* L'Amour de L'Art, *July 1931, p. 305 (ill.); Mauclair, C.,* Degas, *1937, p. 107 (ill.); Cabanne, P.,* Degas, *1958, cat. no. 74 (ill. pl. 74)*

WOMAN IN A ROSE HAT (Mme Dietz-Monin, Portrait après un Bal Costumé)

Painted 1879, signed: Degas.
Pastel, tempera and oil on canvas, 33¾ × 29⅝ in. (85.8 × 75.3 cm.)
The Joseph Winterbotham Collection, 54.325 (Lemoisne no. 534)

This unfinished sketch was done in preparation for a portrait which was presumably destroyed. A fascinating insight into Degas' character is afforded by an unsigned letter to Mme Dietz-Monin found among his papers. Dissatisfied with the arrangements for sittings and displeased with the progress of the portrait, the lady wrote him suggesting that she send the pink Directoire hat and boa instead of appearing herself. Degas answered, "Let us leave the portrait alone, I beg of you. I was so surprised by your letter suggesting that I reduce it to a boa and a hat that I shall not answer you. . . . Must I tell you that I regret having started something in my own manner only to find myself transforming it completely into yours? That would not be too polite and yet. . . . But, dear Madame, I cannot go into this more fully without showing you only too clearly that I am very much hurt." (M. Guérin, *Degas Letters,* 1948, no. 37). There exists also a full scale sketch in pastel, one in charcoal and a study for the head as he may have planned it originally.

Coll: Atelier Degas (1re vente, Paris, Georges Petit, 1918, no. 116, ill.); Jacques Seligmann, Paris; Henry D. Hughes, Philadelphia; Reinhardt, New York

Ref: Charles, E., La Renaissance *1: 4, April 1918 (ill.); New York. American Art Association,* Catalogue J. Seligmann Sale, *1921, no. 34 (ill.); New York. American Art Association,* Catalogue of Sale of Paintings from Various Private Collections, *January 28, 1926, cat. no. 171; Mauclair, C.,* Degas, *1937, p. 64 (ill.); Degas, E.,* Letters, *1947, pp. 60, 61, no. 37*

ON THE STAGE

Painted about 1880, signed: Degas. Pastel on paper, 22½ × 16 in. (57.3 × 40.8 cm.)
Potter Palmer Collection, 22.423 (Lemoisne no. 601)

Ref: Lemoisne, P. A., Gazette des Beaux-Arts *3, per. 5: 227, 1921; Manson, J. B.,* The Life and Works of Edgar Degas, *1927, p. 47; Browse, L.,* Degas Dancers, *1949, cat. no. 143 (pl. 143)*

THE MILLINERY SHOP Illus. p. 336

Painted about 1885, signed: Degas. Oil on canvas, $39\frac{1}{8} \times 43\frac{3}{8}$ in. (17.5 × 110.3 cm.)
Mr. and Mrs. Lewis L. Coburn Memorial Collection, 33.428 (Lemoisne no. 832)

Ref: Paris. Georges Petit, Second Degas Sale, *1918, cat. no. 251; Mongan, A.,* Burlington Magazine *72: 297, 1938 (ill.); Cabanne, P.,* Degas, *1958, p. 111 (ill.)*

DANCERS IN THE WINGS

Painted about 1890, signed: Degas. Pastel on paper, $25\frac{1}{2} \times 19\frac{1}{2}$ in. (64.8 × 49.7 cm.)
Mr. and Mrs. Martin A. Ryerson Collection, 37.1032 (Lemoisne no. 1012)
Coll: Atelier Degas, Paris

Ref: Paris. Georges Petit, Second Degas Sale, *1918, cat. no. 353 (ill.);* Third Degas Sale, *1919, cat. no. 137, 142 (ill.); Manson, J. B.,* Life and Works of Edgar Degas, *1927, p. 47; Browse, L.,* Degas Dancers, *1949, p. 397, cat. no. 187 (ill.)*

THE MORNING BATH

Painted about 1890, signed: Degas. Pastel on paper, $27\frac{3}{4} \times 17$ in. (70.6 × 43.3 cm.)
Potter Palmer Collection, 22.422 (Lemoisne no. 1028)

Ref: Paris. Georges Petit, Third Degas Sale, *1919, cat. no. 348; Manson, J. B.,* op. cit., *p. 47*

TWO DANCERS

Painted about 1890, signed: Degas. Pastel on paper, $28 \times 21\frac{3}{8}$ in. (71.2 × 54.4 cm.)
The Amy McCormick Memorial Collection, 42.458 (Lemoisne no. 1017)

This is one of the pastels found in Degas' studio after his death.

Ref: Browse, L., op. cit., *cat. no. 211 (ill.)*

DANCERS IN THE FOYER

Painted about 1900–1905, signed: Degas. Oil on canvas, $16\frac{1}{4} \times 34\frac{3}{4}$ in. (41.5 × 88.3 cm.)
Charles H. and Mary F. S. Worcester Collection, 47.86 (Lemoisne no. 1394)
Coll: Baron Hatvany, Budapest; Peradon, Paris

THE BATHERS

Painted about 1890–1895. Pastel on paper $44\frac{5}{8} \times 45\frac{1}{2}$ in. (113.4 × 115.7 cm.)
Gift of Nathan Cummings, 55.495 (Lemoisne no. 1079)

This painting was among the objects which were still in the artist's studio at the time of his death. It was purchased by the art dealer Vollard and exhibited only once in Paris in 1936 before entering the Cummings Collection.

Coll: Atelier Degas (First Sale, Galerie Georges Petit, May 4–5, 1918, cat. no. 211, ill.); Ambroise Vollard, Paris

Ref: Paris. Galerie Georges Petit, First Degas Sale, *May 4–5, 1918, cat. no. 211 (ill.)*

WOMAN AT HER TOILETTE Illus. p. 285

Painted about 1903, signed: Degas. Pastel on paper, 29 7/16 × 28 1/2 in. (75 × 72.5 cm.)
Mr. and Mrs. Martin A. Ryerson Collection, 37.1033 (Lemoisne no. 1426)
Coll: Degas Sale no. 1, 1918, no. 127

Ref: Manson, J. B., Life and Works of Edgar Degas, *1927, p. 47*

DE KOONING, Willem ~ *b. 1904 Rotterdam, Holland*

While De Kooning was apprenticed to a decorating firm in Rotterdam, he studied in evening classes at the Academy of Fine Arts, where he came in contact with the de Stijl group. He continued his studies in Brussels and Antwerp. In 1926 De Kooning came to this country, where he first made a living as a housepainter, decorator and designer. In 1935 and 1936 he worked under the auspices of the WPA Art Project. De Kooning became a leading *avant-garde* artist after his first one-man show in New York in 1948.

EXCAVATION Illus. p. 390

Painted 1950, signed: De Kooning. Oil on canvas, 80 1/8 × 100 1/8 in. (203.5 × 254.5 cm.)
Mr. and Mrs. Frank G. Logan Purchase Prize, Gift of Mr. Edgar Kaufmann, Jr. and Mr. and Mrs. Noah Goldowsky, 52.1

Ref: Finkelstein, L., Magazine of Art, *43: 202–6, October 1950 (ill.); Ritchie, A. C.,* Abstract Painting and Sculpture in America, *1951, p. 152, cat. no. 54 (ill. p. 133); New York. Wildenstein & Co.,* Seventy 20th Century American Paintings, *February 20 – March 22, 1952; Venice.* XXVII Biennale, *1954, p. 66 (ill.)*

DELACROIX, Eugène ~ *b. 1798 Charenton-Saint-Maurice, France. d. 1863 Paris*

Delacroix was a pupil of Pierre Guérin but his fellow student Géricault influenced him more than his master. He constantly visited the Louvre and was greatly impressed by the canvases of Veronese and Rubens.

TIGER RESTING

Painted about 1830, signed: Eug. Delacroix. Oil on canvas, 8 × 15 in. (20.3 × 38.2 cm.)
Henry Field Memorial Collection, 94.1049

WOUNDED LIONESS

Probably painted between 1840 and 1850, signed: Eug. Delacroix.
Oil on canvas, 13 1/8 × 22 1/8 in. (33.4 × 56.3 cm.)
Henry Field Memorial Collection, 94.1048

ARAB RIDER ATTACKED BY LION

Painted in 1849, signed: Eug. Delacroix. Oil on canvas, 18 × 14 3/4 in. (45.8 × 37.5 cm.)
Potter Palmer Collection, 22.403 (Robaut no. 1067)

When Delacroix went to Africa in 1832 he had the opportunity of seeing actual combats between Arabs and wild beasts.

Coll: M.D., Paris, 1862; Baron Trétaigne, 1872; Febvre 1885; Mrs. Potter Palmer, Chicago, 1892

Ref: Mireur, H., Dictionnaire des ventes des arts, *II, 1892, p. 422; Mongan, A. and P. J. Sachs,* Drawings in the Fogg Museum of Art, *I, 1940, cat. no. 684 (preliminary drawing for this painting)*

THE LION HUNT Illus. p. 244

Signed and dated: Eug. Delacroix, 1861. Oil on canvas, $30\frac{1}{16}\times 38\frac{3}{4}$ in. (76.5×98.5 cm.)
Potter Palmer Collection, 22.404 (Robaut no. 1350)

On April 26, 1858 Delacroix wrote in his *Journal:* "Worked a lot with good humor on the Lion Hunt, which is as good as finished today." He was possibly making reference to this picture, which was completed and signed three years later.

Coll: Comte d'Aquila, 1868; Faure, 1885; A. Robinson, New York (sale 1892); John Taylor Johnson

Ref: Journal de Eugène Delacroix, *II, 1932, pp. 314, 317, 389, 402; Tietze, H.,* Meisterwerke Europaeischer Malerei in Amerika, *1935, pl. 265 (ill.)*

DELAUNAY Elie ~ *b. 1828 Nantes, France. d. 1891 Paris*

Delaunay, after training at the Ecole des Beaux-Arts became a painter of historical and religious subjects.

MRS. CHARLES L. HUTCHINSON

Signed and dated: Elie Delaunay 1890. Oil on canvas, $31\frac{3}{4}\times 23\frac{1}{2}$ in. (80.8×59.6 cm.)
Gift of Mrs. Charles L. Hutchinson, 36.122

Mrs. Hutchinson was greatly interested in gardening and her books on the subject were well known. Her husband was one of the founders of the Art Institute.

DELAUNAY, Robert ~ *b. 1885 Paris. d. 1941 Montpellier, France*

Delaunay devoted much of his time to the study of color as related to movement. Simultaneously with Léger he discovered the beauty of technology.

CHAMPS DE MARS, THE RED TOWER Illus. p. 429

Signed and dated: r. d. 1911 (inscribed and signed on back: *Champs de Mars, La Tour rouge 1911 r. delaunay époque destructive*). Oil on canvas, $64\times 51\frac{1}{2}$ in. (162.6×130.9 cm.)
The Joseph Winterbotham Collection, 59.1

This painting is one of at least twelve versions which Delaunay worked on from 1909 to 1912. He returned to this theme again during the 1920's and 1930's. On the back of the canvas the artist described this phase of his work as his "destructive period." The painting was exhibited in the Berlin exhibition, Der Sturm, in 1913.

DELVAUX, Paul ~ *b. 1897 Antheit, Belgium*

Delvaux studied at the Academy of Fine Arts in Brussels. Until 1924 he painted entirely from nature and in that year had his first exhibition. His early work shows the influence of Impressionism. During his extensive travels in Italy, he was greatly inspired by early Italian Renaissance painting. Delvaux began to develop his own style around 1936, and from then on his work has tended toward Surrealism.

THE VILLAGE OF THE MERMAIDS

Signed and dated: P. Delvaux 4-42. Oil on panel, 41×49 in. (104.2×124.5 cm.)
Gift of Mr. and Mrs. Maurice E. Culberg, 51.73

Ref: Spaak, C., Paul Delvaux *(Monographies de l'Art Belge), 1948, no. 9 (ill.); Langui, E.,* Paul Delvaux, *1949, p. 22 (ill.)*

DEMUTH, Charles ~ *1883–1935 Lancaster, Pa.*

In 1910 Demuth completed his studies at the Pennsylvania Academy of the Fine Arts, then in 1912 made his second trip to Paris where he studied at the two academies, Colarossi and Julian. In Paris he was exposed to Metzinger and Gleizes, who were experimenting with Cubism, and he was also familiar with the mechanized forms of Léger.

"...AND THE HOME OF THE BRAVE"

Signed with initials and dated: C. D. 1931.
Oil on composition board, 30×24 in. (76.3×61 cm.)
Gift of Georgia O'Keeffe, 48.650

Ref: Ritchie, A. C., Charles Demuth, *1950, p. 15, 86 (ill.), cat. no. 153*

DERAIN, André ~ *b. 1880 Chatou, France. d. 1954 Paris*

A predominately eclectic painter, Derain studied at the Académie Julian and later under Eugène Carrière. Strongly influenced by Matisse, he became identified with the Fauves in 1904. For a brief period he was attracted by the principles of Cubism. His later compositions, particularly his well-constructed landscapes, recall at times Cézanne, at times the more tender style of Corot.

FOREST AT MARTIGUES

Painted about 1908 or 1909. Oil on canvas, 32½×39½ in. (82.6×100.3 cm.)
Arthur Jerome Eddy Memorial Collection, 31.506

Ref: Eddy, A. J., Cubists and Post-Impressionism, *1914 (ill. opp. p. 154); Vaughan, M.,* Derain, *1941, p. 49*

LAST SUPPER

Painted 1911, signed: Derain. Oil on canvas, $89\frac{1}{4} \times 113\frac{1}{2}$ in. (226.7×288.4 cm.)
Gift of Mrs. Frank R. Lillie, 46.339

Studies for this monumental painting (undoubtedly influenced by Italian medieval frescoes) date back to 1910, though the canvas was not completed until four years later.

Ref: Einstein, C., Die Kunst des 20. Jahrhunderts, *1926, pp. 38, 203 (ill.); Manner, M.,* International Studio *94: 28, November 1929; Tselos, D.,* Parnassus *10: 10, March 1938 (ill.)*

LANDSCAPE

Probably painted around 1914, signed: A. Derain.
Oil on canvas, $23\frac{1}{8} \times 28\frac{1}{8}$ in. (58.9×73 cm.)
Helen Birch Bartlett Memorial Collection, 26.190
Coll: Paul Guillaume, Paris

GRAPES

Painted in the early 1920's, signed: A. Derain. Oil on canvas, $9\frac{7}{8} \times 17\frac{3}{8}$ in. (25.1×44.2 cm.)
Helen Birch Bartlett Memorial Collection, 26.191

THE FOUNTAIN

Painted in the early 1920's, signed: A. Derain. Oil on panel, $10\frac{3}{8} \times 13\frac{3}{4}$ in. (27.4×35.3 cm.)
Helen Birch Bartlett Memorial Collection, 26.350

BALLET DANCER

Signed: Derain. Oil on canvas, $17\frac{3}{4} \times 14\frac{1}{2}$ in. (45.2×36.9 cm.)
Charles H. and Mary F. S. Worcester Collection, 47.67

LANDSCAPE IN PROVENCE

Signed: A. Derain. Oil on cradled panel, $14\frac{3}{4} \times 21\frac{5}{8}$ in. (37.5×55 cm.)
Charles H. and Mary F. S. Worcester Collection, 47.67

DESBOUTIN, Marcellin Gilbert ~ *b. 1823 Cévilly, France. d. 1902 Nice, France*

Desboutin spent some time in Couture's studio, but was largely self-taught. He became a professional painter only after the loss of his fortune in 1873.

THE CONVERSATION

Painted about 1879, signed: M. Desboutin. Oil on canvas, $21\frac{13}{16} \times 14\frac{15}{16}$ in. (55.5×38 cm.)
Gift of Annie Swan Coburn to the Mr. and Mrs. Lewis L. Coburn Memorial Collection, 35.71

Ref: Clement-Janin, La Curieuse Vie de Marcellin Desboutin, *1922, p. 265*

DESORIA, Jean Baptiste François ~ *b. 1758 Paris. d. 1832 Cambrai, France*

Desoria was a pupil of Jean Restout the Younger.

MADAME ELISABETH DUNOYER

Signed and dated: Desoria 1797 An V. Oil on canvas, 51⅛ × 38⅝ in. (129.9 × 98.2 cm.)
Simeon B. Williams Fund, 39.533

The sister of General Brun, one of the Marshals of France created by Napoleon, is seated in a Directoire chair.

Coll: Jacques Doucet, Paris

Ref: San Francisco. California Palace of the Legion of Honor, Vanity Fair, *1942, cat. no. 33; Detroit. Institute of Arts,* From David to Courbet, *1950, cat. no. 6 (ill.)*

DESSAU, Paul Lucien ~ *b. 1909 Glendale County, Wood Green, England*

SELF PORTRAIT

Signed: (lower left) Paul Dessau—'40; (upper left) "The Tired Fireman—After Surrey Docks, September 1940". Oil on canvas, 24 × 19 in. (61 × 48.3 cm.)
Gift of the English Speaking Union, 42.309

DETAILLE, Edouard ~ *1848–1912 Paris*

Detaille, like his teacher, Meissonier, was an accomplished master of highly finished technique.

A MOUNTED OFFICER

Signed and dated: Edouard Detaille 1877. Oil on canvas, 19¼ × 15 in. (46.5 × 38.2 cm.)
Henry Field Memorial Collection, 94.1050

The officer represented is the duc de Chartres, grandson of Louis-Philippe.

Ref: Huysmans, J. K., L'Art Moderne, *1908, pp. 76–7*

DEVIS, Arthur ~ *b. 1711 Preston, England. d. 1787 Brighthelmstone, England*

Devis, a pupil of Peter Tillemans, was a frequent exhibitor with the Free Society of Artists from 1761 to 1780.

THE THOMLINSON FAMILY

Signed and dated: A. Devis f. 1745. Oil on canvas, 23¾ × 39¾ in. (60.5 × 101 cm.)
Joseph and Helen Regenstein Foundation Fund, 56.130

This group-portrait is one of the early dated works by Devis, and represents John Thomlinson, his wife, their daughters Bourke and Granger, and Master Thomlinson.

FAMILY IN A PARK WITH TENT

Painted about the middle of the 18th century.
Oil on canvas, 52¼ × 77½ in. (132.8 × 196.9 cm.)
Gift of Emily Crane Chadbourne, 51.206

Ref: Pavière, S. H., The Devis Family of Painters, *1950, p. 60, cat. no. 146*

PORTRAIT OF A GENTLEMAN

Painted probably third quarter of the 18th century.
Oil on canvas, 30¼ × 25¼ in. (76.9 × 64.2 cm.)
Gift of Emily Crane Chadbourne, 51.207

Ref: Pavière, S. H., op. cit., *p. 45, cat. no. 63*

DEWING, Thomas Wilmer ~ *b. 1851 Boston, Mass. d. 1938 New York City*

Dewing had a conventional training at the Académie Julian under Boulanger and Lefèbvre. He became an Impressionist along with Twachtman and J. Alden Weir, who founded the group Ten American Painters.

YOUNG WOMAN WITH VIOLONCELLO

Painted about 1905, signed: T. W. Dewing. Oil on canvas, 20¾ × 15¾ in. (52.8 × 40.1 cm.)
Mr. and Mrs. Martin A. Ryerson Collection, 33.1202

LADY IN GREEN AND GRAY

Painted about 1905, signed: T. W. Dewing. Oil on canvas, 24⅛ × 20 in. (61.3 × 50.9 cm.)
Friends of American Art Collection, 11.5

DE WOLF, Wallace Leroy ~ *b. 1854 Chicago. d. 1930 Pasadena, Calif.*

Wallace De Wolf was a trustee of The Art Institute of Chicago, contributed to the scholarship fund of the School, and gave generously to the Department of Prints and Drawings. Although he was self-taught, he enjoyed considerable popularity as a painter and etcher of Western scenes.

AMONG THE REDWOODS

Signed and dated: W. L. De Wolf 20. Oil on canvas, 30¼ × 25½ in. (76.6 × 64.8 cm.)
Gift of Wallace L. De Wolf, 22.5520

DIAZ DE LA PENA, Narcisse Virgile ~ *b. 1807 Bordeaux. d. 1876 Menton*

Largely self-taught, Diaz began his career as a china painter at Sèvres. Under the influence of Delacroix, color became his main interest. Through Théodore Rousseau he became a great admirer of nature and joined the Barbizon School of painters.

POND IN THE WOODS

Signed and dated: N. Diaz 1862. Oil on canvas, 26 × 35 in. (66.1 × 88.9 cm.)
Mr. and Mrs. W. W. Kimball Collection, 22.4455

LANDSCAPE WITH FIGURES

Painted about 1870, signed: N. Diaz. Oil on panel, $10\frac{1}{4} \times 13\frac{3}{4}$ in. (26 × 35 cm.)
Henry Field Memorial Collection, 94.1052

THREE LITTLE GIRLS

Painted about 1870, signed: N. Diaz. Oil on panel, $15\frac{1}{2} \times 10\frac{1}{2}$ in. (39.5 × 26.7 cm.)
Henry Field Memorial Collection, 94.1051

DICKINSON, Sidney Edward ~ *b. 1890 Wallingford, Conn.*

Dickinson was trained under George B. Bridgman, Douglas Volk, and William Merritt Chase.

UNREST (NUDE)

Painted 1917, signed: Sidney E. Dickinson. Oil on canvas, 62 × 46 in. (157.5 × 116.9 cm.)
Friends of American Art Collection, 19.871

DOESBURG, Theo van ~ *b. 1883 Utrecht, Holland. d. 1931 Davos, Switzerland*

Van Doesburg was one of the most influential artists of the modern Dutch School. Starting as a conventional painter in 1899, he developed revolutionary theories which gradually led him to abstract painting. In 1916 he and Piet Mondrian organized the group de Stijl.

COMPOSITION

Painted 1924. Oil on canvas, $39\frac{3}{8} \times 39\frac{3}{8}$ in. (100 × 100 cm.)
Gift of Peggy Guggenheim, 49.216
Coll: Mrs. Theo van Doesburg

Ref: New York. Art of This Century, Theo van Doesburg, Retrospective, *1947, p. 2*

DOMINGO Y MARQUES, Francisco ~ *b. 1842 Valencia, Spain. d. 1920 Madrid*

After studying at the academy in Valencia, Domingo won the Prix de Rome in 1878. Following his Italian training, he moved to Paris in 1875.

LAZY SPAIN

Signed and dated: F. Domingo 1878. Oil on panel, $8\frac{5}{8} \times 10\frac{5}{8}$ in. (22 × 27 cm.)
Henry Field Memorial Collection, 94.1053

DONGEN, Kees van ~ *b. 1877 Delfshaven, Holland*

Van Dongen, a portrait painter and illustrator of elegant Parisian life, was mainly self-taught. He early became associated with the Fauves, exhibiting with them in 1905.

WOMAN AGAINST WHITE BACKGROUND

Painted between 1910 and 1914, signed: van Dongen.
Oil on canvas, 50⅝ × 31 in. (128.6 × 78.8 cm.)
Gift of Mr. and Mrs. Carter H. Harrison, 46.48

RUE DE LA PAIX, PARIS

Painted between 1910 and 1914, signed: van Dongen.
Oil on canvas, 39 × 31½ in. (99.2 × 80.2 cm.)
Gift of Mr. and Mrs. Carter H. Harrison, 35.303

TEA IN MY STUDIO

Painted between 1910 and 1914, signed: van Dongen.
Oil on canvas, 35¾ × 28¼ in. (90.8 × 71.7 cm.)
Gift of Mr. and Mrs. Carter H. Harrison, 36.7

DOUGHERTY, Paul ~ *b. 1877 Brooklyn, N.Y.*

Dougherty was a landscape and marine painter who received much of his training abroad.

STORM QUIET

Signed and dated: Paul Dougherty 1907. Oil on canvas, 36½ × 48½ in. (92.8 × 123.2 cm.)
Friends of American Art Collection, 14.802

DOVE, Arthur G. ~ *b. 1880 Canandaigua, New York. d. 1946 Centerpoint, L.I.*

Dove began to study art when only nine years of age. After graduating from Cornell University in 1903 he became a successful magazine illustrator and worked for publications like *McClure's* and the old *Life*. Later he supported himself as a chicken farmer and lobster fisherman at Westport, Connecticut. Though influenced by French art which he saw on a trip to Europe, Dove's mature work is personal.

NATURE SYMBOLIZED NO. 2

Painted in 1914, signed: Dove. Pastel on paper, 18 × 21⅝ in. (45.8 × 55 cm.)
Alfred Stieglitz Collection, 49.533

FROM A WASP

Painted about 1914. Oil on panel, 8⅝ × 10½ in. (22 × 26.7 cm.)
Alfred Stieglitz Collection, 49.532

LANTERN

Painted 1921. Oil and silverpoint on panel, 21⅜ × 18 in. (54.4 × 45.8 cm.)
Alfred Stieglitz Collection, 49.539

MONKEY FUR

Made 1928. Tin foil, cloth and fur on metal, 17×12 in. (43.3×30.5 cm.)
Alfred Stieglitz Collection, 49.534

DOGS CHASING EACH OTHER

Painted 1929, signed: Dove. Oil on canvas, 18⅛×21⅛ in. (46.2×53.8 cm.)
Alfred Stieglitz Collection, 49.536

TELEGRAPH POLE Illus. p. 380

Painted 1929, signed: Dove. Oil and metallic paint on metal, 28⅜×21⅛ in. (72×53.8 cm.)
Alfred Stieglitz Collection, 49.535

CROSS AND WEATHER VANE

Painted 1935, signed: Dove. Oil on canvas, 34¾×24⅝ in. (88.3×62.7 cm.)
Alfred Stieglitz Collection, 49.538

SWING MUSIC (LOUIS ARMSTRONG)

Painted 1938, signed: Dove.
Oil, emulsion and wax on canvas, 17⅝×25⅞ in. (44.7×65.8 cm.)
Alfred Stieglitz Collection, 49.540

SILVER AND BLUE

Painted 1940. Oil and metallic paint on canvas, 21⅝×29⅝ in. (55×75.3 cm.)
Alfred Stieglitz Collection, 49.531

DU BOIS, Guy Pène ~ *b. 1884 Brooklyn, N.Y. d. 1958 Boston*

Du Bois studied with some of the notable teachers in this country—Carroll Beckwith, William Merritt Chase, Frank V. Du Mond and Kenneth Hayes Miller—but the most telling influence on his work was study in Paris under Steinlen.

RESTAURANT NO. 1

Painted 1924, signed: Guy Pène Du Bois. Oil on panel, 19½×14¾ in. (49.7×37.5 cm.)
Gift of Chester Dale, 50.1356

Ref: Ely, C. A., Modern Tendencies in American Painting, *1925 (ill. opp. p. 72); Cortissoz, R.,* Guy Pène du Bois, *1931, p. 9 (ill. pl. 40)*

RESTAURANT NO. 2

Signed and dated: Guy Pène Du Bois '24. Oil on panel, 19½×14¾ in. (49.7×37.5 cm.)
Gift of Chester Dale, 50.1357

DUBORDIEU, Pieter ~ *b. 1609/10 Lille-Bouchard, France. d. after 1678 Leyden, Holland*

Dubordieu, about whom little is known, was presumably trained in the Franco-Flemish tradition of realism. After 1630, he was active as a portrait painter in Leyden and Amsterdam where he was influenced by the early work of Rembrandt.

PORTRAIT OF A YOUNG GIRL Illus. p. 191

Painted about 1635. Oil on panel, 23¼×29¾ in. (59.1×75.6 cm.)
Wilson L. Mead Fund, 34.386
Coll: Auspitz, Vienna; Berlin, anonymous private collection

Ref: Cicerone *7: 205, 207, 1915 (ill.—listed as Paulus Moreelse); Tietze, H.,* Meisterwerke Europaeischer Malerei in Amerika, *1935, pl. 251 (ill.); Martin, W.,* Burlington Magazine *41, November 1922 (pl. II D opp. p. 218); Froelich-Bum, L.,* Pantheon *10: 399, December* 1932

DUBUFE, Claude Marie ~ *b. 1790 Paris. d. 1864 La Celle-Saint-Cloud, France*

Dubufe, a pupil of Jacques Louis David, made his reputation as a portrait painter.

PORTRAIT OF A MAN

Painted around 1820, signed: Dubufe. Oil on canvas, 32¼×25½ in. (82×64.8 cm.)
Gift of Samuel Weis, 43.531

DUBUFFET, Jean ~ *b. 1901 Le Havre, France*

The artist studied for several years in various *académies libres*—that is, studios offering space and a model without instruction. He first exhibited in Paris in 1944.

GRAND PORTRAIT MYTHE SUPERVIELLE

Painted about 1945. Oil on canvas, 51½×38½ in. (130.9×97.5 cm.)
Gift of Mr. and Mrs. Maurice E. Culberg, 50.1367

DUDLEY, Frank Virgil ~ *b. 1868 Delavan, Wisc. d. 1957 Chicago*

Frank Dudley studied at the School of the Art Institute.

DUNELAND

Painted about 1918–1920, signed: Frank V. Dudley.
Oil on canvas, 37¾×49¾ in. (95.9×126.4 cm.)
Gift of Gracia M. F. Barnhart in memory of Elizabeth French Barnhart, 21.75

DUDLEY, Katherine ~ *b. 1884 Chicago, Ill.*

Katherine Dudley studied with William P. Henderson in Chicago and New Mexico.

ELVIRA

Painted about 1910. Oil on canvas, 18×12 in. (45.8×30.5 cm.)
Friends of American Art Collection, 15.563

DUFRESNE, Charles Georges ~ *b. 1876 Millemont, France. d. 1938 Paris*

Though Dufresne studied engraving at the Ecole des Beaux-Arts in Paris he had no formal training as a painter. He first exhibited in 1910. In 1912 he became acquainted with Dunoyer de Segonzac and the Cubists.

STILL LIFE WITH COMPOTE

Painted in the late twenties, signed: dufresne. Oil on canvas, $32 \times 21\frac{1}{2}$ in. (81.3×54.7 cm.)
The Joseph Winterbotham Collection, 29.767

Ref: Chicago. Art Institute, Annual Report, *1929, p. 19 (ill.); Chicago. Art Institute,* Bulletin *24: 3–4 (ill.), 1934; Chicago. Art Institute,* Catalogue of the Winterbotham Collection, *1947, p. 16;* The Arts *16: 49, September 1929 (ill. p. 51); New York. Museum of Modern Art,* Painting in Paris from American Collections, *January/February 1930, cat. no. 32; Buffalo. Albright Art Gallery,* Contemporary Paintings of Flowers by International Artists *(25th anniversary), November/December 1930; Chicago. Art Institute,* A Century of Progress Exhibition, *1933, cat. no. 690;* Ibid., *1934, cat. no. 344; Lake Forest, Ill., Garden Club, April/May 1955*

TILL LIFE WITH FLOWERS

Signed: Dufresne. Oil on canvas, $25\frac{3}{8} \times 21\frac{1}{4}$ in. (64.5×54.1 cm.)
Gift of Joseph Winterbotham, 54.309

SYMPHONY

Signed: Dufresne. Oil on canvas, $39\frac{3}{8} \times 31\frac{7}{8}$ in. (100×81 cm.)
Gift of Joseph Winterbotham, 54.310

DUFY, Raoul ~ *b. 1877 Le Havre. d. 1953 Forcalquier, France*

Dufy studied at the Ecole des Beaux-Arts with Léon Bonnat, and together with his friend, Matisse, was an early leader in the Fauve movement.

OPEN WINDOW, NICE

Painted 1928, signed: Raoul Dufy. Oil on canvas, $25\frac{3}{4} \times 21\frac{3}{8}$ in. (65.5×54.4 cm.)
The Joseph Winterbotham Collection, 37.166
Coll: Valentine Galleries, Inc., New York

Ref: Berr de Turique, M., Raoul Dufy, *1930, p. 167 (ill.); San Francisco. Museum of Art,* Quarterly Bulletin, *ser. 2, vol. 3, no. 1–2, 1954 (ill.)*

VILLERVILLE

Painted about 1928, signed: Raoul Dufy. Oil on canvas, $31\frac{7}{8} \times 39\frac{1}{2}$ in. (81×100.3 cm.)
The Joseph Winterbotham Collection, 31.708

THE MARNE AT NOGENT

Signed and dated: Raoul Dufy 1935. Oil on canvas, 51×64 in. (129.6×162.6 cm.)
Gift of Arthur Keating, 51.315

DUNOYER DE SEGONZAC, André ~ *b. 1884 Boussy-Saint-Antoine, France*

Educated as a linguist, Segonzac traveled in the Orient before enrolling as a student at the Ecole des Beaux-Arts in Paris.

PASTURE

Painted 1912, signed: A. D. de Segonzac. Oil on canvas, 28⅞×36 in. (73.4×91.5 cm.)
Arthur Jerome Eddy Memorial Collection, 31.516

This canvas was exhibited at the Armory Show in 1913 in New York.

STILL LIFE

Painted early 1920's, signed: A. Dunoyer de Segonzac.
Oil on panel, $21\frac{11}{16}$×17⅞ in. (55×45.5 cm.)
Helen Birch Bartlett Memorial Collection, 26.194

SUMMER GARDEN (THE HAT WITH THE SCOTTISH RIBBON)

Painted 1926, signed: A. Dunoyer de Segonzac.
Oil on canvas, 18×43 in. (45.8×109.3 cm.)
The Joseph Winterbotham Collection, 29.184
Coll: F. Valentine Dudensing; Mrs. John Alden Carpenter

DUPRÉ, Jules ~ *b. 1811 Nantes, France. d. 1889 L'Isle-Adam, France*

Like Diaz, Dupre began his career as a china painter at Sèvres. Later he was apprenticed to a minor landscapist. In 1850 he established himself at L'Isle-Adam, near the fashionable resort of Pontoise.

COTTAGE BY THE ROADSIDE, STORMY SKY

Painted about 1860, signed: Jules Dupré. Oil on canvas, 10⅞×14 in. (27.6×35.7 cm.)
Henry Field Memorial Collection, 94.1058

ON THE ROAD

Signed and dated: Jules Dupré 1856. Oil on canvas, 15½×20 in. (39.5×50.9 cm.)
Henry Field Memorial Collection, 94.1057

TWO BOATS IN A STORM

Painted between 1870 and 1875, signed: J. D.
Oil on canvas, 10¾×13⅞ in. (27.3×35.3 cm.)
Henry Field Memorial Collection, 94.1056

BARKS FLEEING BEFORE THE STORM

Painted between 1870 and 1875, signed: Jules Dupré.
Oil on canvas, 22×33⅜ in. (56×84.9 cm.)
Henry Field Memorial Collection, 94.1055

DUTCH SCHOOL, 16th century

SAINT MATTHEW AND A DONOR

SAINT PETER AND A DONOR

Painted about 1510 or 1520.
Tempera and oil on panel, each 20 × 8 in. (50.8 × 20.4 cm.)
Charles H. and Mary F. S. Worcester Collection, 36.240, 36.241

This anonymous Dutch master follows the style of Jacob Cornelisz van Amsterdam. On the reverse, painted in grisaille, is the Apostle Andrew. In the corresponding panel a donor kneels in prayer and behind her is Saint Peter. On the reverse is Saint Thomas in grisaille. These panels once formed the wings of a small altarpiece.

Ref: Kuhn, C. L., A Catalogue of German Paintings of the Middle Ages and Renaissance in American Collections, *1936, p. 56, cat. nos. 212, 213; Steinbart, K.,* Das Holzschnittwerk des Jacob Cornelisz van Amsterdam, *c. 1937, p. 121*

PORTRAIT OF A MAN

Painted about 1520–1530. Oil on panel, 14½ × 10 in. (36.9 × 25.5 cm.)
Gift of Adolph Caspar Miller, 53.472

The style of this portrait is reminiscent of the work of Jan Mostaert of Haarlem or Cornelis Engelbrechtsz of Leyden.

DUTCH SCHOOL, 17th century

TRAVELERS ARRIVING AT AN INN

Probably painted between 1630 and 1640. Oil on panel, 7⅝ × 11½ in. (21 × 29 cm.)
Mr. and Mrs. Martin A. Ryerson Collection, 33.1070

This picture carries a false Van Goyen signature. The Fitzwilliam Museum at Cambridge owns a mirror-reversed rendering of the same scene which also has a false signature, but is tentatively attributed to the Dutch painter Pieter de Neyn (1597–1639), who like Van Goyen was a pupil of Esaias van de Velde. A definite attribution of the Art Institute picture is not yet possible.

DUVENECK, Frank ~ *b. 1848 Covington, Ky. d. 1919 Cincinnati, Ohio*

Duveneck was a precocious young artist who had already completed several church decorations before he received any formal art training. In 1870 he went to Munich where he immediately became a star pupil, quickly outstripping his classmates.

J. FRANK CURRIER

Painted 1876, signed: F. Duveneck. Oil on canvas, 24⅞ × 20⅞ in. (63.3 × 53.1 cm.)
Friends of American Art Collection, 17.263

EARLY NORTHERN PAINTINGS

XVth—XVIth Centuries

ILLUSTRATIONS

Gossaert (Mabuse), Madonna and Child, c. 1520. Charles H. & Mary F. S. Worcester Collection

Master of Amiens, The Amiens Altarpiece (two scenes). c. 1480 Mr. & Mrs. Martin A. Ryerson Collection

French School, Lamentation, c. 1490. Max & Leola Epstein Collection

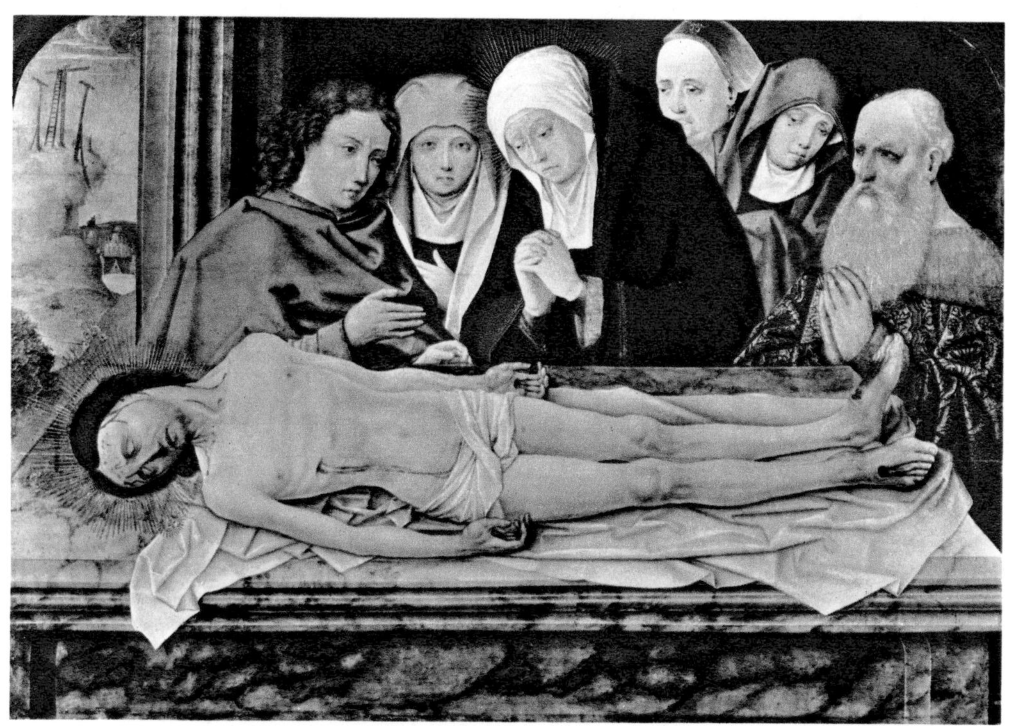

Master of the Pietà of Saint Germain, Entombment, c. 1500. A. A. Munger Collection

Opposite:
Master of Moulins, Annunciation, c. 1490–1500.
Mr. & Mrs. Martin A. Ryerson Collection

Master of the Worcester Panel, Christ Carrying the Cross, c. 1430
Charles H. & Mary F. S. Worcester Collection

Bosch, Hieronymous, Garden of Paradise, c. 1509. Robert A. Waller Fund

Memling, Hans, Diptych: Madonna and Child, c. 1485. Mr. & Mrs. Martin A. Ryerson Collection

Memling, Hans, Diptych: Donor, c. 1485. Gift of Arthur Sachs

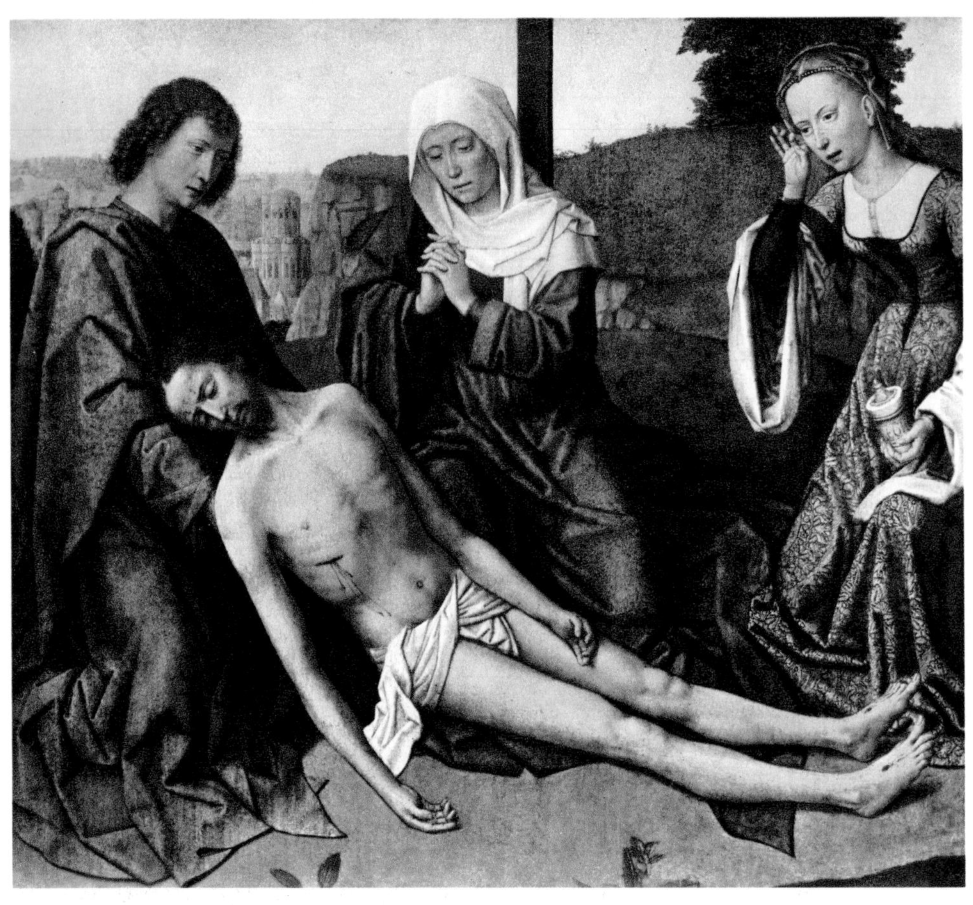

David, Gerard, Lamentation at the Foot of the Cross, c. 1511
Mr. & Mrs. Martin A. Ryerson Collection

Weyden, Rogier van der, Jean de Gros, c. 1450-60. Mr. & Mrs. Martin A. Ryerson Collection

German School, Portrait of a Young Painter, c. 1490. Charles H. & Mary F. S. Worcester Collection

Bruyn, the Younger, Woman with Prayerbook, c. 1560. Charles H. & Mary F. S. Worcester Collection

Cranach, Lucas, the Elder, Crucifixion, 1533. Charles H. & Mary F. S. Worcester Collection

Cranach, Lucas, the Elder, Adam and Eve, c. 1530. Charles H. & Mary F. S. Worcester Collection

Opposite: Leyden, Lucas van, Adoration of the Magi, c. 1510
Mr. & Mrs. Martin A. Ryerson Collection

Coll: A. Juergens, 1917

Ref: Heerman, N., Frank Duveneck, *1918, p. 44 (ill.); Sherman, F. F.,* Art in America *16: 92, 97, February 1928, cat. no. 15*

DYCK, Anthony van ~ *b. 1599 Antwerp. d. 1641 London*

As a boy, Van Dyck studied with Hendrik van Balen, but the great formative influence on his work was Rubens. In 1620 he visited England briefly, and from 1621 to 1627 lived in Italy. From Italy he returned to Flanders for five years, but in 1632 settled in London and became the painter to the court of Charles I.

PORTRAIT OF A GENOESE NOBLEMAN

Painted about 1625. Oil on canvas, $33\frac{3}{8}\times41\frac{3}{4}$ in. (84.9×106 cm.)
Max and Leola Epstein Collection, 54.285

The identity of the sitter is not known. The costume and style of the portrait indicate the same period as Van Dyck's portrait of Cardinal Rivarola. The scheme follows closely a composition by Titian. The painting was attributed to Van Dyck by Glueck.
Coll: Duke of Richmond, Goodwood, England

Ref: Glueck, G., Van Dyck, *1931, p. 162 (ill. called Maximilian of Bavaria) p. 49*

PORTRAIT OF A NOBLEMAN

Painted about 1623–1635. Oil on canvas, $42\frac{1}{2}\times31\frac{1}{2}$ in. (108×80.2 cm.)
Max and Leola Epstein Collection, 54.286

Ref: Glueck, G., Van Dyck, *1931, p. 279 (ill.)*

HELENA TROMPER DU BOIS

Painted about 1631. Oil on canvas, $39\times31\frac{7}{8}$ in. (99.2×81 cm.)
Gift of the Family of William T. Baker in memory of William T. Baker, 94.1027

Helena Du Bois, daughter of Eland Gysbrechts Tromper, married in 1614 Hendrick Du Bois, art dealer and painter of Rotterdam. A pendant portrait of Helena's husband is in the Staedel Museum in Frankfurt. The painting was engraved by Cornelis Visscher.

Coll: Simon du Bois; Earl Somers, 1708; The Lord Chancellor of England; The Earl of Hardwicke at Wimpole (sold 1884); Prince A. Demidoff, San Donato; Prince P. Demidoff, Pratolino, 1890

Ref: Smith, J., A Catalogue Raisonné of the Works of the Most Eminent Dutch, Flemish, and French Painters, *III, 1831, p. 205, cat. no. 723; Waagen,* Treasures of Art in Great Britain, *IV, 1857, p. 519; Cust, L.,* Anthony Van Dyck, *1900, pp. 83, 254; Cust, L.,* Anthony Van Dyck, *1906, pp. 77, 82, 131; Schaeffer, E.,* Van Dyck, *1909, p. 241 (ill.); Glueck,* Van Dyck, *1931, p. 287 (ill.); Tietze, H.,* Meisterwerke Europaeischer Malerei in Amerika, *c. 1935, cat. no. 156 (ill.)*

DYCK, Anthony van (attributed to)

HEAD OF A GIRL

Painted about 1618–1620. Oil on panel, 12¾×9⅞ in. (32.3×25.1 cm.)
Charles H. and Mary F. S. Worcester Collection, 47.69

Given to the artist's early period by Bode and Valentiner. Others have questioned the attribution.

DYER, Charles Gifford ~ *b. 1846 Chicago. d. 1912 Munich*

Dyer, who started his career in the consular service at Bristol and Beirut, decided in1870 to become a painter.

SEVENTEENTH CENTURY INTERIOR

Signed and dated: Chas. G. Dyer, Munich 1877. Oil on canvas, 37×28 in. (94×71.2 cm.)
Gift of Henry W. King, 02.227

EAKINS, Thomas ~ *1844–1916 Philadelphia*

Eakins was a student at the Pennsylvania Academy of the Fine Arts, then went to Paris in 1866 to study with Jean Léon Gérôme and Léon Bonnat. After a trip to Spain he returned to Philadelphia where he spent the rest of his life.

RITER FITZGERALD

Signed and dated: Eakins 95. Oil on canvas, 76×64 in. (193.1×162.6 cm.)
Friends of American Art Collection, Goodman Fund, 50.1511

Riter Fitzgerald, a friend of Eakins, founded the critical review, *The Item.*

Coll: Miss Geraldine M. Hubbard; Whitney Museum of American Art, New York; M. Knoedler & Co., New York

Ref: Philadelphia. Pennsylvania Academy of the Fine Arts, Memorial Exhibition of . . . Eakins, *December 1917 to January 1918, cat. no. 112 (ill.); Goodrich, L.,* The Arts *16: 72–83, October 1929; Philadelphia. Museum,* Bulletin *25, no. 133: 26, March 1930, cat. no. 165; New York. Whitney Museum of American Art,* Catalogue of the Collections, *1931, pp. 23, 101 (ill.); Goodrich, L.,* Thomas Eakins, *1933, p. 186, no. 280 (ill. pl. 45); McKinney, R.,* Thomas Eakins, *1942, p. 72 (ill.); Pittsburgh. Carnegie Institute,* Thomas Eakins Centennial Exhibition, *1945, cat. no. 82*

ADDIE, WOMAN IN BLACK (Miss Mary Adeline Williams) Illus. p. 376

Painted in 1899. Oil on canvas, 24×20 in. (61×50.9 cm.)
Friends of American Art Collection, 39.548

Miss Williams was a life-long friend of the Eakins family and made her home with them after 1900.

Coll: Mrs. M. A. Williams; Mrs. Thomas Eakins, 1938

Ref: Goodrich, L., op. cit., *p. 190, cat. no. 323 (ill. pl. 54); McKinney, R.,* op. cit., *p. 70 (ill.); McHenry, M.,* Thomas Eakins Who Painted, *1946, pp. 131–4*

EARL, Ralph ~ *b. 1751 Shrewsbury, Mass. d. 1801 Bolton, Conn.*

Little is known about Ralph Earl's early career. In 1775 he accompanied the engraver, Amos Doolittle, to Lexington and Concord to make sketches of the first scenes of the Revolution. From these sketches, Doolittle made his famous set of four engravings. Earl spent from 1778 to 1785 in England. He painted a great deal in Connecticut, on Long Island, and in the upper Connecticut valley. In his last years he did several landscapes, among the earliest painted in this country.

NOAH SMITH

Signed and dated: R. Earl pinxt 1798. Oil on canvas, 64¼ × 42¼ in. (163.3 × 107 cm.)
Goodman Fund, 56.126

Born in Suffield, Connecticut in 1756, Noah Smith graduated from Yale in 1778 in the same class with Noah Webster of dictionary fame. He moved to Bennington, was admitted to the Bar in 1779, became States Attorney and County Clerk, and Collector of Internal Revenue. From 1789 to 1790 and from 1798 to 1800, Noah Smith was Judge of the Superior Court. It was during this second term that Earl painted his portrait.

EILSHEMIUS, Louis Michel ~ *b. 1864 Laurel Mansion, Newark, N.J. d. 1941 N.Y. City*

Eilshemius had very little formal art education, studying only for a short time with Bouguereau.

MOONLIGHT ON THE DELAWARE WATER GAP

Painted 1898, signed: Elshemus [sic]. Oil on canvas, 14⅜ × 20½ in. (36.6 × 52.1 cm.)
Gift of Richman Proskauer, 53.25

ELLIOTT, Charles Loring ~ *b. 1812 Scipio, N.Y. d. 1868 Albany, N.Y.*

Elliott, a pupil of John Trumbull and John Quidor, also studied abroad.

H. W. HEWITT

Painted about 1850. Oil on canvas, 27 × 21¾ in. (68.7 × 55.4 cm.)
Gift of Henry J. Willing, 02.161

EMPOLI, Jacopo da Empoli, *see* CHIMENTI, Jacopo

ENGELBRECHTSZ, Cornelis (School of)

The school of Cornelis Engelbrechtsz (1468–1533) in Leyden, was, along with those in Haarlem and Amsterdam, one of the three most important Dutch workshops and art centers at the beginning of the 16th century.

SAINT AUGUSTINE AND A DONOR (a)
SAINT BRIDGET AND A DONOR (b)

Painted about 1510 or 1520.
Oil on panel (a) and (b) each $25\frac{11}{16} \times 8\frac{15}{16}$ in. (65.2×22.5 cm.) (b) $25\frac{5}{8} \times 8\frac{15}{16}$ in. (65.2×22.5 cm.)
Mr. and Mrs. Martin A. Ryerson Collection, 33.1041, 33.1042

These panels were once the wings of an altarpiece. It is known that Cornelis Engelbrechtsz painted two altarpieces for the convent of Marienpoël near Leyden; possibly these two panels also came from this convent.

Coll: Manzi, Paris; Cottier Gallery, New York, 1912

ENGELHARD, Elizabeth ~ *b. 1893 Chicago*

Mrs. Engelhard studied at the School of the Art Institute from 1913 to 1917.

DESIGN FOR SECURITY

Painted 1953, signed: E. Engelhard. Oil on canvas, $41 \times 24\frac{1}{4}$ in. (104.2×61.7 cm.)
Mr. and Mrs. Frank G. Logan Purchase Prize, 53.342

ERNST, Jimmy ~ *b. 1920*

BLUE AND BLACK

Painted 1956, signed: Jimmy Ernst 56. Oil on canvas, $50\frac{3}{16} \times 28\frac{1}{8}$ in. (127.5×71.5 cm.)
Gift of Mr. and Mrs. Edwin A. Bergman, 59.516

ESQUIVEL, Antonio Maria ~ *b. 1806 Seville. d. Madrid 1857*

PORTRAIT OF A MAN

Painted 1843. Oil on canvas, $28\frac{3}{4} \times 22\frac{1}{4}$ in. (73×56.6 cm.)
Gift of Mrs. Chauncey McCormick, 56.134

ESTEVE, Augustin (y Marqués) ~ *b. 1753. d. ca. 1820 Valencia, Spain*

Esteve studied at the academies of Valencia and Madrid. In the 1780's he became Goya's favorite pupil, then his assistant. When Charles IV and Maria Luisa of Parma came to the Spanish throne in 1788, Goya received innumerable commissions for portraits of the royal family and court officials. Esteve helped him fill orders for replicas.

MANUEL GODOY

Painted between 1800 and 1808, signed: Augustin Esteve/ de S. Mag [?], inscribed: Ocidental u Atlantico/ Espagne/ Estrecho de Gibraltar/ Gibraltar/ Mar Mediterraneo. Oil on canvas, $46\frac{1}{8} \times 33\frac{1}{8}$ in. (117.2×84.2 cm.)
Gift of Joseph Winterbotham, 54.312

ETTY, William ~ *b. 1787. d. 1849 York, England*

Etty, who was one of the leading figures in English painting in the second quarter of the 19th century, was a pupil of Anton Fuseli and Thomas Lawrence. Although he began exhibiting his pictures in 1811, his first great success came ten years later when he showed *Cleopatra's Arrival in Cilicia* at the Royal Academy in London. He is best remembered for his portraits and nudes.

DOUBLE PORTRAIT: TWO WOMEN

Painted about 1845–1848. Oil on canvas, $35\frac{7}{8} \times 25\frac{7}{8}$ in. (91.2×65.8 cm.)
Charles H. and Mary F. S. Worcester Collection, 37.460

An unfinished sketch, of which the attribution is uncertain.

EWORTH, Hans ~ *b. Antwerp, active in London 1545–1574*

LADY OF THE WENTWORTH FAMILY

Signed: Aetatis 24 1563 HE. Oil on canvas, $45\frac{5}{8} \times 31\frac{1}{4}$ in. (115.9×79.3 cm.)
Gift of Kate S. Buckingham, 20.1035

Ref: London, South Kensington, National Portrait Exhibition, *1866, cat. no. 310 (as Mary, Queen of Scots); London. Grosvenor Gallery,* Second National Loan Exhibition, *1913/14, cat. no. 39;* Walpole Society *II, 1912/13, pl. xvii, 6; Thieme-Becker,* Kuenstler-Lexikon, *vol. 9, 1915, p. 119*

FABER, Conrad (Conrad von Creuznach) ~ *b. about 1500 Creuznach. d. 1552–3 Frankfurt*

Faber, who was both a painter and an accomplished engraver, has been identified with the monogramist Ↄ v. C., Conrad von Creuznach, and has also been called Master of the Holzhausen Portraits because he painted several members of that family. Little is known of his life except that he became a citizen of Frankfurt in 1538.

FRIEDRICH ROHRBACH

Signed and dated on the reverse with monogram Ↄ v. C–1532, inscribed: Friderich Rorbach Seines Alters XXV—M. D. XXXII. Oil on panel, $19\frac{7}{8} \times 14$ in. (50.7×35.7 cm.)
Charles H. and Mary F. S. Worcester Collection, 35.296
Coll: H. Farrer; Miss I. A. Bodley, Bournemouth

Ref: London. Burlington Fine Arts Club, Early German Art, *1906; Braune, H.,* Monatshefte für Kunstwissenschaft *2: 582, 1909; Friedlaender, M. J.,* Art in America *1: 147, 1913, cat. no. 8; Borenius, T.,* Pantheon *5: 243, 247, 1930 (ill.); London. Sotheby & Co.,* Catalogue of Bodley Paintings, *May 14, 1930, cat. nol 32 (ill.); Goetz, O.,* Art in America *29: 89–97, 1941 (ill.)*

FABRITIUS, Barent ~ *b. 1624 De Beemster, Holland. d. 1673 Amsterdam*

Barent, like his elder brother Carel, was a pupil of Rembrandt. Barent Fabritius adopted the master's mysterious chiaroscuro and psychological characterization. His genre scenes frequently recall the manner of Nicolas Maes and Pieter de Hooch.

JACOB AND BENJAMIN Illus. p. 189

Painted between 1650 and 1660. Oil on canvas, 52×43½ in. (131.5×110.5 cm.)
Wilson L. Mead Fund, 37.463
Coll: Mrs. Wilfred Buckley, Moundsmere Manor, Basingstoke, England; M. Knoedler & Co., New York

Ref: London. Royal Academy, Exhibition of Dutch Art, *1929, p. 37*

FAED, John ~ *b. 1819 Burley Mill, Scotland. d. 1902 Ardmore, Scotland*

John Faed, a brother of the artists, Thomas and James Faed, was self-taught. He first exhibited in the Scottish Academy in 1841. Though Faed began as a miniature painter, he later turned to historical and genre subjects.

THE YOUNG DUCHESS

Signed and dated: J. Faed, '70. Oil on canvas, 46×36 in. (116.9×91.5 cm.)
A. A. Munger Collection, 01.432

FANTIN-LATOUR, Henri ~ *b. 1836 Grenoble. d. 1904 Buré, France*

Fantin-Latour studied with his father Théodore, a painter who specialized in pastel portraits and religious scenes. He also worked for a time in Courbet's studio and knew Manet and his circle. Fantin painted portraits, still lifes of flowers, and allegories on musical themes. A highly disciplined painter, he copied at the Louvre almost daily until 1870. Fantin is also known for his lithographs.

EDOUARD MANET Illus. p. 243

Inscribed, signed and dated: A mon ami Manet—Fantin, 1867.
Oil on canvas, 46×35½ in. (116.9×90.2 cm.)
The Stickney Fund, 05.207 (Mme Fantin-Latour no. 296)

Ref: Proust, A., International Studio *12: 227, 1900 (ill.); Bénédite, L.,* L'Oeuvre de Fantin-Latour, *1906, pl. VIII; Julien, A.,* Fantin-Latour, *1909, p. 31 (ill. opp. p. 92);*

Catalogue de l'oeuvre complet de Fantin-Latour, *1911, p. 42, cat. no. 296;* French Artists of Our Day, Edouard Manet *(intro. by L. Hourticq), 1912 (ill. on frontispiece); Muther, R.,* Histoire Moderne, *1913, p. 107; Kahn, G.,* Fantin-Latour *(Masters of Modern Art), London, 1927 (pl. 6); Bénédite, L.,* L'Art et les Artistes, *N.S. 21–2: 31, October 1930 to July 1931 (ill.); Gibson, F.,* The Art of Henri Fantin-Latour: His Life and Work, *n.d., p. 37 (pl. VII); Mauclair, C.,* Great French Painters from 1830 to the Present Day, *n.d., p. 68 (ill.)*

STILL LIFE: CORNER OF A TABLE Illus. p. 238

Signed and dated: Fantin '73. Oil on canvas, $38\frac{1}{4} \times 49\frac{1}{4}$ in. (97.2×125.1 cm.)
Ada Turnbull Hertle Fund, 51.226 (Mme Fantin-Latour no. 671)

In 1872 Fantin exhibited a canvas showing various of his literary friends gathered together after dinner. Because the poet Albert Mérat was not able to be present, Fantin filled the space which he was to occupy with a large rhododendron plant. This picture, called *Corner of a Table,* is now in the Louvre. A year later Fantin turned to the same setting, painting only the corner of the table and the rhododendron. This is the painting now in the Art Institute.

Coll: G. Tempelaere; M. Mancini, Paris

Ref: Bénédite, L., op. cit.; *Jullien, A.,* Fantin-Latour, Sa Vie et ses Amitiés, *1990, p. 199; Paris.* Catalogue de l'oeuvre complet de Fantin-Latour, *1911, cat. no. 671, p. 76; Grenoble, France.* Exposition du Centenaire de Henri Fantin-Latour, *1936, cat. no. 127; Gibson, F.,* op. cit., *pp. 117, 119, 209 (ill. pl. 34)*

FECHIN, Nicolai ~ *b. 1881 Kazen, Russia*

Fechin developed a style that was based on a late phase of Impressionism and soft-focus photography popular in the twenties.

LILLIAN GISH AS ROMOLA

Signed and dated: N. Fechin, '25. Oil on canvas, $49\frac{1}{8} \times 45\frac{1}{4}$ in. (124.8×115 cm.)
Friends of American Art Collection, 25.392

Romola, the heroine of the novel by George Eliot, was played by Lillian Gish in a movie produced in 1924.

FEININGER, Lyonel ~ *1871–1956 New York City*

As a young man, Feininger earned his living as a cartoonist. During 1906 and 1907 he worked in this capacity for the *Chicago Tribune.* Feininger spent many years in Germany where he taught at the Bauhaus from 1919 to 1924. In 1924 he joined Jawlensky, Klee and Kandinsky to form the exhibiting group known as The Blue Four. After 1937 he lived in New York.

VILLAGE STREET Illus. p. 381

Painted 1929, signed: Feininger. Oil on canvas, $31\frac{3}{4} \times 39\frac{3}{4}$ in. (80.8 × 101 cm.)
Gift of Mr. and Mrs. Sigmund Kunstadter, 55.27

FINSONIUS, Ludovicus (attributed to)

See "CECCO DEL CARAVAGGIO"

FLEMISH SCHOOL, 15th century

SAINT JOHN THE EVANGELIST AND A DONOR (a)
SAINT JOHN THE BAPTIST (b)

Painted about 1490. Oil on panel, each $20\frac{5}{8} \times 5\frac{5}{8}$ in. (52.4 × 14.3 cm.)
Mr. and Mrs. Martin A. Ryerson Collection, 33.1048

These panels have been attributed to the Master of the Morrison Triptych.

Coll: Fievez, Brussels; Edmond Noël, Paris

FLEMISH SCHOOL, 16th century

PORTRAIT OF A MAN

Painted about 1530. Tempera and oil on panel, $16\frac{1}{2} \times 13\frac{1}{2}$ in. (42 × 34.4 cm.)
Robert A. Waller Fund, 24.575

The artist of this portrait has not been definitely identified but might have been Jan van Scorel, or more likely one of his pupils or followers. Although Friedlaender attributed the portrait to Jan Cornelisz Vermeyen (ca. 1500–1559), others have questioned this.

Coll: Countess Dartrey, Monaghan, Ireland, 1780–1923 (as Christoph Amberger); D. Croal Thomson, Barbizon House

Ref: London. Barbizon House, An Illustrated Record, *1924, cat. no. 38 (ill.); Tietze, H.,* Meisterwerke Europaeischer Malerei in Amerika, *1935, cat. no. 208 (ill.);* American-German Review *2, no. 1: 2, September 1935 (ill. only); Kuhn, C. L.,* A Catalogue of German Paintings of the Middle Ages and Renaissance in American Collections, *1936, cat. no. 289*

PORTRAIT OF A MAN

Painted about 1555–1560. Oil on panel, 18 × 14 in. (45.8 × 35.7 cm.)
Gift of Adolph Caspar Miller, 53.470

PORTRAIT OF A YOUNG MAN

Painted about 1560. Oil on panel, $18\frac{1}{2} \times 13\frac{1}{4}$ in. (47.1 × 34 cm.)
Samuel P. Avery Fund, 51.224

The as yet unidentified artist who painted this portrait must have been a contemporary of Anthonis Mor, possibly of the younger generation.

Coll: Mrs. Helen H. Cowie, Rivensleigh, Dowanhill, Glasgow

PORTRAIT OF A LADY

Inscribed and dated: Aetatis Suae 41, A° 1562. Oil on panel, 12¼ × 9 in. (31.2 × 22.8 cm.)
Charles H. and Mary F. S. Worcester Collection, 47.70

This portrait may have been done by some follower of Anthonis Mor. It is perhaps closer in style to the work of Willem Key.

FLIPART, Charles Joseph ~ *b. 1721 Paris. d. 1797 Madrid*

French born, Flipart was trained in Venice under the engraver, Joseph Wagner. He also absorbed much of the late Venetian characteristics of the work of Amigoni, Ricci and Tiepolo, taking these influences with him to Spain where he worked during his later years.

YOUNG WOMAN WITH HUNTER

Painted about 1750. Oil on canvas, 34½ × 27¾ in. (87.6 × 70.6 cm.)
Charles H. and Mary F. S. Worcester Collection, 39.2238

The attribution of this painting to Flipart is tentative.

FORAIN, Jean-Louis ~ *b. 1852 Reims, France. d. 1931 Paris*

Forain was first known as a cartoonist for *Le Rire* and *Le Figaro.*

THE TIGHT-ROPE WALKER

Painted about 1885, signed: Forain. Oil on canvas, 18 3/16 × 15 in. (46.2 × 38.2 cm.)
Gift of Emily Crane Chadbourne, 51.208

IN THE WINGS

Signed and dated: Forain 1899. Oil on canvas, 23⅝ × 28⅞ in. (60.1 × 73.4 cm.)
Mr. and Mrs. Martin A. Ryerson Collection, 33.1118

MATERNITY

Painted about 1904–1905, signed: Forain. Oil on canvas, 26 × 32 in. (66.1 × 81.3 cm.)
Charles H. and Mary F. S. Worcester Collection, 29.920

SENTENCED FOR LIFE

Painted about 1910, signed: Forain. Oil on canvas, 25½ × 31½ in. (64.8 × 80.2 cm.)
The Joseph Winterbotham Collection, 23.6

FORBES, James G. ~ *b. about 1800 Scotland. d. after 1870 London*

Forbes, trained in Scotland, was both a portrait and historical painter. During the decade of the 1860's he worked in Chicago.

ALEXANDER N. FULLERTON

Painted 1865. Oil on canvas, 52⅜ × 39½ in. (133.1 × 100.3 cm.)
Gift of Charles W. Fullerton, 98.226

Alexander Fullerton came to Chicago from Vermont in 1833. Fullerton Hall, in the Art Institute, was built as a memorial to his father by Charles W. Fullerton.

FORTUNY Y CARBO, Mariano ~ *b. 1838 Reus, Spain. d. 1874 Rome*

Fortuny was a student at the academy in Barcelona, then in 1856 went to Rome for further study.

CAVALIER

Painted about 1871. Oil on panel, 5⅜ × 4 in. (13.7 × 10.2 cm.)
Henry Field Memorial Collection, 94.1059

This small study was done in Granada from a model who frequently posed for Fortuny.

FOSTER, Ben ~ *b. 1852 North Anson, Me. d. 1926 New York City*

Foster studied first with Abbott Thayer, and then in Paris.

LITCHFIELD HILLS

Painted about 1912, signed: Ben Foster. Oil on canvas, 42⅛ × 36⅛ in. (107 × 91.8 cm.)
Friends of American Art Collection, 13.131

FOUJITA, Tsugouharu ~ *b. 1886 Tokyo*

Foujita, having studied at the Imperial Art School in Tokyo, moved to Paris in 1913. Though he returned to Japan during World War II, he went back to France again in 1950.

EMILY CRANE CHADBOURNE

Signed and dated: T. Foujita, Paris, 1922.
Tempera on canvas, 35¼ × 57½ in. (89.5 × 146.1 cm.)
Gift of Emily Crane Chadbourne, 52.997

Mrs. Chadbourne, a generous patron of the Art Institute, was a leading figure among the artists and writers in Paris between the wars. Gertrude Stein also described Mrs. Chadbourne in her *Portrait of Emily Crane*.

FRAGONARD, Jean Honoré ~ *1732–1806 Paris* (attributed to)

STILL LIFE WITH EGGS

Painted about 1780. Oil on canvas, 31⅜×36¼ in. (79.7×92.1 cm.)
The Stickney Fund, 24.1042

This picture, which once bore a false signature of Chardin, has stylistic affinities with certain phases of Fragonard's work. If it is not by him, it is by a painter who worked closely in his vein.

FRAZER, Oliver ~ *b. 1808 Fayette Co., Ky. d. 1864 Lexington, Ky.*

Frazer studied with Matthew H. Jouett and Thomas Sully. After traveling abroad, he settled in Lexington as a portrait painter.

CARTER HENRY HARRISON, SR.

Painted about 1835. Oil on canvas, 27¾×22¾ in. (70.6×57.9 cm.)
Gift of Mr. and Mrs. Carter H. Harrison, 52.999

The Harrisons were a Virginia family who moved to Kentucky where this portrait was painted. Later they moved on to Chicago. Carter Harrison (1825–1893), Mayor of Chicago for five terms, was assassinated during his last term. His son, Carter Harrison, the donor of this painting, was also Mayor of Chicago for five terms.

FREER, Frederick Warren ~ *1849–1908 Chicago*

Freer studied at the Munich academy from 1867 to 1873 and later in Paris. In 1880 he established himself as a portrait painter in New York. In 1890 he moved to Chicago to continue his career and teach at the School of the Art Institute.

CHARLES W. FULLERTON

Signed and dated: Frederick W. Freer, 1901. Oil on canvas, 52×41½ in. (132.2×105.4 cm.)
Gift of Martha S. Hill, 01.424

Charles W. Fullerton, prominent in Chicago real estate, was a Trustee of the Art Institute, and gave Fullerton Hall in memory of his father.

FRENCH SCHOOL, 15th century

LAMENTATION Illus. p. 139

Painted about 1490. Oil on panel, 16¾×11¼ in. (42.6×28.6 cm.)
Max and Leola Epstein Collection, 54.294

Friedlaender suggested a date around 1460; Sterling, however, points out that the general style of the painting would indicate a date nearer the end of the 15th century, perhaps about 1490.

Ref: Tietze, H., Meisterwerke Europaeischer Malerei in Amerika, *1935, p. 341, cat. no. 245; Sterling, Ch.,* La Peinture Française, Les Maîtres du Moyen Age, *1941, pp. 60, 61, no. 30; Goldblatt, M. H.,* Connoisseur *122: 6, September 1948 (ill., called Jean Hay Clouet); Sterling, Ch.,* La Revue des Arts *5: 25–46, 1955*

FRENCH SCHOOL, 16th century

JEAN, SIRE DE RIEUX

Painted about 1550. Oil on panel, 7⅞×6¼ in. (20×15.8 cm.)
Frederick T. Haskell Collection, 40.1144

The sitter, a nobleman of the time of Henry II of France, has been identified on the basis of three replicas of this portrait, all bearing his name.

FRENCH SCHOOL, 17th century

THE PEASANT FAMILY AT THE WELL

Painted between 1640 and 1648. Oil on canvas, 38½×40 in. (97.9×101.7 cm.)
Robert A. Waller Fund, 23.415
Coll: O. Sirèn, Stockholm, 1923

Ref: London. Burlington Fine Arts Club, Illustrated Catalogue of Pictures by the Brothers Le Nain, *1910, p. 15 (pl. 13); Chicago. Art Institute,* Annual Report, *1923 (ill.); Chicago. Art Institute,* Bulletin *17: 94–6, 1923 (ill. p. 59); Wilenski, R. C.,* French Painting, *1931, p. 49; Chicago. Art Institute,* A Century of Progress Exhibition, *1933, cat. no. 221 (ill. p. 44);* Ibid., *1934, cat. no. 145; Toledo, Ohio. Museum of Art,* The Brothers Le Nain, *October 1947, cat. no. 16 (ill.)*

FRENCH SCHOOL, 19th century

THE CAROUSALS (two panels)

Painted about 1860–1870.
Oil on panel (a) 7×10 in. (17.8×25.5 cm.) (b) 7⅞×13⅞ in. (20×35.3 cm.)
Charles H. and Mary F. S. Worcester Collection, 47.72, 47.73

The subjects of these two panels have not been identified. One of them might conceivably be from Goethe's *Faust* representing a scene in Auerbach's Cellar in Leipzig. The other may represent a masked ball in Paris during the cholera epidemic of 1831.

FRIESEKE, Frederick Carl ~ *b. 1874 Owosso, Mich. d. 1939 Normandy, France*

After studying at the School of the Art Institute, Frieseke went to the Académie Julian in Paris in 1898. He remained in France most of his life. He was at one time a pupil of Whistler, and was strongly influenced by Impressionism.

LADY TRYING ON A HAT

Signed and dated: F. C. Frieseke, 1909. Oil on canvas, $63\frac{3}{4} \times 51$ in. (162×129.6 cm.)
Walter H. Schulze Memorial Collection, 24.908

ON THE BANK

Painted about 1915, signed: F. C. Frieseke.
Oil on canvas, $40\frac{1}{2} \times 57\frac{1}{2}$ in. (102.9×146.1 cm.)
Friends of American Art Collection, 16.439

SEMI-NUDE

Signed and dated: F. C. Frieseke, 1925. Oil on canvas, $36\frac{1}{8} \times 28\frac{1}{8}$ in. (91.8×71.5 cm.)
Gift of Mr. and Mrs. Carter H. Harrison, 36.15

FRIESZ, Emile Othon ~ *b. 1879 Le Havre, France. d. 1949 Paris*

Friesz began his studies in Le Havre, but later moved to Paris where he was a pupil of Bonnat. For a brief period he became interested in Impressionism but by 1903 Friesz joined forces with several artists who were to become the Fauves.

PORT OF TOULON

Painted in the late 1920's, signed: E. Othon Friesz.
Oil on canvas, $24\frac{7}{8} \times 31\frac{3}{4}$ in. (63.3×80.8 cm.)
The Joseph Winterbotham Collection, 28.258

FROMENTIN, Eugène ~ *b. 1820 La Rochelle, France. d. 1876 Saint Maurice, France*

A pupil of Louis Cabat, Fromentin was influenced by the orientalism of Alexandre Decamps. He visited Algiers often and was as successful with the paintings he produced from these trips as he was with his travel accounts. He became a member of the Academy by virtue of his writings, which included a review of Dutch and Flemish art called *Les maîtres d'autrefois.*

WOMEN OF THE OULED NAYLS

Signed and dated: Eug. Fromentin, 1867. Oil on canvas, $43\frac{3}{8} \times 28\frac{1}{2}$ in. (110.3×72.5 cm.)
Henry Field Memorial Collection, 94.1060

Fromentin's third trip to Africa in 1853 took him to El Agouath, a little place on the border of the Sahara settled by the tribe, Ouled Nayls, whose women were allowed to appear unveiled before men.

ON THE NILE, NEAR PHILAE

Signed and dated: Eug. Fromentin '71. Oil on canvas, $25 \times 43\frac{1}{2}$ in. (63.6×110.6 cm.)
Nickerson Collection, 00.580

In the fall of 1869 Fromentin traveled in Egypt. His diary mentions Philae, where he did sketches of the famous temple seen in the right background of this painting.

Ref: Rhode Island. School of Design, Yearbook, *1935, p. 167; Portland, Oregon. Museum of Art,* Fiftieth Anniversary Exhibition, *1892–1942, December 1942 to January 1943, cat. no. 26*

FULLER, George ~ *b. 1822 Deerfield, Mass. d. 1884 Brookline, Mass.*

Fuller studied in Albany with the sculptor Henry K. Brown, then traveled as an itinerant portrait painter. He met with small success and returned to the family farm at Deerfield.

GATHERER OF SIMPLES

Painted between 1878–1883, signed: G. Fuller.
Oil on canvas, 36×47⅞ in. (91.5×121.6 cm.)
Gift of William T. Cresmer, 55.746
Coll: G. Fuller Sale, Boston, 1884; Mrs. F. D. Kimball, Boston; Ralph Cudney, Chicago; William T. Cresmer, Chicago

Ref: Caffin, C. H., American Masters of Painting, *1913 (ill. opp. p. 106)*

AN EXAMINATION OF WITNESSES IN A TRIAL FOR WITCHCRAFT

Painted about 1880. Oil on canvas, 36×54 in. (91.5×137.2 cm.)
Friends of American Art Collection, 17.62

PSYCHE

Painted in 1884, signed: G. Fuller. Oil on composition board, 36×28 in. (91.5×71.2 cm.)
Friends of American Art Collection, 18.31

FYT, Jan (attributed to) ~ *1611–1661 Antwerp*

Pupil of the distinguished animal and still life painter, Frans Snyders, Fyt became a member in 1629 of the Painters' Guild of St. Luke in Antwerp. He worked for several years in Paris and Rome, but returned to Antwerp in 1645, where he lived the rest of his life.

STILL LIFE WITH DEAD BIRDS

Painted about 1650. Oil on canvas, 12¾×17 in. (32.6×43.3 cm.)
A. A. Munger Collection, 55.747
Coll: Adolf Mayer, The Hague; Adolf Mayer, Jr. and H. Herbert Mayer

Ref: Oberlin, Ohio. Allen Memorial Art Museum, Bulletin *5: 13, January 1948 (ill.)*

GARBER, Daniel ~ *b. 1880 North Manchester, Ind. d. 1958 Lumberville, Pa.*

Garber studied in Cincinnati and at the Pennsylvania Academy of the Fine Arts. After travel and study abroad he returned to Philadelphia where he taught at the Academy.

HILLS OF BYRAM

Painted 1909, signed: Daniel Garber. Oil on canvas, 42×46½ in. (106.7×118.2 cm.)
Walter H. Schulze Memorial Collection, 10.309

GASPARD, Leon ~ *b. 1882 Vitebsk, Russia*

Gaspard, who studied in Odessa, later went to Paris where he became interested in the late phases of Impressionism. He came to this country in 1919 and has for many years been living in Taos, N.M.

MRS. JULIETTE ROSENTHAL

Signed and dated: Leon Gaspard, 1913. Oil on canvas, 23½×17⅜ in. (59.6×44.2 cm.)
Gift of Lessing Rosenthal, 50.165

TO THE DANCE

Signed and dated: Leon Gaspard, Taos 1919. Oil on canvas, 32½×36½ in. (82.6×92.8 cm.)
Gift of Friends of the Artist, 20.95

GATCH, Lee ~ *b. 1902 Baltimore, Md.*

Gatch studied at the Maryland Institute with Leon Kroll and John Sloan. In 1927 he spent a year in France, attended classes at the American School in Fontainebleau, and studied in Paris with André Lhote, Moïse Kisling and Jean Metzinger.

THE THESPIAN TREE

Painted 1956, signed: Gatch. Oil on canvas, 25×40 in. (63.6×101.7 cm.)
Goodman Fund, 56.136

GAUGUIN, Paul ~ *b. 1848 Paris. d. 1903 Atuana, Hiva-Oa (La Dominique)*

During his early years Gauguin was influenced by the Impressionists, with whom he first exhibited in 1880. Three years later he decided to give up business and become a professional painter. Eventually this move broke up his family life. In 1887 Gauguin and his friend, Charles Laval, went to Martinique. It was a short experience for Gauguin and resulted in his complete break with Impressionism. From 1886 to 1890 the artist spent considerable time in Brittany, at Pont-Aven and later at Le Pouldu, where he became the leader of the Synthesis group, a school of painting emphasizing simplification of color, form and line. In 1888 he lived at Arles with Van Gogh for a few tragic months, this being the time when Vincent's malady reached its height. Gauguin went to the South Seas in 1890 where he stayed until his death, with only one short trip back to Paris.

OLD WOMEN OF ARLES Illus. p. 333

Signed and dated: P. Gauguin '88. Oil on canvas, 28¾×36 in. (73×91.5 cm.)
Gift of Annie Swan Coburn to the Mr. and Mrs. Lewis L. Coburn Memorial Collection, 34.391

Late in 1888 Gauguin accepted Van Gogh's invitation to join him at Arles. Here he painted this canvas. There are preparatory drawings for the painting in a sketchbook Gauguin used in Brittany and Arles. He also made a zincograph in reverse after the picture. Van Gogh, at the same time, painted an almost identical scene called *Promenade at Arles—Souvenir of the Garden at Etten* (Pushkin Museum, Moscow). There can be no question that the two artists inspired each other, even though Gauguin denied it. Gauguin's painting may also have been influenced by the contemporary literary movement of the Symbolists who had turned against naturalism and whose work greatly interested Gauguin.

Coll: J. W. Barney, New York

Ref: de Rotonchamp, J., Paul Gauguin, *1925, pp. 66, 68; Guérin, M.,* L'Oeuvre Gravé de Gauguin, *I, 1927, p. X, no. 11; Basle. Kunsthalle Basle,* Exhibition, *1928, cat. no. 39 (ill.); Van Gogh, V.,* Letters to his Brother, *III, 1929, p. 469; Barth, W.,* Paul Gauguin, *1929, pp. 81, 82 (pl. XVI); New York. Museum of Modern Art,* First Loan Exhibition . . ., *1929, cat. no. 40 (pl. 40); St. Louis. City Art Museum,* An Exhibition of . . . Post-Impressionism, *1931; San Francisco. Museum of Art,* Paul Gauguin, *1936, cat. nos. 60, 61; Meyerson, A.,* Konsthistorisk Tidskrift *15: 145, 146, 1946 (ill. fig. 20);* Art et Style *34, 1955 (ill.); Paris. Musée de l'Orangerie,* De David à Toulouse-Lautrec, *1955, cat. no. 28 (pl. 74); Rewald, J.,* Post-Impressionism, *1956, p. 254 (ill.); Chicago. Art Institute,* Gauguin, *1959, cat. no. 13*

HUMAN MISERY (SCENE IN BRITTANY)

Painted 1889, signed: P. Gauguin. Oil on canvas, 28⅞ × 36⅝ in. (73.4 × 93 cm.)
The Joseph Winterbotham Collection, 54.313

In June 1886 Gauguin left Paris for Brittany, where he spent the rest of the year at Pont-Aven. Many of his artist friends joined him there, among others Emile Bernard, Paul Serusier, and Charles Laval. He returned again in 1888 and 1889. An entry from Gauguin's note-book written for his daughter, Aline, during this period says, "I have known extreme misery, meaning that I have been hungry and cold and all the like. That is nothing or nearly nothing; one gets used to it and with some will, one comes to laugh at it. But the terrible thing about misery is that it keeps one from working and from the development of the intellectual faculties." (J. Rewald, *Gauguin,* 1938, p. 1). The sketch-book which Gauguin used during this period lists twelve paintings, with prices, to be sent to Brussels for the exhibition of *Les Vingt* of 1889. The price of this picture, 1500 francs, is highest on the list. Gauguin used the same theme in several other compositions.

Coll: Ambroise Vollard, Paris; Joseph Winterbotham, Burlington, Vt.

Ref: Meyer-Riefstahl, R., Deutsche Kunst und Dekoration *27: 109, November 1910 (ill.); Rewald, J.,* Gauguin, *1938, pl. 77; Malingue, M.,* Gauguin, Le Peintre et son Oeuvre, *1948 (pl. 129); Rewald, J.,* Post-Impressionism, *1956, pp. 271, 276–7, 286 (ill.); Chicago. Art Institute,* Gauguin, *1959, cat. no. 11*

MARIE DERRIEN Illus. p. 332

Signed and dated: P. Go./90. Oil on canvas, 25⅝ × 21½ in. (65.2 × 34.1 cm.)
The Joseph Winterbotham Collection, 25.753

The sitter for this portrait was once thought to be Marie Henry, owner of the inn at Le Pouldu. Gauguin stayed at Le Pouldu from October 1889 until the end of 1890. The portrait is influenced by Cézanne, whose painting in the background of the portrait was once owned by Gauguin.

Ref: Alexandre, A., Paul Gauguin, sa vie et le sens de son oeuvre, *1930 (ill. p. 29);* Paul Gauguin's Intimate Journals, *1936, p. 235 (ill.); Rewald, J.,* Gauguin, *1938, p. 52 (ill.); Malingue, M.,* Gauguin, *1948, cat. no. 153 (ill.); Rewald, J.,* Post-Impressionism, *1956, pp. 271, 276–7, 309 (ill.); Kerr, J. O'Connell,* The Studio *150: 172, December 1955 (ill.)*

THE BIG TREE (TE RAAU RAHI)

Signed and dated: P. Gauguin '91. Inscribed: Te raau rahi.
Oil on canvas, 28⅝ × 36 in. (72.8 × 91.5 cm.)
Gift of Kate L. Brewster, 49.513

One of the early canvases painted in Tahiti.

Coll: Mme Gauguin, Copenhagen; Mr. and Mrs. Walter S. Brewster, Chicago

Ref: Lettres de Gauguin, 1946, p. 235

THE BURAO TREE (TE BURAO)

Signed and dated: P. Gauguin 92. Inscribed: Te Burao.
Oil on canvas, 35½ × 26½ in. (89.9 × 67.4 cm.)
The Joseph Winterbotham Collection, 23.308

It has been suggested that Te Burao, painted in 1892 in Tahiti, shows the artist's hut in a richly colored tropical setting. In his book *Noa Noa,* Gauguin describes the scene: "On one side was the sea, on the other, the mountain, a deeply fissured mountain; an enormous cleft closed by a great mango leaning against the rocks. Between the mountain and the sea stood my hut, made of the wood of the burao tree."

Coll: Marius de Zayas, New York (sale 1923, cat. no. 83)

Ref: New York. Metropolitan Museum of Art, Loan Exhibition of Impressionist and Post-Impressionist Paintings, *1921, cat. no. 50; Rewald, J.,* Post-Impressionism, *1956, p. 510 (ill.)*

THE DAY OF THE GOD (MAHANA NO ATUA) Illus. p. 335

Signed and dated: Gauguin 94. Inscribed: MAHANA no Atua.
Oil on canvas, 27⅜ × 35⅝ in. (69.6 × 89.9 cm.)
Helen Birch Bartlett Memorial Collection, 26.198

In *Noa Noa,* Gauguin describes figures from his dream world, the ancient gods of Oceania, whose idols were set up on the seashore to mark the boundaries between earth and sea and to maintain the balance between the two "elements." Though painted in Paris, this is one of Gauguin's compositions which more or less sums up his ideas of ancient Maori life. There is a woodcut of the same composition, and many of the figures, the tree and the idol appear repeatedly in other paintings.

Coll: Frederic Clay Bartlett, Chicago, 1924

Ref: New York. Museum of Modern Art, First Loan Exhibition, *1929, cat. no. 46 (ill.); Cambridge, Mass. Fogg Museum of Art,* Paul Gauguin, *1936, cat. no. 28; Goldwater, R. C.,* The Art Bulletin *23: 129, 1941 (ill.); Jacobson, E.,* Basic Color, *1948, pp. 181–3 (ill.); Washington, D. C. Corcoran Gallery,* Visionaries and Dreamers, *1956, cat. no. 12 (ill.); Chicago. Art Institute,* Gauguin, *1959, cat. no. 57*

WHY ARE YOU ANGRY? (NO TE AHA OE RIRI)

Signed and dated: P. Gauguin 96. Inscribed: No te aha oe riri.
Oil on canvas, 37⅜×51 in. (95×129.6 cm.)
Mr. and Mrs. Martin A. Ryerson Collection, 33.1119

Five years earlier, Gauguin painted two other pictures with similar compositions, *The Big Tree* (*Te Raau Rahi,* F. Griesinger Collection, Cleveland), and *The Maori House* (*Te Fare Maorie,* Rhienfelden Collection, Switzerland). There is a drawing in the Louvre for the semi-nude seated figure; this same figure appears in Gauguin's manuscript *Avant et Après,* and again in a painting, *The Sisters of Charity,* 1902 (Marion Koogler McNay Art Institute, San Antonio, Texas).

Ref: Rey, R., Gauguin *(Masters of Modern Art), 1924, p. 31; Alexandre, A.,* Paul Gauguin, sa vie et le sens de son oeuvre, *1930, pp. 245, 260 (ill.); Rewald, J.,* Paul Gauguin, *1938, p. 115 (ill.); Malingue, M.,* Gauguin, *1948, cat. no. 209; Edinburgh. Royal Scottish Academy,* The Edinburgh Festival, *1955, cat. no. 54;* Emporium *124: 80, August 1956 (ill.); Chicago. Art Institute,* Gauguin, *1959, cat. no. 60*

TAHITIAN WOMAN WITH CHILDREN

Signed and dated: Paul Gauguin/1901. Oil on canvas, 38¼×29¼ in. (97.2×74.3 cm.)
Helen Birch Bartlett Memorial Collection, 27.460

This canvas was painted when Gauguin was about to leave Tahiti for Oa-Hiva, in the Marquesas. The woman and the children are intended simply as portraits, with no symbolic overtones.

Ref: Meyer-Riefstahl, R., Deutsche Kunst und Dekoration *27: 115, 1910–1911 (ill.); New York. Museum of Modern Art,* First Loan Exhibition, *1929, cat. no. 49 (ill.); Goldwater, R. C.,* The Art Bulletin *23: 129, 1941 (footnote 46); Chicago, Art Institute,* Gauguin, *1959, cat. no. 66*

GAY, Walter ~ *b. 1856 Hingham, Mass. d. 1937 Paris*

Walter Gay studied with Léon Bonnat in Paris in 1878. He later became interested in Impressionism.

THE COMMODE

Painted about 1900, signed: Walter Gay. Oil on canvas, 25¾×21 7/16 in. (65.5×54.1 cm.)
Friends of American Art Collection, 14.357

GELDER, Aert de ~ *1645–1727 Dordrecht, Holland*

De Gelder was a pupil of Samuel van Hoogstraten in Dordrecht. In the early 1660's he went to Amsterdam to study with Rembrandt.

PORTRAIT OF A GIRL

Painted about 1690. Oil on canvas, 26¼×21 in. (66.4×53.5 cm.)
Wirt D. Walker Fund, 33.1175
Coll: H. Ker-Colville, Jr., Bellport Towers, England

Ref: Chicago. Art Institute, A Century of Progress Exhibition, *1933, cat. no. 60 (pl. 39);* Ibid., *1934, cat. no. 89; Tietze, H.,* Meisterwerke Europaeischer Malerei in Amerika, *1935, pl. 191*

GELLEE, Claude (Lorraine) ~ *b. 1600 Chamagne (Mirecourt), France. d. 1682 Rome*

Like Poussin, Claude spent most of his life in Italy. When only thirteen years of age he went there for the first time and settled permanently in Rome in 1627 where he became a pupil of Agostino Tassi. Later he was influenced by Annibale Carracci, Paul Bril and Adam Elsheimer.

LANDSCAPE WITH SACRIFICIAL PROCESSION Illus. p. 230

Painted 1673, signed: Gelée. Oil on canvas, 40×50 in. (101.7×127 cm.)
Robert A. Waller Fund, 41.1020
Coll: Comissioned by Camillo Cardinal Massimo, Rome; Earl of Derby, England

Ref: Liber Veritas, II, 1777, no. 182; Smith, J., A Catalogue Raisonné of the Works of the Most Eminent Dutch, Flemish, and French Painters, *VIII, 1837, cat. no. 182; Dullea, O. J.,* Claude Gellée Le Lorrain, *1887, p. 5; Borenius, T.,* Burlington Magazine *77: 195, 1940*

GELLER, Todros ~ *b. 1889 Vinnitsa, Russia. d. 1949 Chicago*

Geller studied in Odessa and later at the Ecole d'Art in Montreal, Canada. He came to Chicago in 1918, where he attended classes at the Art Institute until 1923.

STRANGE WORLDS

Painted 1928, signed: Todros Geller. Oil on canvas, 28¼×26⅛ in. (71.7×66.4 cm.)
Gift of Leon Garland Foundation, 49.27

GENIN, Robert ~ *b. 1884 Wisokoje, Russia*

A self-taught painter, Genin was educated in Germany and has lived in Paris, Munich, and Berlin. In 1926 he visited Bali, Java, and Sumatra.

THIRST

Signed and dated: R. Genin '13. Oil on canvas, 39½ × 31½ in. (100.3 × 80.2 cm.)
Arthur Jerome Eddy Memorial Collection, 31.520

Ref: Deutsche Kunst und Dekoration *33: 294–5, October 1913 to March 1914 (ill.); Eddy, A. J.,* Cubists and Post-Impressionism, *1914, p. 47; Chicago. Art Institute,* Catalogue of the Eddy Collection, *1922, cat. no. 21; Chicago. Art Institute,* A Century of Progress Exhibition, *1933, cat. no. 728*

GERICAULT, Théodore ~ *b. 1791 Rouen, France. d. 1824 Paris*

Géricault, who studied with Pierre Guérin, was also influenced by David, though his main inspiration came from Baron Gros and Delacroix, with whom he became friendly during his student days. A trip to Italy where he stayed mostly in Rome during 1816 and 1817 centered his interest on Baroque art. Later, during a visit to England (1820–1822), he was much impressed by Constable's color and his insistence on realism.

PRANCING HORSE

Painted between 1808 and 1812. Oil on canvas, 10⅜ × 15½ in. (26.4 × 39.5 cm.)
Gift of Annie Swan Coburn to the Mr. and Mrs. Lewis L. Coburn Memorial Collection, 44.687
Coll: Vente Delacroix, 1864 [?]; Foinard, Paris

Ref: Connoisseur *119: 42, 1947*

AFTER DEATH (Study) Illus. p. 232

Painted about 1818 or 1819. Oil on canvas, 17¾ × 22 in. (45.2 × 56 cm.)
A. A. Munger Collection, 37.502

This was a study for *The Raft of the Medusa.* The artist prepared for this painting by observing corpses in the morgue and the sick in a hospital near his studio. In this study the head was a model for the man at the extreme left of the Raft. There are related sketches in the Museum of Rouen, in the National Museum of Stockholm, and in a private collection in London. Neither this painting nor the other studies were used directly in the final composition.

Coll: Chamartin, Paris, 1914; Foynard, Paris

Ref: Guey, F., La Renaissance de l'Art Français, *VII, pt. 1, 1924, p. 103; Gauthier, M.,* Géricault *(Collection des Maîtres), 1935, no. 59 (ill.);* L'Amour de l'Art *18: 41, May 1937; Friedlaender, W.,* David to Delacroix, *1952, p. 97 ff. (ill. pl. 57);* Art et Style *34, 1955 (ill.); Berger, K.,* Géricault and His Work, *1955, pp. 53, 54, 55 (pl. 52); Aimé-Azam, D.,* Mazeppa: Géricault et son temps, *1956, chapter xiv, ill. opp. 216*

GERINI, Niccolò di Pietro ~ *About 1368–1415 Florence*

Gerini was highly esteemed in his day but little is known about him except that he collaborated with Jacopo di Cione. His style derives from Bernardo Daddi.

MADONNA AND CHILD

Painted 1375–1400.
Tempera on canvas, transferred from panel, 38¾ × 20¼ in. (98.5 × 51.5 cm.)
Mr. and Mrs. Martin A. Ryerson Collection, 37.1003
Coll: Kerr Lawson, Florence, 1910; Martin A. Ryerson, Chicago

Ref: Offner, R., Art in America *9: 153, 238, 1921; van Marle, R.,* The Development of the Italian Schools of Painting, *III, 1924, p. 614; Berenson, B.,* Pitture Italiane del Rinascimento, *1936, p. 339*

GERMAN SCHOOL, 14th century

SAINT CATHERINE

Painted between 1350 and 1400. Tempera on panel, 14¼ × 13 in. (36 × 33 cm.)
A. A. Munger Collection, 32.989

This representation of Saint Catherine was formerly attributed to the French, the English and even to the Norwegian School. More recently it has been found that this panel has a sylistic relationship to the work of the Nuremberg Master of the Claren Altar.

Ref: Chicago. Art Institute, A Century of Progress Exhibition, *1933, cat. no. 17;* Ibid., *1934, cat. no. 13; Chicago. Art Institute,* Bulletin *28: 13, 1934*

GERMAN SCHOOL, 15th century

CRUCIFIXION (triptych)

Painted about 1420. Tempera on panel, 21⅜ × 31¾ in. (57.9 × 80.8 cm.)
Mr. and Mrs. Martin A. Ryerson Collection, 47.394

The center panel represents the Crucifixion; the left wing shows above the Temptation of Saint Anthony; and, below, Saint Christopher carrying the Christ Child across the stream; the right wing represents above Saint James and below Saint George and the Dragon. With the coming of Protestantism to northern Europe, many religious pictures were destroyed, thus accountıng for the rarity of German and Dutch devotional panels. Here is, however, an exceptional case where the origin of such a painting can be traced. In the Monastery of the Holy Cross at Rostock were once listed thirteen processional altarpieces, done perhaps by various artists of the same school. Some of them were later transfered to the Landesmuseum in Schwerin, others were lost. Stylistic comparison places this little triptych among those panels which are related to the upper Rhine area, particularly to a group of illuminated manuscripts done around 1400.

Ref: de Tolnay, C., Miscellanea Leo van Puyvelde, *1949, pp. 49–54; Panofsky, E.,* Early Netherlandish Painting, *I, 1953, pp. 97, 395*

THE CRUCIFIXION

Painted about 1420. Oil on panel, 16×9¼ in. (40.8×23.5 cm.)
Charles H. and Mary F. S. Worcester Collection, 36.242

This painting has been tentatively attributed to the Master of Saint Veronica, a painter who was active in Cologne. The scene here represented is an allegory symbolizing the triumph of the Church over the Synagogue.

Coll: Winandus Gulich [?], Cologne, 1684; Lersch, Aix-la-Chapelle; Worcester, 1928

Ref: Firmenich-Richartz, E., Zeitschrift für Christliche Kunst, *VIII, 1895, pp. 302–3; Scheibler, L. and C. Aldenhoven,* Geschichte der Kölner Malerschule, *1896–1902, pp. 90, 91, 384; Schafer, K.,* Geschichte der Kölner Malerschule, *1923, p. 25 (pl. 25); Wilm, H.,* Cicerone *20: 350–1, 1928; Freund, F. E. W.,* Belvedere *8: 285, 1929; Chicago. Art Institute,* A Century of Progress Exhibition, *1933, cat. no. 29; Chicago. Art Institute,* Catalogue of the Worcester Collection, *1936, cat. no. 28 (pl. 20); Kuhn, C. L.,* A Catalogue of German Paintings of the Middle Ages and Renaissance in American Collections, *1936, p. 23, cat. no. 3*

CHRIST BEARING THE CROSS

Painted about 1450. Oil on panel, 38½×42 in. (97×106.7 cm.)
Gift of Frederic Clay Bartlett, 16.371

This master from the upper Rhine is one of several painters who were grouped around the Master of the Housebook, but now appear as separate personalities.

PORTRAIT OF A YOUNG ARTIST Illus. p. 148

Painted about 1490, signed M. N. Oil on tempera on panel, 18×12⅞ in. (45.8×32.6 cm.)
Charles H. and Mary F. S. Worcester Collection, 47.77

This portrait is now ascribed to an artist of the Augsburg School. Formerly believed to be a youthful self-portrait of Matthias Grünewald (Mathis Gothardt-Neithardt), it was given by Ernst Buchner to the Augsburg School. He suggests that it might possibly be a portrait of the young Mathis by a contemporary of Dürer (the painting being inscribed with the initials M. N.). Certain stylistic elements point to an artist in the circle of Hans Burgkmair. Buchner also points out that the utensils shown in the painting suggest rather a draughtsman than a painter. The delicate drawing may be a representation of Eve after Dürer.

Coll: Private collection, Sweden, 1928; Worcester, 1937

Ref: Cicerone, *col. 20, pt. 2, 1928, p. 516; Zuelch, A. K.,* Pantheon *3: 222, 223, 1929; Jatho, K.,* Cicerone *22, pt. 2: 415, 1930; Pariset, F. G.,* Archives Alsaciennes *9: 63–100, 1930; Naumann, H. H.,* Schriften des Schongauer-Nithart-Archivs *1: 19–36, 1930;*

Pariset, F. G., Gazette des Beaux-Arts *6, per. 6: 259, 260, 262–3, 1931;* Zeitschrift für Bildende Kunst *65: 98, 1932; Naumann, H. H.,* Burlington Magazine *64: 203, 204, 210, 213, 1934; Haug, H.,* Gazette des Beaux-Arts *12, per. 6: 191, 200, 202, 1934; Chicago. Art Institute,* Catalogue of the Worcester Collection, *1936, cat. no. 29; Burkhard, A.,* Mathias Gruenewald, Personality and Accomplishment, *1936, pp. 6, 88; Fraenger, W.,* Matthias Gruenewald in seinen Werken, *1936, pp. 40, 42, 43, 45;* Les Archives Alsaciennes d'Histoire de l'Art, *15, 1936, pp. 10, 13, 66, 68, 76, 77, 153; Zuelch, A. K.,* Der Historische Gruenewald, *1938, pp. 13, 323; Henze, H.,* Marburger Jahrbuch für Kunstwissenschaft *11–12: 281–7, 1938–1939; Chicago. Art Institute,* Bulletin *41, 1947; Buchner, E.,* Das Deutsches Bildnis der Spätgotik und der Fruehen Dürerzeit, *1953, pp. 87, 88*

GERMAN SCHOOL, 16th century

MADONNA AND CHILD WITH SAINTS

Painted about 1525.
Oil and tempera on panel, center 54½ × 39½ in. (138.5 × 100.3 cm.),
wings 54½ × 16¾ in. (138.5 × 42.6 cm.)
Mr. and Mrs. Martin A. Ryerson Collection, 33.1065

This triptych by a painter of the Swabian School, done somewhat in the manner of Martin Schaffner, is an allegory dealing with the virtues of the Virgin, a conception based on an Old Testament prophecy. On the back of the wings, probably by the hand of an assistant, are (left) Pilate washing his hands before the multitude and (right) the multitude crying, "Crucify Him."

LEONHART FUCHS

Painted 1525. Oil on panel, 15⅜ × 10¼ in. (39.1 × 26 cm.)
Charles H. and Mary F. S. Worcester Collection, 47.88

Fuchs was one of the most famous botanists of his time, the fuchsia having been named for him. In 1542 he published a book on herbs illustrated by Heinrich Füllmaurer, who included a life-size drawing of Fuchs probably based on his portrait. The professor wears a fur-trimmed gown according to his rank and holds a carnation indicating that this was probably a marriage portrait, pendant, no doubt, to one of his wife Anna Friedberger. On the back of the panel are two coats of arms presumably of Fuchs and his wife, and the date 1525. Formerly thought to be by the hand of Hans Maler zu Schwaz, this portrait can only be designated as by an unknown Swabian painter.

Coll: Baron Eugen von Kohner, Budapest; Worcester, 1928

Ref: Freund, F. E. W., Belvedere *8, pt. 2: 285, 1929; Chicago. Art Institute,* Catalogue of the Worcester Collection, *1932, cat. no. 37; Kuhn, C. L.,* A Catalogue of German Paintings of the Middle Ages and Renaissance in American Collections, *1936, p. 65, cat. no. 270*

GERUNG, Matthias ~ *b. c. 1500 Noerdlingen, Germany. d. c. 1568–1570 Lauingen*

Gerung was one of the several minor followers of Lucas Cranach the Elder. He lived in the household of Duke Ottheinrich of Neuburg where he was employed as a painter, miniaturist, engraver and designer of tapestries.

THE JUDGMENT OF PARIS

Dated and inscribed: OW 1536 P G - PARIS TRRM.
Oil on panel, 18¾ × 12½ in. (47.7 × 31.8 cm.)
Charles H. and Mary F. S. Worcester Collection, 40.935

Coll: Reuling, Baltimore, 1920; John E. Stillwell, New York (sale Anderson Galleries, 1927, no, 454); Worcester, 1928

Ref: Art News *27: 5, November 10, 1928;* The Arts *14: 31, 1928; Freund, F. E. W.,* Belvedere *8, pt. 2: 285, 1929; Wescher-Kauert, H.,* Zeitschrift für Bildende Kunst *63: 150–3, 1929–1930; Chicago. Art Institute,* A Century of Progress Exhibition, *1934, cat. no. 14; Chicago. Art Institute,* Catalogue of the Worcester Collection, *1936, cat. no. 40 (pl. 29); Kuhn, C. L.,* A Catalogue of German Paintings . . . , *1936, p. 57, cat. no. 215*

GHIRLANDAIO, Ridolfo ~ *1483–1561/2 Florence*

A pupil of Fra Bartolommeo, Ghirlandaio was influenced by Piero di Cosimo, Lorenzo di Credi, Raphael, and Leonardo da Vinci. He was the son of the great fresco painter, Domenico Ghirlandaio, and is best remembered for his portraits.

PORTRAIT OF A GENTLEMAN OF FLORENCE Illus. p. 41

Painted about 1550. Oil on panel, 26¾ × 19⅜ in. (68 × 49.4 cm.)
Mr. and Mrs. Martin A. Ryerson Collection, 33.1009
Coll: Prince Brancacci, Rome; William Beattie, Glasgow; Arthur T. Sully, London; Ryerson, Chicago

Ref: Armstrong, W., Art Journal *53: 46–7, 1901; Venturi, L.,* Pitture Italiane in America, *1931, pl. 338; Chicago. Art Institute,* A Century of Progress Exhibition, *1933, cat. no. 116;* Ibid., *1934, cat. no. 47; Berenson, B.,* Pitture Italiane del Rinascimento, *1936, p. 194*

GIACOMETTI, Alberto ~ *b. 1901 Stampa, Switzerland*

PORTRAIT OF ISAKU YANAIHARA

Signed and dated: Alberto Giacometti 1956. Oil on canvas, 32 × 25⅝ in. (81.3 × 65.2 cm.)
Gift of Silvain and Arma Wyler, 59.11

GIAQUINTO, Corrado ~ *b. 1699 Molfetta, Italy. d. about 1765 Naples*

A pupil of Francesco Solimena, Giaquinto worked in Rome and Turin with Sebastiano Conca. In 1752 he went to Madrid where he was court painter to Ferdinand VI.

FIGURES FROM THE OLD TESTAMENT (Sketch for the cupola of the Cathedral of Cesena)
Painted about 1750. Oil on canvas, 16×41 in. (40.8×104.2 cm.)
Gift of Mrs. John H. Harmon and Mrs. Everett L. Millard in memory of their mother Mrs. Charles T. Boynton, 41.830

Sketch for a part of the fresco of *The Triumph of the Virgin,* in the chapel of the Vergine del Popolo of the Cathedral of Cesena (1750), a work highly praised by Count Algarotti in a letter to Mariette ("rinomata cupola . . . un fresco di grandissima vaghezza"). The present sketch varies the finished work and seems at the same state of development as two sketches for the fresco in the collection Villafalletto, Rome (each 40×30 cm.), and to be earlier than the three sketches at Capodimonte (each 40×98 cm., signed and dated Rome, 1749). Other sketches, also in lunette format exist: two formerly and one still (1959) in propr. Jandolo, Rome; a small early sketch in coll. Capparoni, Rome; and a sketch in the Maser coll., Lawrence, Kansas. A drawing for the *King David Playing the Harp* is in the Cianfaroni coll., Rome.

Ref: Algarotti, Opere complete, *Venice, 1792, vol. VII, 181; Lazzarini, G. A.,* Opere . . . di belle arti, *Pesaro 1806, vol. II; Aguselli, F. A.,* Sul famoso dipinto a fresco della cupola di M. Vergine del Popolo nella Cattedr. di Cesena, *Bologna, 1841; Mauceri, E.,* Brutium, *1934;* Bolletino d'Arte, *1953, p. 379; Volpi, M.,* Boll. d'Arte, *1958, p. 280; d'Orsi, Mario,* Corrado Giaquinto, *Rome, 1958, pp. 82, 91, figs. 89–91*

GILES, Howard ~ *b. 1876 Brooklyn, N.Y. d. 1955 Woodstock, N.Y.*

Giles' work was much influenced by the color theories of Denman W. Ross and the system of dynamic symmetry taught by Jay Hambidge.

MACMAHON'S, MAINE
Painted 1916, signed: H. Giles. Oil on canvas, 30×30 in. (76.3×76.3 cm.)
Friends of American Art Collection, 17.265

GINZEL, Roland ~ *1921 Lincoln, Illinois*

Ginzel lives in Chicago where he teaches at the University of Illinois and the University of Chicago. He studied at the Art Institute of Chicago, at the State University of Iowa and at the Slade School in London.

MARCH 10TH
Painted 1955, signed: Ginzel. Oil on canvas, 41¼×48 in. (104.8×122 cm.)
Mr. and Mrs. Seymour Oppenheimer Purchase Prize, 55.650

GIOVANNI DI PAOLO ~ *About 1403–1482/3 Siena, Italy*

Giovanni di Paolo worked in the tradition of Taddeo di Bartolo and Sassetta. He also learned from the style of Gentile da Fabriano, the Umbrian painter who spent two years in Siena. It is possible that Giovanni visited Florence, as his work of about 1440 suggests contact with the style of Fra Angelico.

JOHN THE BAPTIST Illus. p. 36–37

Painted about 1450 or 1460.

Tempera on panel, a. c. d. and f., 27 × 14¼ in. (68.7 × 36.3 cm.); b. 27 × 15 9/16 in. (68.7 × 39.8 cm.) and e. 27 × 15⅜ in. (68.7 × 39.1 cm.)

Mr. and Mrs. Martin A. Ryerson Collection, (a) 33.1010; (b) 33.1011; (c) 33.1012; (d) 33.1013; (e) 33.1014; (f) 33.1015

These six scenes from the life of John the Baptist with six other panels (four in other collections and two lost) once formed the wings of an altarpiece, the center of which may have been a painting or a sculptured group.

(a) John in the Wilderness.
(b) John Meets Christ.
(c) John in Prison.
(d) Salome Asks Herod for the Head of the Baptist.
(e) Beheading of John the Baptist.
(f) The Head of the Baptist Brought Before Herod.

Another set of four paintings on the same subject by Giovanni di Paolo is owned by the National Gallery in London. In style and composition they are closely related to the Chicago panels.

Coll: Edouard Aynard, London; Martin A. Ryerson, 1913

Ref: Reinach, S., Repertoire *1: 516, 523, 1905; Perkins, F. M.,* Rassegna d'Arte Senese *3: 82–3, 1907; Berenson, B.,* The Central Italian Painters of the Renaissance, *1909, p. 177; Crowe, J. A. and G. B. Cavalcaselle,* A History of Painting in Italy, *V, 1914, p. 179; Schubring, P.,* Cassoni, *1915, pp. 324–5; de Nicola, G.,* Burlington Magazine *33: 163–8, 1918; New York. Metropolitan Museum of Art,* Loan Exhibition of the Arts of the Italian Renaissance, *1923, cat. nos. 12–17, pl. 17; Mather, F. J., Jr.,* A History of Italian Painting, *1923, pp. 93–5; van Marle, R.,* The Development of the Italian Schools of Painting, *IX, 1927, pp. 427–430; Offner, R.,* Italian Primitives at Yale University, *1927, p. 40; London. Royal Academy,* Exhibition of Italian Art, *1930, cat. nos. 96–101; Venturi, L.,* Pitture Italiane in America, *1931, cat. nos. 136–141; Berenson, B.,* Italian Pictures of the Renaissance, *1932, p. 245; Edgell, G. H.,* A History of Sienese Painting, *1932, pp. 218–9; Chicago. Art Institute,* A Century of Progress Exhibition, *1933, cat. no. 85; Chicago. Art Institute,* Bulletin *27: 8, 1933; Tietze, H.,* Meisterwerke Europaeischer Malerei in Amerika, *1935 (pls. 37–8); Pope-Hennessy, J.,* Giovanni di Paolo, *1937, pp. 80–90; Chicago. Art Institute,* Bulletin *32: 106–9, 1938; Pope-Hennessy, J.,* Burlington Magazine *72: 95, 1938; Langton-Douglas, R.,* Burlington Magazine *72: 43–7, 1938; Boston. Museum of the Fine Arts,* Arts of the Middle Ages, *1940, cat. nos. 65–7; Carli, E.,* La Pittura Senese, *1955, pp. 224, 226 (fig. 147); Carli, E.,* Sienese Painting, *1956, pl. 116*

GIRARD, Pedro (attributed to) ~ *Active second half of 15th century, Valencia, Spain*

A Valencian master, Pedro Girard, is known to have worked in Vich in the province of

Catalonia, in 1479. Although his work is not clearly identified, a group of Catalan paintings has tentatively been attributed to this artist. This painter shows a relationship with the Valencian artists Jacomart and Rexach.

SAINT SEBASTIAN

Painted second half 15th century. Tempera on panel, 70 × 36 in. (117.9 × 91.5 cm.)
Gift of Mr. and Mrs. Chauncey McCormick, 42.603

Ref: Post, C. R., A History of Spanish Painting, *vol. 8, pt. 2, 746–8*

GLACKENS, William J. ~ *b. 1870 Philadelphia. d. 1938 Westport, Conn.*

Glackens who started as an illustrator in Philadelphia, later went to New York where he joined a group of painters under Robert Henri, who were known as the New York Realists or The Eight.

CHEZ MOUQUIN Illus. p. 377

Signed and dated: W. Glackens '05. Oil on canvas, $48\frac{3}{16}$ × $36\frac{1}{4}$ in. (122.3 × 92.1 cm.)
Friends of American Art Collection, 25.295

The man at the right was James Moore, the well-known New York café owner. This picture was shown at the Macbeth Gallery in 1908, the only exhibition ever held by The Eight.

Ref: American Art Annual *6: 60, 1907; Gallatin, A. E.,* International Studio *40, 1910;* The Arts *3: 249, 1923; Watson, F.,* William Glackens, *1923; Chicago, Art Institute,* Bulletin *19: 97, 1925; Pène du Bois, Guy,* William J. Glackens, *1931, pl. 52;* Index of 20th Century Artists, *II, 1935, no. 4, p. 64;* Magazine of Art *30: 175, 1937*

GOERG, Edouard ~ *b. 1893 Sydney, Australia*

Of French-British extraction, Goerg studied in Paris with Maurice Denis. However, the three great influences in his work are Goya, Daumier and Rouault.

THE EPICURE

Signed and dated: Ed. Goerg 1923. Oil on canvas, $39\frac{3}{8}$ × 32 in. (100 × 81.3 cm.)
The Joseph Winterbotham Collection, 29.765

THE HUNTERS' CAR

Painted between 1920 and 1930, signed: Goerg.
Oil on canvas, $23\frac{1}{8}$ × $21\frac{7}{8}$ in. (58.7 × 81 cm.)
Gift of Mr. and Mrs. Carter H. Harrison, 37.379

THE STROKE OF LIGHTNING

Painted between 1920 and 1930, signed: E. Goerg.
Oil on canvas, $28\frac{1}{4}$ × $35\frac{1}{4}$ in. (71.7 × 89.5 cm.)
Gift of Mr. and Mrs. Carter H. Harrison, 36.8

TABLE D'HOTE

Painted about 1928, signed: E. Goerg. Oil on canvas, 35½×28 in. (90.2×71.2 cm.)
Gift of Mr. and Mrs. Carter H. Harrison, 35.304

VAN GOGH, Vincent ~ *b. 1853 Groot-Zundert, Holland. d. 1890 Auvers, France*

Van Gogh was the son of a Dutch clergyman. During his early years he worked along with his brother Theo in The Hague at Goupil & Co., art dealers. In 1876 Van Gogh turned to missionary and religious work and two years later volunteered for service in the Borinage (a Belgian coal-mining district). The artist began to draw seriously in 1880. At this time he was much influenced by the work of Millet. Supported by Theo, he painted dark canvases of Dutch peasants until 1886 when he came to Paris where he worked under the influence of the Impressionists. In 1888 he lived in Arles; here his personal style fully matured. During this period Gauguin joined Van Gogh for a short time. The following year his sickness forced him to live in the asylum at Saint-Rémy and finally in 1890 he moved to Auvers where shortly thereafter he killed himself.

MONTMARTRE

Painted about 1886. Oil on canvas, mounted on masonite, 17⅛×13 in. (43.6×33 cm.)
Helen Birch Bartlett Memorial Collection, 26.202 (de la Faille no. 272)

This view of Paris from the hill of Montmartre, is one of the early paintings done by Van Gogh during his Paris period.

Coll: Mme J. van Gogh-Bonger, Amsterdam; Viaud, Paris; Birch Bartlett

Ref: Amsterdam. Stedelijk Museum, Exhibition, *1905, no. 40; London. Leicester Galleries,* Exhibition of... Vincent van Gogh, *1923, cat. no. 25;* The Arts *6: 294, 1924; Chicago. Art Institute,* Bulletin *19: 81–2, 1925; Chicago. Art Institute,* Birch Bartlett Handbook, *1926, p. 8; Watson, F.,* The Arts *9: 306, 1929; Chicago. Art Institute,* A Century of Progress Exhibition, *1933, cat. no. 380;* Ibid., *1934, cat. no. 313; Frankfurter, A. M.,* Art News *37, pt. 1: 9, January 1, 1939 (ill.); New York. M. Knoedler & Co.,* Views of Paris, *January 1939, cat. no. 36 (ill.); New York. M. Wildenstein & Co.,* The Art and Life of Vincent van Gogh, *1943, p. 23 (ill. no. 16); Chicago. Art Institute,* Catalogue of the Birch Bartlett Collection, *1946, pp. 22–3; Cleveland. Museum of Art,* Work by Vincent van Gogh, *1948, cat. no. 5 (ill.); New York. Metropolitan Museum of Art,* Van Gogh, Paintings and Drawings, *1949–1950, cat. no. 46; Schapiro, M.,* Vincent van Gogh, *1950, p. 42; Chicago. Art Institute,* Van Gogh, Paintings and Drawings, *1950, cat. no. 46; Houston, Texas. Contemporary Arts Association,* Vincent van Gogh, *1951, cat. no. 3 (ill.); Andover, Mass. Phillips Academy, Addison Gallery of American Art,* Variations . . . Three Centuries of Painting, 1954, *cat. no. 12*

SELF PORTRAIT Illus. p. 331

Painted 1886–1888. Oil on cardboard, 16½×13¼ in. (42×33.7 cm.)
The Joseph Winterbotham Collection, 54.326 (de la Faille no. 345)

While in Paris from 1886 to 1888 Van Gogh stayed with his brother Theo. Through him he met most of the leading Impressionists. Pissarro became his friend and he also met Seurat whose work he admired greatly. For a short period he was intensely interested in the "pointillist" color theories of Seurat and Pissarro. During this brief time in Paris, Van Gogh painted an astonishing number of self portraits, twenty-four in all.

Coll: Mme J. van Gogh-Bonger, Amsterdam; Leonard Tietz, Cologne; Alfred Tietz, Cologne

Ref: Cologne, Internationale Kunstausstellung . . . , *1912, cat. no. 11; Berlin. Paul Cassirer,* Exhibition, *1914, cat. no. 28; Berlin. Paul Cassirer,* Vincent van Gogh, Gemaelde, *January/March 1928, cat. no. 29; Frankfort-on-Main. M. Goldschmidt Art Gallery,* Exhibition, *March/April 1928, cat. no. 18; Amsterdam. Municipal Museum,* Vincent van Gogh, en zijn tijdgenooten, *1930, cat. no. 25 (ill.); Barr, A. H., Jr.,* Vincent van Gogh, *1935, cat. no. 20 (ill.); Chicago. Arts Club,* Loan Exhibition of the Winterbotham Collection, *1936, cat. no. 43 (ill.); Davidson, M.,* Art News *36: 10, March 5, 1938; De la Faille, J.-B.,* Vincent van Gogh, *1939, p. 294, no. 406 (ill.)*

STILL LIFE: FRUIT

Painted 1887. Oil on canvas, 18×21½ in. (45.8×54.7 cm.)
Gift of Kate L. Brewster, 49.215 (de la Faille no. 382)
Coll: H. G. E. Degas, Paris; H. J. Laroche, Paris; Walter S. Brewster, Chicago

Ref: L'Amour de l'Art *3: 207, 1922; New York. Museum of Modern Art,* First Loan Exhibition . . . , *1929, cat. no. 94, pl. 94; Cambridge, Mass. Fogg Museum of Art,* Exhibition of French Painting . . . , *1929, cat. no. 94 (pl. 42); Northampton, Mass. Smith College Museum of Art,* Bulletin, *1935, no. 16, p. 18; Vitali, L.,* Vincent van Gogh, *1936, XIV, (pl. 5); New York. Metropolitan Museum of Art,* Van Gogh, Paintings and Drawings, *1949–1950, cat. no. 55 (ill. p. 41)*

SUNNY MIDI, ARLES

Painted 1888. Oil on canvas, 28¾×36¼ in. (73×92.1 cm.)
Mr. and Mrs. Lewis L. Coburn Memorial Collection, 33.433 (de la Faille no. 468)

As a welcoming gesture for Gauguin when he came to live with him in Arles, Van Gogh painted four pictures, all of which depicted the public gardens facing his little house. Among them were two which were supposedly companion pieces, one dominated by a blue sky, the other (the Art Institute version) by a lemon sky. As Van Gogh wrote about the latter, the colors have "the richness and intensity of autumn. And also it is in still heavier paint than the other, plain and thick." In both pictures there are clumps of oleander in the background "raving mad; the blasted things are flowering so riotously. . . They are loaded with fresh flowers, and heaps of faded flowers as well, and their green is continually renewing itself in fresh, strong jets, apparently inexhaustibly."

Coll: Van Gogh Family; M. Gieseler, The Hague (sale A. Mak, Amsterdam, October 1925, no. 33)

DUTCH PAINTINGS

XVIIth Century

ILLUSTRATIONS

Rembrandt, Girl at an Open Half-Door, 1645. Mr. & Mrs. Martin A. Ryerson Collection

Claesz, Pieter, Still Life, c. 1630. Simeon B. Williams Fund

Below: Steen, Jan, The Family Concert, 1666. Gift of T. B. Blackstone

Rembrandt, Harmen Gerritsz van Rijn, c. 1631. Mr. and Mrs. W. W. Kimball Collection

Opposite: Fabritius, Barent, Jacob and Benjamin, c. 1650–60. Wilson L. Mead Fund

Witte, Emanuel de, Church Interior, c. 1670. Charles H. & Mary F. S. Worcester Collection

Dubordieu, Pieter, Portrait of a Young Girl, c. 1635. Wilson L. Mead Fund

Hobbema, Meindert, The Watermill with the Great Red Roof, c. 1670. Gift of Mr. & Mrs. Frank G. Logan

Ruisdael, Jacob van, *Ruins of Egmond*, c. 1650–60. Potter Palmer Collection

Ostade, Adriaen van, The Golden Wedding, 1674. George B. & Mary R. Harris Fund

Hals, Frans, The Rommelpot Player, c. 1626
Charles H. & Mary F. S. Worcester Collection

Ochtervelt, Jacob, The Musicians, c. 1670. Mr. & Mrs. Martin A. Ryerson Collection

Ref: Copenhagen, Denmark, Den Frie Udstilling, *1893, cat. no. 183; Van Gogh, V.,* Further Letters to His Brother, *1886–1889, III, London, 1929, no. 537; New York. Museum of Modern Art,* Retrospective, *1930, cat. no. 105; Chicago. Art Institute,* Catalogue of the *Coburn Collection, 1932, cat. no. 13 (ill. p. 41); Chicago. Art Institute,* Bulletin *27: 116, 1933 (ill.); Chicago. Art Institute,* A Century of Progress Exhibition, *1934, cat. no. 315; Springfield, Mass. Museum of Art,* French Painting, Cézanne to the Present. *1935–1936, cat. no. 52; Nordenfalk, C.,* Konsthistorisk Tidskrift *15: 92–3, December 1946 (ill. fig. 4); Cleveland, Ohio. Museum of Art,* Work by Vincent van Gogh, *1948, cat. no. 12 (pl. 10)*

BEDROOM AT ARLES Illus. p. 328

Painted 1888. Oil on canvas, 28¾ × 36 in. (73 × 91.5 cm.)
Helen Birch Bartlett Memorial Collection, 26.417 (de la Faille no. 484)

This touching painting, Van Gogh's bedroom at Arles, represented in his own words the security of "solidity, lastingness and quiet." In writing about the painting he said it was intended to be "as simple as a Seurat; flat tones crudely brushed on, and with a heavy impasto." A year later in Saint-Rémy (1889) Van Gogh painted this same subject from memory but used somewhat different color. The second version is in the collection of V. W. van Gogh. Still another much smaller version was also executed in Saint-Rémy (1889) and was sent by Vincent to Theo who in turn was instructed to give the painting to their mother. It is now in the collection of Prince Matsukata, Kobe, Japan.

Coll: Miss Wilhelmina van Gogh; Carl Reininghaus, Vienna

Ref: Minneapolis, Minn. Institute of Arts, Forty Paintings from the Birch Bartlett Collection, *1925, cat. no. 29; Chicago. Art Institute,* Annual Report, *1926; Chicago. Art Institute,* Bulletin *20: 92–4, 1926; Watson, F.,* The Arts *9: 306, 1926; Chicago. Art Institute,* Birch Bartlett Handbook, *1929, pp. 22–3; Van Gogh, V.,* Further Letters to His Brother, *1886–1889, London, 1929, nos. 573, 604, 554; New York. Museum of Modern Art,* First Loan Exhibition . . . , *1929 ,cat. no. 79 (ill.); Chicago. Art Institute,* A Century of Progress Exhibition, *1933, cat. no. 376;* Ibid., *1934, cat. no. 310; Toledo, Ohio. Museum of Art,* French Impressionists and Post-Impressionists, *1934, cat. no. 24; Chicago. Art Institute,* Catalogue of the Birch Bartlett Collection, *1946, pp. 18–9; Jacobson, E.,* Basic Color, *1948, pp. 174–6; Schapiro, M.,* Vincent van Gogh *(Library of Great Painters), 1950, p. 78*

MADAME ROULIN ROCKING THE CRADLE (LA BERCEUSE)

Signed and dated: Vincent, Arles 89. Inscribed: La Berceuse.
Oil on canvas, 36⅝ × 28⅞ in. (93 × 73.4 cm.)
Helen Birch Bartlett Memorial Collection, 26.200 (de la Faille no. 506)

A discussion with Gauguin about Icelandic fishermen (from a novel of Pierre Loti) inspired Van Gogh to paint this picture which was intended to give sailors a sense of security, a feeling of being cradled and of hearing old lullabies. Van Gogh purposely planned the painting like a chromo where "discordant sharps of crude pink, crude orange, and crude green are softened by flats of red and green." Mme Roulin and her husband, the postman, were Van Gogh's best friends in Arles. It was she who served as the model for this painting. The canvas was originally intended as the middle section of a triptych, the other two parts to have been paintings of sun flowers. The decorative floral background suggests the influence of Gauguin who was living with Van Gogh at this time. There are five other versions of this painting; one in the Oscar Reinhart Collection, Winterthur, Switzerland; one in the Kroeller-Mueller Museum, Holland; one belongs to V. W. van Gogh; still another was formerly in a private collection in Paris, and the fifth is owned by the Museum of Fine Arts, Boston.

Coll: Paul Gauguin, Paris; Pellerin, Paris; A. Schuffenecker, Saint-Maur, Paris

Ref: Chicago. Art Institute, Bulletin *17: 77, 1923; Minneapolis, Minn. Institute of Arts,* Forty Paintings from the Birch Bartlett Collection, *1925, cat. no. 20; Chicago. Art Institute,* Bulletin *20: 92–4, 1926; Zabel, M. D.,* Art and Archaeology *26: 231, 233, December 1928; Chicago. Art Institute,* Catalogue of the Birch Bartlett Collection, *1929, pp. 20–1, 58 (ill.); Van Gogh, V.,* Further Letters to His Brother, *1886–1889, III, London, 1929, nos. 573–6, 578, 582, 592; Chicago. Art Institute,* A Century of Progress Exhibition, *1933, cat. no. 377;* Ibid., *1934, cat. no. 311; Scherjon, W. and J. de Gruyter,* Vincent van Gogh's Greatest Period, *1937, p. 171; Chicago. Art Institute,* Catalogue of the Birch Bartlett Collection, *1946, pp. 20–1 (ill.); Van Gogh, V. W.,* Museumjournaal, *ser. 1, nol 3, October 1955, pp. 46–8; New York. Wildenstein & Co.,* Loan Exhibition, Van Gogh, *March/April 1955, cat. no. 45 (ill.)*

THE DRINKERS

Illus. p. 330

Painted February 1890. Oil on canvas, 23⅜×28⅞ in. (59.4×73.4)
The Joseph Winterbotham Collection, 53.178 (de la Faille no. 667)

During the last year of his life in the asylum at Saint-Rémy, Van Gogh spent much time copying prints by Millet, Delacroix and Daumier. This he did not do for lack of original ideas but rather in an attempt to restrain his emotions and his imagination both of which tended to overpower him. In Daumier's work Van Gogh found a passion close to his own. In letters to his brother Theo he explained that he was not really making a copy of Daumier's famous woodcut *The Drinkers* but rather a translation into the language of color. While retaining the original composition, Van Gogh transformed Daumier's sketch into a more detailed scene, adding a landscape with houses and factory chimneys as his background and filling the sky with a mass of turbulent clouds. The emotional tension dominant in his late work is brilliantly expressed by an unusual color scheme restricted almost exclusively to blues and greens, and by the abrupt use of his brush.

Coll: Carl Reininghaus, Vienna; Aghion, Paris

Ref: Meier-Graefe, J., Vincent van Gogh, *Munich, 1912, pp. 56–7; Berlin. Paul Cassirer,* Exhibition, *May/June 1914, cat. no. 113; Meier-Graefe, J.,* Vincent van Gogh, *London/Boston, 1922, pp. 68–71; Coquiot, G.,* Vincent van Gogh, *Paris, 1923, p. 319; Vienna. Secession,* The Leading Masters of the French Art of the 19th Century, *1925, cat. no. 89 (ill.); Van Gogh, V.,* Letters to His Brother, *1872–1886, II, Boston/New York, 1927, p. 83; Meier-Graefe, J.,* Entwicklungsgeschichte der Modernen Kunst, *III, 1927, pl. 518; Van Gogh, V.,* Further Letters to His Brother, *1886–1889, III, 1929, pp. 427–30, 437–8; Von Udhe, W. (introd.),* Vincent van Gogh, *1936, pp. 16–7; Chicago. Arts Club,* Exhibition of the Winterbotham Collection, *December 1936, cat. no. 44; Scherjon, W. and J. de Gruyter,* Vincent van Gogh's Great Period, *1937, p. 291 (ill.);* Art Quarterly *16, no. 4: 356, 357, Winter 1953 (ill.)*

GONZALES, Eva ~ *1849–1883 Paris*

Eva Gonzalès was a pupil of Charles Chaplin. In 1869 she began her studies with Edouard Manet and followed his style closely.

GIRL WITH CHERRIES

Painted about 1870, signed: Eva Gonzalès. Oil on canvas, 21⅞ × 18¼ in. (55.7 × 46.5 cm.)
Gift of Annie Swan Coburn to the Mr. and Mrs. Lewis L. Coburn Memorial Collection, 40.32

This study of a girl, conceived in the 18th century tradition, shows the influence of Manet.

Coll: William Merritt Chase (sale Anderson Galleries, 1896, no. 1095); Miss M. Mott, Randor, Pa., 1904; Mrs. Haven Emerson

Ref: W. S. Sparrow, Women Painters of the World, *1905, p. 231; Chicago. Art Institute,* Bulletin *34: 73–5, 1940 (ill.); Roger-Marx,* Eva Gonzalès, *1950, p. 4*

GOSSAERT, Jan (called Mabuse) ~ *b. about 1478 Maubeuge, Flanders. d. about 1535 Antwerp*

Gossaert's style developed from the tradition of Gerard David and Quentin Massys. In 1503 he was accepted as Master in Antwerp and in 1508/9 he went to Italy in the entourage of Philip of Burgundy. This trip brought him in contact with the Humanists. Leonardo da Vinci more than any other Italian painter influenced Gossaert, who was one of the first to introduce the Mannerist style in the North.

MADONNA AND CHILD Illus. p. 137

Painted about 1520. Oil on panel, 21 × 15⅞ in. (53.5 × 40.4 cm.)
Charles H. and Mary F. S. Worcester Collection, 57.47
Coll: Baron de Beurnonville, Paris; Max von Wasserman, Paris

Ref: Paris. Georges Petit Gallery, Catalogue . . . Beurnonville, *May 14–16, 1881, cat. no. 289; Segard, A.,* Jean Gossaert, dit Mabuse, *1923, pp. 68, 69, 185 (cat. no. 53); Friedlaender, M. J.,* Die Altniederlaendische Malerei, *VIII, 1930, p. 156, no. 33; engraved by Guérard*

GOYA Y LUCIENTES, Francisco ~ *b. 1746 Fuendetodos, Spain. d. 1828 Bordeaux, France*

Goya studied in Saragossa under José Luzan, in Madrid under Francisco Bayeu, and later in Rome. He designed tapestries, painted murals, altarpieces, and portraits and made many etchings and lithographs. In 1799 he was appointed official painter to the court of Charles IV. Deeply affected by the events of the Napoleonic Wars and the Restoration of the Bourbons in Spain, he chose self-imposed exile, and moved in 1824 to France. He was first recognized outside Spain as the etcher of the *Caprichos,* satires on contemporary social and political customs. The *Disasters of War* also helped to establish Goya's fame after 1863 when the complete series of satires had its first public edition.

ISIDORO MAIQUEZ

Painted about 1807. Oil on canvas, $32\frac{3}{8} \times 24\frac{7}{8}$ in. (82.3×63.3 cm.)
Mr. and Mrs. Martin A. Ryerson Collection, 33.1077

Maiquez (1766–1820), who had studied in Paris with the great Talma, was a successful actor. The painting is a replica of the portrait of Maiquez in the Prado which is signed and dated 1807. Another, more finished version, is in a private collection in Madrid.

Ref: Calvert, A. F., Goya, An Account of His Life and Works, *1908, p. 63; V. von Loga,* Francisco de Goya, *1910, p. 199, no. 270; Mayer, A. L.,* Zeitschrift für Bildende Kunst, *N.F. 33: 70, 1922; Mayer, A. L.,* Francisco de Goya, *1924, pp. 28, 61; Guidol, J.,* Goya, *1941, p. 88*

CAPTURE OF THE BANDIT MARAGATO BY THE MONK PEDRO DE ZALDIVIA

(in six panels) Illus. p. 102

Painted about 1806–1807. Oil on panel, $11\frac{1}{2} \times 15\frac{1}{8}$ in. (29.2×38.5 cm.)
Mr. and Mrs. Martin A. Ryerson Collection, 33.1071–33.1076

(Desparmet Fitz-Gerald Nos. 215-220)

In 1806 a bandit named Maragato attacked Fray de Zaldivia. The monk resisted and overpowered the bandit.

(a) Maragato Robs a Fat Purser
(b) Maragato Points His Gun at Fray Pedro de Zaldivia to Get His Shoes
(c) Fray Pedro Wrests the Gun from Maragato
(d) Fray Pedro Clubs Maragato
(e) Fray Pedro Shoots Maragato
(f) Fray Pedro Binds Maragato

The detailed accounts of this incident fired the imagination of the Spanish public. Songs and poems about the monk and the bandit were circulated, and the episode was illustrated in popular prints. If Goya used the popular prints as basis for his own representation, he extracted the scenes from the merely anecdotal, creating dramatic and vividly narrative paintings where action moves vigorously from panel to panel. Goya must have painted these scenes for his own pleasure or intended them as a kind of record to be used for some future compositions. They were still listed among his possessions in the inventory of 1812.

Coll: Lafitte, Madrid (sale Hôtel Drouot, Paris, March 7, 1861); Lafitte, Paris, 1911

Ref: Lafond, P., Goya, *1902, p. 110, nos. 64–9; V. von Loga,* Francisco de Goya, *1903, p. 215, no. 485; Calvert, A. F.,* Goya, *1908, pp. 152–3, cat. nos. 24–9; Stokes, H.,* Francisco

Goya, *1914, p. 351, nos. 501–6; A. de Beruete y Moret,* Goya: Composiciones y Figuras, *II, 1918, pp. 95–6; Mayer, A. L.,* Francisco de Goya, *1924, pp. 65, 117, cat. no. 597; Chicago. Art Institute,* A Century of Progress Exhibition, *1933, cat. no. 166;* Ibid., *1934, cat. no. 69; Chicago. Art Institute,* Goya, *1941, pp. 46–9, cat. nos. 71–6; Gudiol, J.,* Goya, *1941, p. 88; Estarico, L.,* Francisco de Goya, *1942, figs. 123–5; Hilton, R.,* Margato Y El Ocaso del Bandalerismo Español, *1946, pp. 1–10; Font, E. S.,* Gazette des Beaux-Arts, *November 1958, pp. 289–304*

THE HANGED MONK Illus. p. 103

Painted about 1810. Oil on panel, $12\frac{3}{16} \times 15\frac{7}{16}$ in. (31 × 39.2 cm.)
Robert A. Waller Fund, 36.225 (Desparmet Fitz-Gerald no. 230 [?])
Coll: Baron Adolf Kohner, Budapest; Duc de Trévise, Paris

GOYEN, Jan van ~ *b. 1596 Leyden, Holland. d. 1656 The Hague*

Van Goyen was mainly influenced by the landscape painter, Esaias van de Velde. Settling in Leyden about 1618, he later also worked in Leyden and The Hague.

FISHING BOATS OFF AN ESTUARY

Signed with monogram, dated: V G 1633. Oil on panel, $13\frac{9}{16} \times 22\frac{7}{16}$ in. (34.5 × 57 cm.)
Mr. and Mrs. Martin A. Ryerson Collection, 33.1078 (HdG 1079)

GRABACH, John R. ~ *b. 1886 Greenfield, Mass.*

Grabach, both a painter and sculptor, was trained at the Art Students League in New York.

WASHDAY IN SPRING

Painted 1924, signed: John R. Grabach. Oil on canvas, $30\frac{3}{4} \times 29$ in. (78.1 × 73.7 cm.)
Friends of American Art Collection, 24.951

GRAHAM, Ellwood ~ *b. 1911 St. Louis, Mo.*

Graham studied at the Washington University School of Fine Arts in St. Louis.

EMBLAZONMENT

Painted about 1949, signed: Graham. Oil on canvas, $35\frac{3}{4} \times 27\frac{1}{2}$ in. (90.8 × 70 cm.)
Gift of Mr. and Mrs. Ainsley K. Salz, 51.15

GRANDI, Ercole ~ *About 1463 to about 1521 Ferrara, Italy*

Grandi was in the service of the Este family, Dukes of Ferrara. He was influenced by Lorenzo Costa and Francesco Francia.

MADONNA AND CHILD

Painted about 1490. Oil and tempera on panel, 21⅛×14⅜ in. (53.8×36.6 cm.)
Charles H. and Mary F. S. Worcester Collection, 47.90

While the attribution to Grandi must remain tentative, the style of the painting definitely suggests the School of Ferrara.

Coll: A. von Beckerath, Berlin; Worcester, 1929

Ref: Borenius, T., The Painters of Vicenza, *1909, p. 158; Crowe and Cavalcaselle,* A History of Painting in North Italy, *II, New York, 1912, p. 140; Venturi, A.,* Storia dell'Arte Italiana, *VII, Milan, 1915, pp. 636–7, fig. 408; Longhi, R.,* Officina Ferrarese, *Rome, 1934, pp. 67, 169; Chicago. Art Institute,* Catalogue of the Worcester Collection, *1936, cat. no. 6; Longhi, R.,* Ampliamenti Nell'Officina Ferrarese, *1940, p. 8*

GREAVES, Walter ~ *b. 1841 Chelsea, England. d. 1930 London*

Walter Greaves and his brother Henry were boatmen who rowed Whistler about the Thames while he made sketches. In 1863 they became his pupils and, of the two, Walter attained some degree of recognition.

JAMES MCNEILL WHISTLER

Signed and dated: W. Greaves 1869. Oil on canvas, 32⅞×22⅞ in. (83.5×58.2 cm.)
A. A. Munger Collection, 26.259

GRECO, EL (Domenico Theotocopuli) ~ *b. 1541 Phoedele, Crete. d. 1614 Toledo*

At an unknown date El Greco left Crete for Venice. There he was influenced by Titian, Tintoretto, the Bassani and later, Correggio. By 1570 he was established in Rome, and left for Spain before 1577, very likely because of a commission to paint an altarpiece for Santo Domingo el Antiguo in Toledo. In 1577 the artist settled in Spain, remaining in Toledo until his death. It was in the environment of this medieval town that the developed his own individual style which epitomized the Mannerist style.

THE ASSUMPTION OF THE VIRGIN Illus. pp. 89-90-91

Signed and dated: Dominico Theotocopuli, 1577.
Oil on canvas, 158×90 in. (301.3×228.7 cm.)
Gift of Nancy Atwood Sprague in memory of Albert Arnold Sprague, 06.99 (Aznar no. 3)

The concept of this painting is related to Titian's Assumption in the Frari Church, Venice. El Greco's canvas originally served as the center of the main altarpiece in the convent church of Santo Domingo el Antiguo of Toledo. In its original arrangement, the Assumption was crowned by a Trinity (now in the Prado, Madrid). The various sections of the altarpiece were separated in 1830 when the Assumption and the Trinity were sold by the nuns.

The Infante Don Sebastian became the owner of the Assumption and had it replaced in the convent by a copy. Thought to be El Greco's first important known work executed in Spain, the Assumption is strongly Italianate, showing the influence of Titian and Veronese. The drawing, particularly in the lower figures, recalls the power of Michelangelo whose work in the Sistine Chapel El Greco undoubtedly saw when he was in Rome. Already certain specific characteristics of El Greco are evident in the heads of the Apostles, in the elongated hands throughout, and in certain color combinations.

Coll: Santo Domingo el Antiguo, Toledo, Spain, 1577; Museo Nacionale de Fomento, Spain, 1864; Don Sebastian Gabriel de Borbón, Pau and Madrid; The Prado, Madrid, 1902–1905; Infanta Doña Cristina of Spain [?]

Ref: Levice, Revue des Musées d'Espagne, *1864; Madrid. Prado Museum,* Exposición del Greco, *1902, cat. no. 6; Lafond, P.,* Les Arts *5: 4, 18, October 1906; Chicago. Art Institute,* Bulletin *1: 20, 21, 1908; Cossio, M. B.,* El Greco, *1908, pp. 132–41, 594, no. 279; Calvert, A. F. and C. G. Hartley,* El Greco, *1909, pp. 78–81; Mayer, A. L.,* El Greco, *1911, p. 24, 25; Mayer, A. L.,* El Greco, *1916, p. 16; Chicago. Art Institute,* Bulletin *18: 30, 31, 1024; Mayer, A. L.,* Dominico Theotocopuli El Greco . . . , *1926, p. 19, cat. no. 114; Willumsen, J.-F.,* La Jeunesse du Peintre El Greco, *I, 1920, pp. 566–8; Waterhouse, E. K.,* Art Studies *8, pt. 1: 88, 1930; Mayer, A. L.,* El Greco, *1931, pp. 41, 42, 54; Chicago. Art Institute,* A Century of Progress Exhibition, *1933, cat. no. 169;* Ibid., *1934, cat. no. 70; Hagen, O.,* Patterns of Principles of Spanish Art, *1936, p. 117; Legendre, M. and A. Hartmann,* Dominikos Theotocopulos called El Greco, *1937, pp. 22, 236; Chicago. Art Institute,* Bulletin *41: 5, 1947; Ponz y Piquier, A.,* Viaje de Espana, *1947 ed., p. 78; Kimball, F. and L. Venturi,* Great Paintings in America, *1948, p. 94; Aznar, J. Camon,* Dominico Greco, *I, 1950, pp. 243, 246–53, II, p. 1356; Bronstein, A.,* El Greco, *1950, p. 32; Iniguez, D. A.,* Ars Hispaniae, *XII, 1954, pp. 268, 283; Vallentin, A.,* El Greco, *1955, pp. 92–100; Cossio, M. B.,* Dominico Theotocopuli El Greco, *1955, p. 30, pl. 12; Florisoone, M.,* Gazette des Beaux-Arts *59: 19–44, 1957*

SAINT FRANCIS Illus. p. 100

Painted between 1590 and 1604, signed: Domenikos Theotocopulos [second line illegible].
Oil on canvas, $36\frac{5}{16} \times 29\frac{3}{8}$ in. (92.6×74.6 cm.)
Robert A. Waller Fund, 35.372 (Aznar no. 58)

Probably in part by Jorge Manuel Theotocopuli. The picture exists in numerous variants and replicas.

Coll: Don Clemente de Velasco, Madrid

Ref: Cossio, M. B., El Greco, *1908, p. 42, cat. no. 267; Mayer, A. L.,* El Greco, *1926, p. 139, cat. no. 576; Chicago. Art Institute,* Bulletin *31: 1, 2, 4, 1937; Legendre, M. and A. Hartmann,* op. cit., *p. 377; Chicago. Art Institute,* Bulletin *32: 50, 1938; Aznar, J. Camón,* Dominico Greco, *I, 1950, pp. 342–65, II, p. 1385, no. 580*

SAINT MARTIN AND THE BEGGAR

Painted between 1599 and 1604, signed: Domenikos Theotocopulos Kres epoiei.
Oil on canvas, 43⅜ × 24⅞ in. (110.3 × 63.3 cm.)
Gift of Mr. and Mrs. Chauncey McCormick, 49.1093

St. Martin, protector of the poor, is represented as a knight on horseback, cutting his cloak in two to share with a beggar. The view of Toledo is precisely that section of the city which El Greco saw from his house in Santo Tomé and which he repeatedly introduced into his paintings. This is one of several smaller replicas of the famous composition which the artist painted for the Chapel of San José in Toledo between 1597 and 1599 (now in the Widener Collection, National Gallery in Washington, D.C.). It was done in El Greco's workshop and signed by him. There exists a companion picture to our painting, representing Saint Joseph and the Christ Child (Museo San Vicente, Toledo). This is presumably a workshop replica.

Coll: Marques de Perinat, Madrid; Diego de Canovas [?]; Charles Deering; Chauncey McCormick, 1931

Ref: Bachelin, L., El Greco, *1898, cat. no. 168; Cossio, M.,* El Greco, *1908, pp. 60, 330, no. 309; King, G. G.,* Art Bulletin *5: 9, 1922–1923; Chicago. Art Institute,* Bulletin *18: 29, 32, 33, 1924; Mayer, A. L.,* El Greco, *1926, pp. 45, 48, cat. no. 298; Mayer, A. L.,* Apollo *10: 151, 1929; Mayer, A. L.,* El Greco, *1931, pp. 104, 146; Chicago. Art Institute,* A Century of Progress Exhibition, *1933, cat. no. 176;* Ibid., *1934, cat. no. 76; Legendre, M. and A. Hartmann,* op. cit., *1937, p. 464; Chicago. Art Institute,* Bulletin *44: 2, 1950; Aznar, J. Camón,* Dominico Greco, *II, 1950, pp. 697–708, 1382, no. 524; Halldor, S.,* Zeitschrift für Kunstwissenschaft *3–4; 210–5 (n.d.)*

THE FEAST IN THE HOUSE OF SIMON Illus. p. 96

Probably painted between about 1610 and 1614.
Oil on canvas, 56¼ × 39⅜ in. (143 × 100 cm.)
The Joseph Winterbotham Collection, 49.397 (Aznar no. 77)

Heavy architectural forms and a mosque in the center of the background are the setting for this religious scene (John 12: 1–8). El Greco may have seen related compositions on the same subject by Jacopo da Ponte during his early years in Venice. Even the mosque immediately behind the figure of Christ points symbolically upwards. Another version of this picture, perhaps an earlier one, with some architectural differences, is in the Cintas Collection in Havana, Cuba. This may be in part by Jorge Manuel Theotocopuli.

Coll: M. Guinea, Bilbao, Spain; M. Plasencia, Bilbao, Spain; Prince de Wagram, Paris; Joseph Winterbotham, Burlington, Vermont

Ref: Cossio, M. B., El Greco, *1908, pp. 353, 602, no. 325; Kehrer, H.,.* Die Kunst des El Greco, *1914, p. 41; Mayer, A. L.,* El Greco, *1916, pp. 27–8; Mayer, A. L.,* Art in America *14: 253–4, 1916; Mayer, A. L.,* El Greco, *1926, p. 9, cat. no. 46a; Willumsen, J.-F.,* La Jeunesse du Peintre El Greco, *II, 1928, pp. 657–8; Chicago. Art Institute,* Bulletin *24: 17,*

24, 1930; Mayer, A. L., El Greco, *1931, pp. 116–8, 132; Chicago. Art Institute,* A Century of Progress Exhibition, *1933, cat. no. 172;* Ibid., *1934, cat. no. 72; Legendre, M. and A. Hartmann,* op. cit., *1937, p. 171; Trapier, E. du Gue,* Notes Hispanic *3: 12, 1943; Chicago. Art Institute,* Bulletin *44: 22–6, 1950; Aznar, J. Camón,* Dominico Greco, *II, 1950, pp. 897–902*

GREUZE, Jean-Baptiste ~ *b. 1725 Tournus, France. d. 1805 Paris*

Greuze was a pupil of Charles Grandon, a portrait painter of Lyon. He later went to Paris where in 1769 he became a member of the academy.

LITTLE GIRL POUTING

Painted about 1760. Oil on canvas, 15½ × 12⅝ in. (39.5 × 32.1 cm.)
Mr. and Mrs. Martin A. Ryerson Collection, 33.1079

Greuze had two daughters, Anne Geneviève and Louise Gabrielle. Probably this little girl was a portrait of his older daughter, Anne Geneviève, who later became a painter herself. The artist exhibited a picture of the same title at the Salon of 1761 which may have been this canvas.

GRIFFEN, Davenport ~ *b. 1894 Millbrook, N.Y.*

Griffen studied at the Chicago Academy of Fine Arts and at the School of the Art Institute under George Oberteuffer and John Norton. He taught at the Art Institute from 1927 to 1930.

SLEEP

Signed and dated: D. Griffen 29. Oil on canvas, 35¾ × 45⅞ in. (90.8 × 114.7 cm.)
Mr. and Mrs. Frank G. Logan Purchase Prize, 30.82

GRIS, Juan (Gonzales, José Vittorio) ~ *b. 1887 Madrid. d. 1927 Boulogne-sur-Seine, France*

Gris studied with an academic painter in Madrid, later moving to Paris in 1906 where he settled in Montmarte and became friendly with Picasso and Braque. To earn money he drew for illustrated magazines. In 1912 the dealer Daniel-Henry Kahnweiler contracted with the artist to buy all his future paintings. Along with Braque, Picasso and Léger he is considered a pioneer in the Cubist movement.

A TABLE AT A CAFE (ABSTRACTION IN GRAY)

Painted 1912, signed: Juan Gris. Oil on canvas, 18⅛ × 15 in. (46.2 × 38.2 cm.)
Gift of Kate L. Brewster, 50.122

Ref: Ozenfant, A., Foundations of Modern Art, *1931, p. 105; George, W.,* Juan Gris, *1931, p. 19, no. 44; Seuphor, Michael,* L'Art Abstrait, *1949, p. 143; Chicago. Art Institute,* Bulletin *3: 53–4, 1950*

PORTRAIT OF PICASSO

Painted 1912, inscribed and signed: Homage à Pablo Picasso/Juan Gris.
Oil on canvas, 29¼ × 36¾ in. (74 × 93.4 cm.)
Gift of Leigh B. Block, 58.525

Ref: Soby, James Thrall, Juan Gris, *N.Y. Museum of Modern Art, 1958, 18, 20 (ill.)*

THE CHECKERBOARD Illus. p. 470

Signed and dated: Juan Gris 9–1915. Oil on canvas, 36¼ × 28¾ in. (92.1 × 73 cm.)
Gift of Mrs. Leigh B. Block with a contribution from the Ada Turnbull Hertle Fund, 56.16

This canvas was painted in 1915, a year after Picasso, Braque and Gris had been working in Paris and Collioure experimenting chiefly with collage. In 1914 Gris made a series of large collages in which he used wall-paper and imitation wood paper as well as superimposed cubist designs in gouache and oil. Though painted on canvas, the *Checkerboard* obviously grows out of collage.

Ref: Soby, James Thrall, op. cit., *57, 59 (ill.)*

GROVER, Oliver Dennett ~ *b. 1861 Earlville, Ill. d. 1927 Chicago*

Grover studied at the academy in Munich as well as in Paris, and under Frank Duveneck in Florence.

MISS MARION ROGERS (Mrs. James A. Vincent)

Signed and dated: Oliver Dennett Grover 1897. Oil on canvas, 24 × 31 in. (61 × 78.8 cm.)
Gift of James A. Vincent, 51.247

JUNE MORNING: LAKE ORTA

Signed and dated: Oliver Dennett Grover, 1913.
Oil on canvas, 38⅛ × 47 in. (96.9 × 119.4 cm.)
Friends of American Art Collection, 13.789

GUARDI, Francesco ~ *1712–1793 Venice*

Guardi was a pupil of his brother, Giovanni Antonio, with whom he worked until the latter's death in 1760. Francesco began as a figure painter in collaboration with Marieschi, but after his brother's death became increasingly active as a landscape painter. He was influenced by Canaletto, with whom he probably studied.

THE GRAND CANAL, VENICE Illus. p. 54

Painted about 1745, signed: Fran Guardi. Oil on canvas, 28¾ × 47 in. (75.6 × 119.4 cm.)
Wirt D. Walker Fund, 51.21
Coll: S. C. Weston, 1840; A. Anderson Weston, 1884; Mrs. Isabella Frances Weston, 1949

Ref: Berenson, B., Venetian Painters of the Renaissance, *1894, p. 109; Graves, A.,* A Century of Loan Exhibitions, *1813, 1912, I, pp. 452, 454; Morassi, A.,* Emporium *57: 195–219, 1951; Chicago. Art Institute,* Quarterly *46, no. 4, 1952;* Studies in the History of Art, Dedicated to W. Suida on his Eightieth Birthday, *Morassi, A., pp. 338–53, 1959*

RUINED ARCHWAY

Probably painted between 1775 and 1793. Oil on canvas, 11⅝ × 19½ in. (29.5 × 49.7 cm.)
Mr. and Mrs. Martin A. Ryerson Collection, 33.1080

GUERCINO ~ *b. 1591 Cento, Italy. d. 1666 Bologna*

(Barbieri, Giovanni Francesco—called Il Guercino)

Guercino was a pupil of Ludovico Carracci. In 1621, Pope Gregory XV invited him to Rome, where he worked until the death of the Pope in 1623. He then returned to Cento, but in 1642, following the death of Guido Reni, established himself in Bologna as the leader of the Bolognese School.

ENTOMBMENT OF CHRIST

Probably painted 1656. Oil on canvas, 47¾ × 87 in. (121.3 × 211.6 cm.)
Mead Fund Income, 56.128
Coll: Palazzo Colonna (by 1783); Sir Simon Clarke; William Buchanan; John Humble (sale at Christie's, April 1812, no. 56); T. B. Bulkeley Owen of Tedsmore Hall

Ref: Catalogo dei Quadri, e pitture esistenti nel Palazzo dell'eccellentissima Casa Colonna in Roma, *1783, p. 32, no. 205; F. W. B. von Ramdohr,* Ueber Mahlerei und Bildhauerarbeit in Rom, *1787, II, pp. 104–5; Malvasia,* Felsina Pittrice, *ed. 1841, II, p. 270 (under 1656), p. 337 (6 Settembre 1656); Buchanan, William,* Memoirs of Painting, *1824, vol. II, pp. 117–8; Redford, George,* Art Sales, *London, 1888, vol. II, p. 234; Graves, Algernon,* Art Sales, *London, 1918, vol. I, p. 385, no. 56; Thieme-Becker,* Kuenstler-Lexikon *(Hermann Voss), XV, p. 219*

GUGLIELMI, O. Louis ~ *b. 1906 Cairo, Egypt*

Guglielmi, the child of Italian parents, came to the United States in 1914. He attended the National Academy of Design for five years.

THE RIVER

Painted 1942, signed: Guglielmi. Oil on canvas, 34 × 30 in. (86.4 × 76.3 cm.)
Gift of the Society for Contemporary American Art, 45.6

GUILLAUMIN, Jean-Baptiste Armand ~ *1841–1927 Paris*

Chiefly self-taught, Guillaumin met Cézanne at the Académie Suisse in Paris, where they became life-long friends. Under the influence of Courbet he tried his hand at portraiture.

Through Cézanne he met most of the Impressionists and became a member of their group. Though Monet was his greatest early influence, it was Cézanne's work which had the strongest impact on him.

THE WATER MILL OF PONT MAUPUIT (CROZANT)
Painted about 1900, signed: Guillaumin. Oil on canvas, 25¾ × 32 in. (65.5 × 81.3 cm.)
Mr. and Mrs. Martin A. Ryerson Collection, 33.1123

Ref: Borgmeyer, C. L., Fine Arts Journal *30: 50–75, 1914; 33: 461, 1915*

GUSTON, Philip ~ *b. 1913 Montreal*

RITE
Painted 1958, signed: Philip Guston. Oil on canvas, 48 × 64 in. (122 × 162.6 cm.)
Gift from the Society for Contemporary American Art in memory of Beulah Zachary, 59.9

HAHN, Walter ~ *b. 1927 Milwaukee, Wis.*
Hahn studied at The Art Institute of Chicago.

STILL LIFE
Painted 1951. Oil on canvas, 44 × 29¾ in. (111.9 × 75.6 cm.)
Pauline Palmer Purchase Prize, 51.128

HALS, Frans ~ *b. 1580/85 Antwerp. d. 1666 Haarlem*
Hals spent most of his life in Haarlem. There he studied with Karel van Mander, and painted the group portraits for which he is best known. His technique and brushwork, and his brilliant handling of the problems of group portraiture exercised an influence on far into the 19th century, especially on Manet and the Impressionists.

THE ROMMELPOT PLAYER Illus. p. 195
Painted about 1626. Oil on panel, 15 1/16 × 12 5/16 in. (39.1 × 30.5 cm.)
Charles H. and Mary F. S. Worcester Collection, 47.78 (HdG no. 137 (4))

PORTRAIT OF A LADY
Painted about 1640. Oil on canvas, 34¼ × 26⅜ in. (87 × 67 cm.)
Max and Leola Epstein Collection, 54.287

PORTRAIT OF AN ARTIST
Signed and dated: F. H. Aeta 32, 1644. Oil on canvas, 32½ × 25½ in. (82.6 × 64.8 cm.)
Gift of Charles L. Hutchinson, 94.1023 (HdG no. 185)

A palette hanging on the wall suggests the title. Possibly the sitter was Hals' son, Harmen, also a painter, whose age would correspond to the dated inscription (Aeta 32, 1644) on the picture. Some have suggested that it portrays Leendert van der Cooghen, a well-to-do Haarlem burgher who painted occasionally and whose portrait by Hals is mentioned in early documents. There is no definite proof for either theory.

HARDING, Chester ~ *b. 1792 Conway, Mass. d. 1866 Boston*

Harding established himself as a self-taught portrait painter in Paris, Kentucky, about 1819. Afterwards, he studied briefly at the Pennsylvania Academy, and then went to Boston in 1822, where he had a phenomenal success.

GEORGE HALLETT

Painted about 1822. Oil on panel, 27½×22½ in. (70×57.3 cm.)
Samuel P. Avery Fund, 15.565

MRS. GEORGE HALLETT

Painted about 1822. Oil on panel, 28×23 in. (71.2×58.6 cm.)
Samuel P. Avery Fund, 15.566

The portraits of Mr. and Mrs. Hallett were probably painted in Boston.

THOMAS ABTHORPE COOPER

Painted about 1822. Oil on canvas, 30¼×25 5/16 in. (76.9×64.2 cm.)
Friends of American Art Collection, 27.4

HARNETT, William Michael ~ *b. 1848 Clonakilty, Ireland. d. 1892 New York City*

Harnett was trained as an engraver and studied at the Pennsylvania Academy of the Fine Arts and at Cooper Union in New York. From 1879 to 1885 he lived in Europe where he was influenced by the 17th century Dutch still life painters.

FOR SUNDAY'S DINNER

Signed and dated: WM Harnett/1888. Oil on canvas, 37⅛×21⅛ in. (94.3×53.8 cm.)
Wilson L. Mead Fund, 58.296

JUST DESSERT Illus. p. 386

Signed and dated: W. M. Harnett 1891. Oil on canvas, 22¼×26¾ in. (56.6×68 cm.)
Friends of American Art Collection, 42.50

Ref: Born, W., Still Life Painting in America, *1947, fig. 80; Frankenstein, A.,* After the Hunt, *1953, pp. 67, 92, 173, 174, cat. no. 124*

HARSHE, Robert B. ~ *b. 1879 Salisbury, Mo. d. 1938 Chicago*

Robert Harshe was Director of The Art Institute of Chicago from 1921 until his death. He was a graduate of the University of Chicago, studied design and painting at the School of the Art Institute, then worked with Arthur Dow at Columbia University and attended the Art Students League. Later he went to the Académie Colarossi in Paris and to the Central School of Arts and Crafts in London where he came in contact with Frank Brangwyn and Philip de Lászlό. He taught art from 1902 to 1913.

ENGLISH HARBOR, THE PIER AT BRIGHTON
Painted about 1930. Oil on canvas, 19½ × 23¼ in. (49.7 × 59.1 cm.)
Friends of American Art Collection, 38.238

GIRL WITH CIGARETTE
Painted about 1935. Oil on canvas, 19⅞ × 23⅛ in. (50.7 × 59.6 cm.)
Friends of American Art Collection, 38.237

HARTIGAN, Grace (George) ~ *b. 1922 Newark, N.J.*

MASQUERADE
Signed and dated: Hartigan '54. Oil on canvas, 81¾ × 86¼ in. (207.7 × 219 cm.)
Anonymous Gift, 55.493

HARTLEY, Marsden ~ *b. 1877 Lewiston, Me. d. 1943 Ellsworth, Me.*

Hartley studied with Frank Vincent Du Mond and William Merritt Chase and at the National Academy of Design.

LANDSCAPE NO. 26
Painted about 1909. Oil on cardboard, 12 × 12 in. (30.5 × 30.5 cm.)
Alfred Stieglitz Collection, 49.543

THE DARK MOUNTAIN
Painted 1909. Oil on composition board, 19¼ × 23¼ in. (49 × 59.1 cm.)
Alfred Stieglitz Collection, 49.542

MOVEMENTS, 1913
Painted 1913. Oil on canvas, 47¼ × 47¼ in. (120 × 120 cm.)
Alfred Stieglitz Collection, 49.544

PROVINCETOWN
Painted 1916. Oil on composition board, 24⅛ × 20 in. (61.3 × 50.9 cm.)
Alfred Stieglitz Collection, 49.545

MOVEMENT NO. 10
Painted 1917. Oil on composition board, 15¼ × 19½ in. (38.8 × 49.7 cm.)
Alfred Stieglitz Collection, 49.548

THE LAST OF NEW ENGLAND—THE BEGINNING OF NEW MEXICO
Painted about 1920. Oil on cardbord, 24 × 30 in. (61 × 76.3 cm.)
Alfred Stieglitz Collection, 49.546

LANDSCAPE NO. 3—CASH ENTRY MINES—NEW MEXICO

Signed and dated: Marsden Hartley 1920. Oil on canvas, 27¾×35¾ in. (70.6×90.8 cm.)
Alfred Stieglitz Collection, 49.549

STILL LIFE NO. 15 (In Vase)

Painted before 1921. Oil on masonite, 23⅜×19½ in. (59.4×49.7 cm.)
Alfred Stieglitz Collection, 49.547

STILL LIFE NO. 3

Painted 1923. Oil on canvas, 22¾×41 in. (57.9×104.2 cm.)
Alfred Stieglitz Collection, 49.550

PORTRAIT OF A SEA-DOVE

Signed and dated on back: Marsden Hartley Jan 7–1935.
Oil on composition board, 9¾×13¾ in. (24.8×35 cm.)
Alfred Stieglitz Collection, 49.551

A poem Hartley wrote on the back of this picture tells its story:

This Portrait of Dead Sea-Dove /

Sea-dove in a shroud / of sand—all shiny with / thick crisps of sun / Sea-dove in a shroud / of sand—and the last word / spoke alone. / I did not carry messages / for wars or love to end their ways / I only bore flicked wave caresses / and took them to a timely place; / I gave them to my brood to drink / a draft of silence on the brink / of death I gave—telling them / also to be brave—have grace / to face the loneliness of their days; / I shut my eyes on a kiss / of sun / and this I give to everyone.

Jan 7–1935 Marsden Hartley

HASSAM, Childe ~ *b. 1859 Dorchester, Mass. d. 1935 East Hampton, N.Y.*

Hassam began as an illustrator and later decided to become a painter. He studied at the Lowell Institute in Boston and with Gaugengigl, then at the Académie Julian in Paris. Settling in New York, he joined The Ten, an American group influenced by French Impressionism.

NEW ENGLAND HEADLANDS

Signed and dated: Childe Hassam 1899. Oil on canvas, 27×26¾ in. (68.7×68 cm.)
Walter H. Schulze Memorial Collection, 30.349

AT SUNSET

Painted about 1900, signed: Childe Hassam. Oil on canvas, 24¼×29½ in. (61.7×75 cm.)
Gift of Mr. and Mrs. Carter H. Harrison, 36.14

BAILEY'S BEACH, NEWPORT, R.I.

Signed and dated: Childe Hassam 1901. Oil on canvas, 24×26 in. (61×66.1 cm.)
Walter H. Schulze Memorial Collection, 36.243

AGAINST THE LIGHT (Contre-Jour)
Signed and dated: Childe Hassam 1910. Oil on canvas, 29¼×24½ in. (74.3×61.7 cm.)
Friends of American Art Collection, 11.4

SPRING MORNING IN OLD LYME
Signed and dated: Childe Hassam 1911. Oil on canvas, 30×25 in. (76.3×63.6 cm.)
Gift of Mr. and Mrs. Carter H. Harrison, 37.380

NYMPH OF THE BERYL GORGE
Signed and dated: Childe Hassam, 1914. Oil on canvas, 34×16¼ in. (86.4×41.5 cm.)
Gift of Mr. and Mrs. Carter H. Harrison, 35.312

HAWTHORNE, Charles Webster ~ *b. 1872 Lodi, Ill. d. 1930 Baltimore, Md.*

Hawthorne studied at the National Academy of Design, the Art Students League, and with William Merritt Chase.

LITTLE SYLVIA
Painted about 1912, signed: C. W. Hawthorne.
Oil on canvas, 40×40 in. (101.7×101.7 cm.)
Friends of American Art Collection, 12.193

ALBIN POLASEK
Painted 1917, signed: C. W. Hawthorne. Oil on canvas, 40×40 in. (101.7×101.7 cm.)
Friends of American Art Collection, 17.266

SELECTMEN OF PROVINCETOWN
Painted about 1924. Oil on canvas, 48½×59¾ in. (122.6×151.8 cm.)
Friends of American Art Collection, 24.952

HEALY, George Peter Alexander ~ *b. 1813 Boston. d. 1894 Chicago*

Healy, who started modestly as a painter in Boston, later went to Europe where he was soon established as a portrait painter.

ARMENIAN FATHERS
Painted about 1870. Oil on canvas, 54×40 in. (137.2×101.7 cm.)
Gift of G. P. A. Healy, 79.2

SELF PORTRAIT
Signed and dated: G. P. A. Healy 1873. Oil on canvas, 29¾×24⅜ in. (75.6×62 cm.)
Gift of George L. Healy, 13.134

MRS. GEORGE P. A. HEALY
Signed and dated: G. P. A. Healy 1873. Oil on canvas, 30×24¾ in. (76.3×63 cm.)
Gift of George L. Healy, 13.135

JAMES N. AND JAMES F. PAINE (after Reynolds)
Painted about 1840. Oil on canvas, 16 × 13 in. (40.8 × 33 cm.)
Gift of Mrs. Edward N. Hurley, Jr., 44.400

HEBERT, Ernest ~ *1817–1908 La Tronche, France*
Hébert studied in Paris. He won the Prix de Rome in 1839. In 1882 he was appointed professor in the Ecole des Beaux-Arts and twice was given the directorship of the French Academy in Rome (1867–1873 and 1885–1891).

ON GUARD
Painted about 1860–1870, signed: Hébert. Oil on canvas, 18¾ × 14⅜ in. (47.7 × 36.6 cm.)
Henry Field Memorial Collection, 94.1061

HELIKER, John Edward ~ *b. 1909 Yonkers, N.Y.*
Though originally trained in the realistic school of American landscape painting, Heliker has been strongly influenced by Klee and Kandinsky.

SCAVE (Excavation)
Painted 1952, signed: Heliker. Oil on canvas, 11½ × 18 in. (29.2 × 45.8 cm.)
Gift of the Childe Hassam Fund of the American Academy of Arts and Letters, 51.244

HELION, Jean ~ *b. 1904 Couterne, France*
Hélion first exhibited at the Salon des Indépendants in Paris in 1927.

TWIN FIGURES
Signed and dated on the reverse: Hélion 22 Janv.–7 Mars 38
Oil on canvas, 52 × 69 in. (132.2 × 175.3 cm.)
Gift of Peggy Guggenheim, 57.14

HELLEU, Paul ~ *b. 1859 Vannes, France. d. 1927 Paris*
Helleu studied with Gérôme at the Ecole des Beaux-Arts in Paris.

KATHERINE VAN ETTA MEDILL
Pastel on paper, mounted on canvas, 59⅛ × 39½ in. (150.2 × 100.3 cm.)
Bequest of Colonel Robert R. McCormick, 56.759

Katherine van Etta Medill was the wife of Robert Sanderson McCormick and the mother of Colonel Robert R. McCormick.

HEMESSEN, Jan Sanders van ~ *b. about 1500 Hemixem. d. after 1575 Haarlem*
Hemessen was a pupil of Hendrick van Cleve in Antwerp where he was recorded in 1523 as Master Jan Sanders de Meyere van Hemessen. Hemessen continued in the direction of

Barend van Orley and Jan Gossaert. He also received direct Italian influences while working in Florence in 1534. Some time after 1551 Hemessen moved to Haarlem where he was still recorded in 1575.

JUDITH

Painted about 1560. Oil on panel, 39¼ × 30 7/16 in. (99.8 × 77.2 cm.)
Wirt D. Walker Fund, 56.1109
Coll: Marquis de la Pallu, Paris

Ref: Lebel, R., Journal de l'Amateurs d'Art *10: 3, 1956; Chicago. Art Institute,* Quarterly *51: 2–3, 1957;* Emporium *125, no. 748: 186, 1957*

HENRI, Robert ~ *b. 1865 Cincinnati, Ohio. d. 1929 New York City*

Henri studied at the Pennsylvania Academy and later in Paris. Dissatisfied with academic teaching, he turned to the study of the old masters. From Frans Hals he learned broad, fluid brushwork. In New York he gathered around him John Sloan, George Luks, Everett Shinn and William Glackens, most of whom had been illustrators in Philadelphia, and together they formed the group of New York Realists, later called the "Ash Can" School.

YOUNG WOMAN IN BLACK

Painted 1902, signed: Robert Henri. Oil on canvas, 77 × 38½ in. (195.7 × 97.9 cm.)
Friends of American Art Collection, 10.317

HIMSELF

Painted 1913, signed: Robert Henri. Oil on canvas, 32¼ × 26⅛ in. (82 × 66.4 cm.)
Walter H. Schulze Memorial Collection, 24.912

HERSELF

Painted 1913, signed: Robert Henri. Oil on canvas, 32 × 26 in. (81.3 × 66.1 cm.)
Walter H. Schulze Memorial Collection, 24.911

HERBIN, Auguste ~ *b. 1882 Quiévy, France*

Herbin studied painting in Lille. About 1901 he went to Paris where he painted in the impressionist manner, but after 1909 his work changed under the influence of Cubism. Like other Cubists, Herbin returned to naturalistic painting in 1921, but in 1926 he again concerned himself with abstract experiments.

HOUSE AND FLOWERING CHERRY TREES, HAMBURG

Probably painted about 1910–1912, signed: Herbin.
Oil on canvas, 23 3/16 × 28⅞ in. (59 × 73.4 cm.)
Arthur Jerome Eddy Memorial Collection, 31.507

HIGGINS, Victor ~ *b. 1884 Shelbyville, Ind. d. 1949 Taos, N.M.*

Higgins was a student at The Art Institute of Chicago and taught there after returning from Paris and Munich.

SPRING RAINS

Painted about 1924, signed: Victor Higgins. Oil on canvas, 40×43 in. (101.7×109.3 cm.)
Friends of American Art Collection, 24.18

HITCHCOCK, George ~ *b. 1850 Providence, R.I. d. 1913 Marken, Holland*

Hitchcock studied painting in Paris with Bourguereau and Lefèbvre. Later he went to Düsseldorf and to Holland where he worked with his fellow American, Gari Melchers.

FLOWER GIRL IN HOLLAND

Signed and dated: Geo Hitchcock, Op. XXXV, 1887.
Oil on canvas, 31⅛×58 in. (79×147.4 cm.)
Potter Palmer Collection, 88.169

HOBBEMA, Meindert ~ *1638–1709 Amsterdam*

With Ruysdael, who greatly influenced him and probably was his teacher, Hobbema was a leading Dutch landscape painter of the 17th century.

WOODED LANDSCAPE WITH COTTAGE AND HORSEMAN

Signed and dated: M. Hobbema, 1663. Oil on canvas, 39½×52½ in. (100.3×133.4 cm.)
Mr. and Mrs. W. W. Kimball Collection, 22.4460 (HdG no. 130)
Coll: Thomas Emmerson, London, 1835; D. McIntosch, London, 1857; Nieuvenhuis, Amsterdam, 1860; Adrian Hope, London, 1894; Charles Wertheimer, London

Ref: Smith, J., Catalogue Raisonné of the Most Eminent Dutch and Flemish Painters, *VI, 1835, p. 149, cat. no. 99; Chicago. Art Institute,* Bulletin *14: 77, 1920*

THE WATERMILL WITH THE GREAT RED ROOF Illus. p. 192

Painted about 1670, signed: Hobbema. Oil on canvas, 32×43⅛ in. (81.3×109.6 cm.)
Gift of Mr. and Mrs. Frank G. Logan, 94.1031 (HdG no. 71)
Coll: John Ellis, 1755; Lord Mount Temple, 1870–1890; Prince Anatole Demidoff, San Donato; Prince Paul Demidoff, Pratolino, 1890

Ref: Smith, J., Catalogue Raisonné . . . , *VI, 1835, p. 151, cat. no. 105; W. von Bode,* Die Meister der Hollaendischen und Vlaemischen Malerschulen, *1919, p. 191; Chicago. Art Institute,* A Century of Progress Exhibition, *1933, cat. no. 66, pl. 38;* Ibid., *1934, cat. no. 93; Broulheit, G.,* Meindert Hobbema, *1938, p. 378, cat. no. 13*

HODLER, Ferdinand ~ *b. 1853 Berne, Switzerland. d. 1918 Geneva*

All his life Hodler struggled with philosophic problems which he tried to express in his paintings through symbolism and allegory. Post-Impressionism exerted a strong influence on his style.

JAMES VIBERT, SCULPTOR

Signed and dated: F. Hodler, 1907. Oil on canvas, 25×25 in. (63.6×63.6 cm.)
Helen Birch Bartlett Memorial Collection, 26.212
Coll: W. Russ-Young, Serrières

Ref: Loosli, C. A., Ferdinand Hodler, *II, 1920; Chicago. Art Institute,* Catalogue of the Birch Bartlett Collection, *1929, pp. 26–7; Chicago. Art Institute,* A Century of Progress Exhibition, *1934, cat. no. 319*

THE GRAND MOUVERAN

Painted about 1912, signed: F. Hodler. Oil on canvas, 27¾×37½ in. (70.6×95.3 cm.)
Helen Birch Bartlett Memorial Collection, 26.211
Coll: W. Russ-Young, Serrières

Ref: Chicago. Art Institute, Bulletin *19: 81–2, 1925; Watson, F.,* The Arts *9: 313, 1926; Chicago. Art Institute,* Catalogue of the Birch Bartlett Collection, *1929, pp. 16, 54; Chicago. Art Institute,* A Century of Progress Exhibition, *1933, cat. no. 729; Myers, B.,* American Artists *15: 57, November 1951*

A HEAD OF A SOLDIER

Painted between 1915–1917, signed: F. Hodler.
Oil on canvas, 18½×17⅛ in. (47.1×43.6 cm.)
Helen Birch Bartlett Memorial Collection, 26.213
Coll: W. Russ-Young, Serrières

Ref: Loosli, C. A., Ferdinand Hodler, *III, 1920, pl. 143; Chicago. Art Institute,* Bulletin *19: 81, 1925; Chicago. Art Institute,* Catalogue of the Birch Bartlett Collection, *1929, pp. 20, 21; Chicago. Art Institute,* A Century of Progress Exhibition, *1934, cat. no. 318*

HOFER, Carl ~ *b. 1878 Karlsruhe, Germany. d. 1955 Berlin*

Hofer was a member of the Expressionist group called *Die Bruecke* (The Bridge). He settled in Berlin in 1918 where he taught at the Academy. In 1946 he was appointed Director of the Berlin Academy.

GIRLS THROWING FLOWERS

Signed and dated: C H 34. Oil on canvas, 48½×38⅝ in. (132.2×98.2 cm.)
The Joseph Winterbotham Collection, 36.221

HOFF, Margo ~ *b. Tulsa, Okla.*

Margo Hoff has traveled widely in Mexico, Haiti, Dalmatia, Spain, Egypt and Beirut.

MURDER MYSTERY

Painted 1946, signed: M. Hoff. Oil and casein on canvas, 30×19⅞ in. (76.3×50.7 cm.)
Walter M. Campana Memorial Prize, 46.50

HOFFMAN, Harry Leslie ~ *b. 1874 Cressona, Pa.*

Hoffman studied with Du Mond at the Art Students League and in Paris at the Académie Julian.

THE COTTON GIN

Signed and dated, H L Hoffman '19. Oil on canvas, 30×40 in. (76.3×101.7 cm.)
Friends of American Art Collection, 19.782

HOFMANN, Hans ~ *b. 1880 Weissenberg, Germany*

Hofmann studied in Munich and in Paris. His first exhibition was held in 1909 in Berlin. In 1930 he came to the United States to teach at the University of California and four years later founded his famous schools of art in New York and in Provincetown.

BLUE RHYTHM

Painted 1950. Oil on canvas, 48×36 in. (122×91.5 cm.)
Gift of the Society for Contemporary American Art, 52.200

HOMER, Winslow ~ *b. 1836 Boston. d. 1910 Prout's Neck, Me.*

Homer began his career as a lithographer, did magazine illustrations, and made his reputation during the Civil War as an artist-reporter for *Harper's Weekly*. Although he visited France and England, his work remained largely free of European influences.

CROQUET SCENE Illus. p. 378

Signed and dated: Winslow Homer 66. Oil on canvas, 15 7/8×26 1/16 in. (40.4×66.1 cm.)
Friends of American Art Collection, 42.35

MOUNT WASHINGTON

Signed and dated: Winslow Homer 1869. Oil on canvas, 16×24 1/8 in. (40.8×61.3 cm.)
Gift of Mrs. Richard E. Danielson and Mrs. Chauncey McCormick, 51.313

PEACH BLOSSOMS

Signed with monogram, dated: 1878. Oil on canvas, 13 3/16×19 3/4 in. (33.7×50.4 cm.)
Gift of George B. Harrington, 46.338

THE HERRING NET Illus. p. 379

Signed and dated: Homer 85. Oil on canvas, 29 1/2×47 1/2 in. (75×120.6 cm.)
Mr. and Mrs. Martin A. Ryerson Collection, 37.1039

COAST OF MAINE

Signed and dated: Homer 93. Oil on canvas, 24×30 1/8 in. (61×76.6 cm.)
Arthur Jerome Eddy Memorial Collection, 31.505

HOPKINS, James R. ~ *b. 1877 Irwin, Ohio*

Hopkins studied at the Academy in Cincinnati, traveled abroad extensively and worked in Paris from 1904 to 1914.

A KENTUCKY MOUNTAINEER

Painted in 1915, signed: James R. Hopkins. Oil on canvas, 32×36 in. (81.3×91.5 cm.)
Friends of American Art Collection, 15.561

HOPPER, Edward ~ *b. 1882 Nyack, N.Y.*

Hopper studied in New York under Henri and Kenneth Hayes Miller, and then spent a year in Paris.

NIGHTHAWKS Illus. p. 384

Painted 1942, signed: Edward Hopper. Oil on canvas, $33\frac{3}{16}\times 60\frac{1}{8}$ in. (84.2×152.8 cm.)
Friends of American Art Collection, 42.51

HOPPNER, John ~ *1758 [?]–1810 London*

Hoppner began his studies at the Royal Academy in 1775 and formed his early style under the influence of Reynolds.

MARK PRINGLE

Painted about 1800. Oil on canvas, 30×25 in. (76.3×63.6 cm.)
Gift of Spencer Stuart and Waldo H. Logan in memory of Mr. and Mrs. Frank G. Logan, 44.700

THOMAS TURNER, J.P.

Painted ca. 1775. Oil on canvas, 30×25 in. (76.3×63.6 cm.)
Gift of Arthur Keating, 48.568

HOWARD, Charles ~ *b. 1889 Montclair, N.J.*

Howard studied at the University of California.

TRINITY

Signed and dated: Charles Howard 1:VIII:41. Oil on canvas, 24×34 in. (61×86.4 cm.)
Wilson L. Mead Fund, 45.292

HOYER, Torvalt Arnt ~ *b. 1872 Copenhagen. d. 1949 Chicago*

Hoyer studied in his native Denmark, but gave up art to become an acrobat in a traveling troupe. Later he settled in Chicago.

WHEAT FIELD

Signed and dated: T. A. Hoyer, 1940. Oil on canvas, $30\frac{1}{4}\times 24$ in. (76.9×61 cm.)
Gift of Olga Pegelow, 49.519

HUGUET, Victor Pierre ~ *b. 1835 Le Lude, France. d. 1902 Paris*
Huguet studied first in Marseilles, then with Fromentin in Paris.

RAVINE NEAR BISKRA
Painted about 1890–1900, signed: V. Huguet. Oil on canvas, 14⅞ × 18⅛ in. (37.8 × 46.2 cm.)
Mr. and Mrs. Martin A. Ryerson Collection, 33.1128

HURD, Peter ~ *b. 1904 Roswell, N.M.*
After Hurd resigned from West Point to become an artist, he studied with the noted illustrator, N. C. Wyeth.

EL MOCHO
Painted 1936, signed: Peter Hurd. Egg tempera on panel, 30 × 25⅛ in. (76.3 × 63.9 cm.)
Watson F. Blair Purchase Prize, 37.53

HUYSMANS, Cornelis ~ *b. 1648 Antwerp. d. 1727 Mechlin, Belgium*
Huysmans, a pupil of Gaspard de Witte and Jacques d'Arthois, spent his active career in Brussels, Antwerp and Mechlin. His work shows strong Italian influence.

THE HOLLOW ROAD
Painted around 1700 [?]. Oil on canvas, 9½ × 12¼ in. (24.2 × 31.2 cm.)
Mr. and Mrs. Martin A. Ryerson Collection, 33.1084
Coll: Prince Demidoff, San Donato; G. Rothan, Paris

Ref: Chicago. Art Institute, A Century of Progress Exhibition, *1934, cat. no. 94*

INGERLE, Rudolph, F. ~ *1879 Vienna. d. 1950 Highland Park, Ill.*
Ingerle came to America as a boy, and spent most of his life in Chicago. He attended the School of the Art Institute and Smith's Art Academy.

SWAPPIN' GROUNDS
Signed and dated: R. F. Ingerle '28. Oil on canvas, 52 × 58½ in. (132.2 × 148.7 cm.)
Friends of American Art Collection, 28.523

INMAN, Henry ~ *b. 1801 Utica, N.Y. d. 1846 New York City*
Inman, trained as a miniature painter, learned portrait painting from J. W. Jarvis.

WILLIAM INMAN
Painted about 1825. Oil on composition board, 30 × 24½ in. (76.3 × 62.4 cm.)
Friends of American Art Collection, 17.269

INNESS, George ~ *b. 1825 Newburgh, N.Y. d. 1894 Bridge of Allan, Scotland*
Inness made his first contact with the Barbizon painters, especially Rousseau, Daubigny, and Corot, who were to have profound influence on his style, in Paris in 1854.

OUR OLD MILL
Signed and dated: G. Inness 1849. Oil on canvas, 29⅞×42⅛ in. (76×107 cm.)
The William Owen and Erna Sawyer Goodman Collection, 39.388

SUMMER IN THE CATSKILLS
Signed and dated: G. Inness 1867. Oil on canvas, 20×30 in. (50.9×76.3 cm.)
Edward B. Butler Collection, 12.1837

DELAWARE VALLEY
Painted about 1869, signed: G. Inness.
Oil on composition board, 15½×24 in. (39.8×61 cm.)
Edward B. Butler Collection, 11.43

CATSKILL MOUNTAINS Illus. p. 372
Signed and dated: G. Inness 1870. Oil on canvas, 48½×72½ in. (123.2×184.2 cm.)
Edward B. Butler Collection, 12.1623

VILLA BARBERINI
Signed and dated: G. Inness 1872. Oil on canvas, 9×13 1/16 in. (22.8×33.2 cm.)
Mr. and Mrs. Martin A. Ryerson Collection, 33.1206

TWILIGHT
Signed and dated: G. Inness 1874. Oil on panel, 16½×25⅞ in. (42×65.8 cm.)
Edward B. Butler Collection, 11.44

THE STORM
Signed and dated: G. Inness 1876. Oil on canvas, 25⅜×38¼ in. (64.5×97.2 cm.)
Edward B. Butler Collection, 12.1

ALEXANDRIA BAY, ST. LAWRENCE RIVER
Painted about 1878, signed: G. Inness.
Oil on composition board, 16×24 in. (40.8×61 cm.)
Charles H. and Mary F. S. Worcester Collection, 35.74

TWO SISTERS IN THE GARDEN
Painted about 1880–1885, signed: G. Inness. Oil on canvas, 19¼×15¼ in. (49×38.8 cm.)
Edward B. Butler Collection, 26.132

A SILVERY MORNING
Signed and dated: G. Inness 1884. Oil on canvas, 35½×45½ in. (90.2×115.7 cm.)
Edward B. Butler Collection, 25.38

COAST OF CORNWALL

Signed and dated: G. Inness 1887. Oil on canvas, 32×42 in. (81.3×106.7 cm.)
Charles H. and Mary F. S. Worcester Collection, 47.80

LANDSCAPE, SUNSET

Signed and dated: G. Inness 1887. Oil on canvas, 22½×36¼ in. (57.3×92.1 cm.)
Edward B. Butler Collection, 11.35

THE MILL POND

Signed and dated: G. Inness 1889. Oil on canvas, 37½×28⅞ in. (95.3×73.4 cm.)
Edward B. Butler Collection, 11.30

AT NIGHT

Signed and dated: G. Inness, 1890. Oil on canvas, 22×27 in. (56×68.7 cm.)
Edward B. Butler Collection, 11.36

SUNSET IN THE VALLEY

Signed and dated: G. Inness 1890. Oil on canvas, 22¼×36¼ in. (56.6×92.1 cm.)
Edward B. Butler Collection, 11.38

EVENING LANDSCAPE

Signed and dated: G. Inness 1890. Oil on canvas, 20×30 in. (50.9×76.3 cm.)
Edward B. Butler Collection, 11.42

MOONRISE

Signed and dated: G. Inness 1891. Oil on canvas, 30×25 in. (76.3×63.6 cm.)
Edward B. Butler Collection, 11.39

THREATENING

Signed and dated: G. Inness 1891. Oil on canvas, 30¼×45¾ in. (76.9×116.2 cm.)
Edward B. Butler Collection, 11.33

ETRETAT, NORMANDY

Painted about 1892, signed: G. Inness. Oil on canvas, 30×45¼ in. (76.3×115 cm.)
Edward B. Butler Collection, 13.90

THE LONE FARM, NANTUCKET

Signed and dated: G. Inness 1892. Oil on canvas, 30×45 in. (76.3×114.4 cm.)
Edward B. Butler Collection, 14.189

EARLY MORNING, TARPON SPRINGS

Signed and dated: G. Inness 1892. Oil on canvas, 42×32¼ in. (106.7×82 cm.)
Edward B. Butler Collection, 11.32

THE HOME OF THE HERON

Signed and dated: G. Inness, 1893. Oil on canvas, 30×45 in. (76.3×114.4 cm.)
Edward B. Butler Collection, 11.31

AUTUMN WOODS

Painted about 1893, signed: G. Inness. Oil on canvas, 29¼×45 in. (74.3×114.4 cm.)
Edward B. Butler Collection, 11.34

MOONLIGHT ON PASSAMAQUODDY BAY

Signed and dated: G. Inness 1893. Oil on canvas, 30×45¼ in. (76.3×115.7 cm.)
Mr. and Mrs. Martin A. Ryerson Collection, 33.1207

THE AFTERGLOW

Signed and dated: G. Inness 1893. Oil on canvas, 30×25¼ in. (76.3×64.7 cm.)
Edward B. Butler Collection, 11.441

IN THE VALLEY

Signed and dated: G. Inness 1893. Oil on canvas, 24×36¼ in. (61×92.1 cm.)
Edward B. Butler Collection, 11.37

LANDSCAPE NEAR MONTCLAIR

Painted about 1893, signed: G. Inness. Oil on canvas, 15×26⅛ in. (38.2×66.4 cm.)
Edward B. Butler Collection, 11.40

AFTER A SUMMER SHOWER

Signed and dated: G. Inness 1894. Oil on canvas, 32×42 in. (81.3×106.7 cm.)
Edward B. Butler Collection, 11.29

IPSEN, Ernest Ludwig ~ *b. 1869 Malden, Mass. d. 1951 Miami, Fla.*

Ipsen was trained at the School of the Museum of Fine Arts, Boston, and at the Royal Academy in Copenhagen.

BENJAMIN FRANKLIN FERGUSON

Signed and dated: E. L. Ipsen 1899. Oil on canvas, 30×25 in. (76.3×63.6 cm.)
Gift of Mary Ferguson Olden, 11.449

MRS. BENJAMIN FRANKLIN FERGUSON

Painted probably about 1899. Oil on canvas, 30×25 in. (76.3×63.6 cm.)
Gift of Mary Ferguson Olden, 11.450

IRVINE, Wilson H. ~ *b. 1869 Byron, Ill. d. 1936 Lyme, Conn.*

AUTUMN

Painted c. 1914, signed: Irvine. Oil on canvas, 32×40 in. (81.3×101.7 cm.)
Friends of American Art Collection, 15.558

ISENBRANDT, Adriaen ~ *Active 1510. d. 1551 Bruges*

Isenbrandt may have studied with Gerard David, whose influence is apparent in his work.

MADONNA AND CHILD

Painted between 1510 and 1540. Oil on panel, 15¼ × 12 in. (38.8 × 30.5 cm.)
Mr. and Mrs. Martin A. Ryerson Collection, 33.1053 (Friedlaender no 182a)

Ref: Friedlaender, M. J., Die Altniederlaendische Malerei, *XI, 1933, p. 136, no. 182a; Chicago. Art Institute,* A Century of Progress Exhibition, *1933, cat. no. 41;* Ibid., *1934, cat. no. 120*

SAINT CATHERINE

Painted about 1510–1520. Oil on panel, 14 × 21½ in. (35.7 × 54.7 cm.)
Max and Leola Epstein Collection, 54.288 (Friedlaender no. 209)

Ref: Pantheon *8: 436–7, October 1931; Friedlaender, M. J.,* op. cit., *XI, 1933, p. 139, no. 209*

ISRAELS, Josef ~ *b. 1824 Groningen, Holland. d. 1911 The Hague*

During Israëls' early years in Holland he copied the works of Rembrandt. In 1845 he went to Paris where he was influenced by Horace Vernet and Paul Delaroche.

OLD AGE

Painted probably between 1890 and 1900, signed: Josef Israëls.
Oil on canvas, 46⅜ × 33⅜ in. (117.8 × 84.9 cm.)
Gift of Mrs. Francis Neilson, 44.35

ITALIAN SCHOOL, 13th century

DIPTYCH: VIRGIN AND CHILD, CRUCIFIXION

Painted between 1250 and 1300. Tempera on panel, each 11½ × 8¾ in. (29.2 × 22.3 cm.)
Mr. and Mrs. Martin A. Ryerson Collection, 33.1035
Coll: Albin Chalandon, Paris, 1850; Henri Chalandon, La Grange Blanche, Parcieux

Ref: Chicago. Art Institute, Bulletin *20: 77–80, 1926; Vávala, E. S.,* International Studio *95: 32–6, 88, April 1930; Chicago. Art Institute,* A Century of Progress Exhibition, *1933, cat. no. 100;* Ibid., *1934, cat. no. 39*

ITALIAN SCHOOL, 14th century

CRUCIFIXION

Painted about 1340. Tempera on panel, 20 × 9¼ in. (50.9 × 23.5 cm.)
Mr. and Mrs. Martin A. Ryerson Collection, 33.1032

Ref: Chicago. Art Institute, Bulletin *22: 74–5, 1928; Berenson, B.,* Italian Pictures of the Renaissance, *1932, p. 165; Chicago. Art Institute,* A Century of Progress Exhibition, *1933, cat. no. 97*

MADONNA OF HUMILITY

Painted about 1375–1400. Tempera on panel, 38⅞ × 23¼ in. (98.9 × 59.1 cm.)
Charles H. and Mary F. S. Worcester Collection, 47.56
Coll: Count Ambroz-Migazzy, Sarvar, Hungary

Ref: Pantheon *3: 102, 104, 1929; Chicago. Art Institute,* Bulletin *24: 85–9, 1930; Venturi, L.,* Pitture Italiane in America, *1931; Chicago. Art Institute,* A Century of Progress Exhibition, *1933, cat. no. 86; Chicago. Art Institute,* Catalogue of the Worcester Collection, *1936, cat. no. 2; Meiss, M.,* Art Bulletin *18: 441, 1936*

ITALIAN SCHOOL, 15th century

THE BETROTHAL AND WEDDING DANCE

Painted about 1465. Tempera on panel, 15¾ × 53⅝ in. (40.1 × 136.3 cm.)
Mr. and Mrs. Martin A. Ryerson Collection, 33.1036

This painting once formed the front panel of a wedding chest.

Coll: Emile Gavet

Ref: Berenson, B., Pitture Italiane del Rinascimento, *1936, p. 283*

PIETA

Painted during the last quarter of the 15th century.
Tempera on panel, 28¼ × 21¾ in. (71.7 × 55.4 cm.)
Mr. and Mrs. Martin A. Ryerson Collection, 33.1037

This painting is a free copy after Tura's Pietà in the Museo Civico Correr in Venice. It bears certain stylistic characteristics of the work of Marco Zoppo.

MADONNA AND CHILD

Painted about 1475. Tempera and oil on panel, 30¾ × 21¾ in. (78.1 × 55.4 cm.)
Mr. and Mrs. Martin A. Ryerson Collection, 37.1009

The artist of this panel painted in a manner close to the early work of Botticelli and Antonio Pollaiuolo.

Coll: Alexander Barker, London; G. P. Boyce, Chelsea; Consul E. F. Weber, Hamburg

Ref: Berenson, B., Italian Pictures of the Renaissance, *1932, p. 101; Chicago. Art Institute,* A Century of Progress Exhibition, *1933, cat. no. 111*

EPIPHANY

Probably painted after 1475. Tondo, tempera on panel, 31 in. diameter (78.8 cm.)
Mr. and Mrs. Martin A. Ryerson Collection, 37.997

Ascribed by Berenson to Francesco Botticini.

Coll: Emile Gavet, Paris

Ref: Kühnel, E., Francesco Botticini, *1906, pp. 16–7, 37; R. van Marle,* The Development of the Italian Schools of Painting, *XIII, 1931, pp. 398–9; Berenson, B.,* Italian Pictures of the Renaissance, *1932, p. 107; Chicago. Art Institute,* A Century of Progress Exhibition, *1934, cat. no. 46a; Berenson, B.,* Pitture Italiane del Rinascimento, *1936, p. 92; Neilson, K. B.,* Filippino Lippi, *1938; Chicago. Art Institute,* Bulletin *32: 3, 101, 1939*

ITALIAN SCHOOL, 16th century

TWO CHERUBS

Painted about 1500. Tempera and oil on panel, 18 × 14 5/16 in. (45.8 × 36.4 cm.)
Mr. and Mrs. Martin A. Ryerson Collection, 37.1001

This painting once formed part of the decorated lid of a wooden box. Such boxes were customarily given to a lady after the birth of a child. In adjusting the painting to a rectangular panel, part of the owner's coat of arms was destroyed. This artist followed the tradition of Francesco di Giorgio and Neroccio.

THE MARRIAGE OF SAINT CATHERINE

Probably painted about 1510. Oil on panel, 23⅝ × 19⅛ in. (60.1 × 48.6 cm.)
Mr. and Mrs. Martin A. Ryerson Collection, 37.1002

This painting was attributed to a follower of Francesco Francia by Adolfo Venturi.

ALLESSANDRO DE' MEDICI

Painted probably between 1533–1537. Oil on panel, 13⅞ × 10⅛ in. (35.3 × 25.7 cm.)
Mr. and Mrs. Martin A. Ryerson Collection, 33.1002

Berenson attributed this painting to Bronzino, Van Marle to Andrea del Sarto; other scholars do not agree with these attributions.

Coll: Earl Dudley, London

Ref: McComb, A., Agnolo Bronzino, *1928, p. 44; Berenson, B.,* Pitture Italiane del Rinascimento, *1936, p. 98*

PORTRAIT OF A YOUNG FLORENTINE LADY

Painted about 1540–1550. Oil on panel, 21⅝ × 17 in. (55 × 43.3 cm.)
Charles H. and Mary F. S. Worcester Collection, 37.459

FRENCH AND ENGLISH PAINTINGS

XVIIth—XIX Centuries

ILLUSTRATIONS

Opposite: Chardin, Jean-Baptiste, The White Tablecloth, c. 1737
Gift of Annie Swan Coburn to the Mr. & Mrs. Lewis L. Coburn Memorial Collection

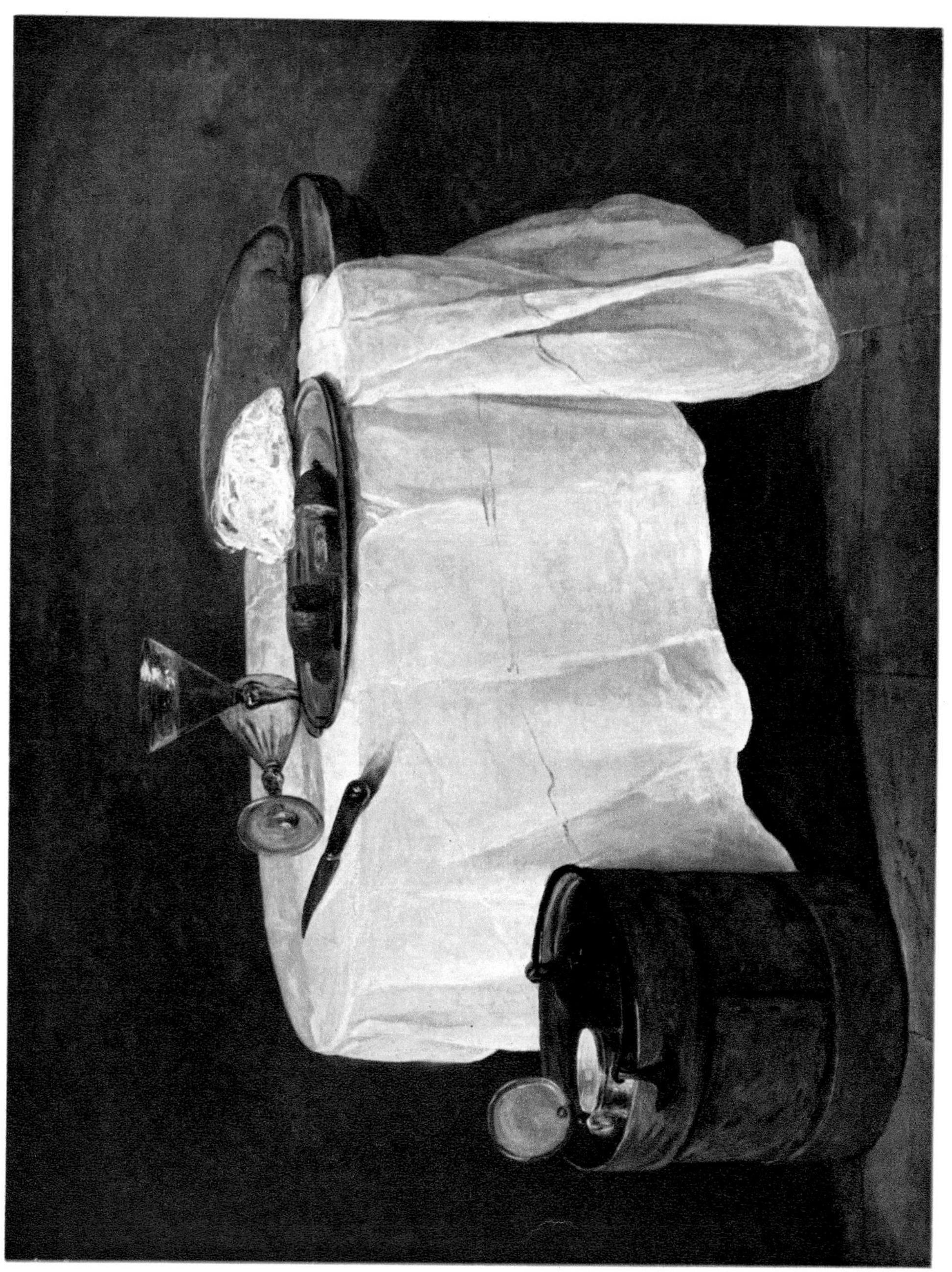

Gelée, Claude (Lorraine), Landscape with Sacrificial Procession, 1673. Robert A. Waller Fund

Poussin, Nicolas, Saint John on Patmos, c. 1645–50. A. A. Munger Collection

Opposite:
Daumier, Honoré, The Print Collector, c. 1857–63
Gift of the Estate of Marshall Field III

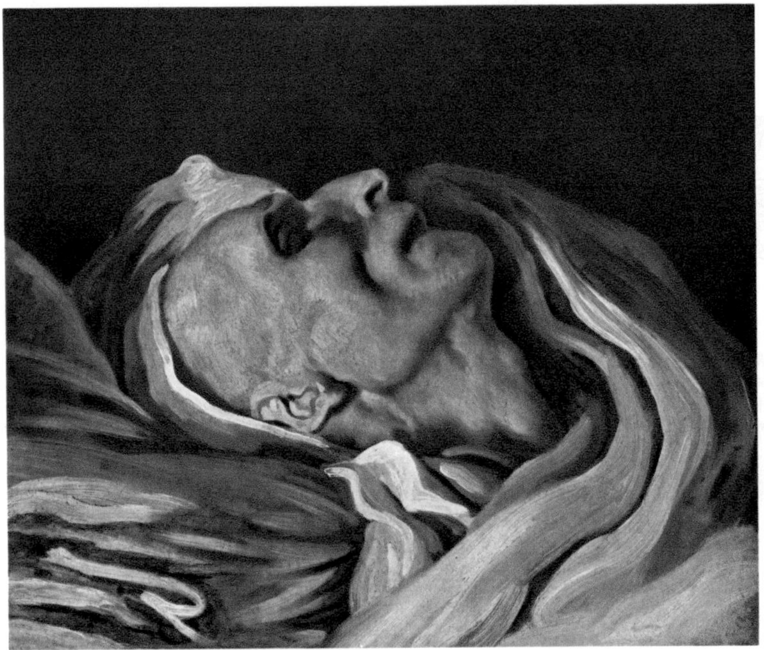

Géricault, Théodore, After Death (Study), c. 1818/19. A. A. Munger Collection

h. Daumier

Millet, Jean François, Young Woman, c. 1845. Potter Palmer Collection

Opposite:
Monticelli, Adolphe, Portrait of a Lady, c. 1870–79
A. A. Munger Collection

Turner, Joseph Mallord William, Valley of Aosta – Snowstorm, c. 1836/37. Frederick T. Haskell Collection

Constable, John, Stoke-by-Nayland, 1836. Mr. & Mrs. W. W. Kimball Collection

Fantin-Latour, Henri, Still Life: Corner of a Table, 1873. Ada Turnbull Hertle Fund

Courbet, Gustave, The Brook of Les Puits-Noir, 1868. Gift of Mr. & Mrs. Morris Kaplan

Corot, Jean-Baptiste, Monte Pincio, Rome, c. 1840–50
Gift of Annie Swan Coburn to the Mr. & Mrs. Lewis L. Coburn Memorial Collection

Opposite: Corot, Jean-Baptiste, Interrupted Reading, c. 1865–70
Potter Palmer Collection

Courbet, Gustave, Mère Grégoire, 1855. Wilson L. Mead Fund

Fantin-Latour, Henri, Edouard Manet, 1867. The Stickney Fund

Opposite: Delacroix, Eugène, The Lion Hunt, 1861
Potter Palmer Collection

This painting is in the tradition of Bronzino, F. Salviati and M. Ridolfi.

Coll: E. Volpi, Rome

Ref: Chicago. Art Institute, A Century of Progress Exhibition, *1933, cat. no. 127; Chicago. Art Institute,* Catalogue of the Worcester Collection, *1936, cat. no. 7*

PORTRAIT OF A LADY

Painted about 1575. Oil on canvas, 70½ × 45¾ in. (179.1 × 116.2 cm.)
Gift of Chester Dale, 46.382

This picture, sometime attributed to Veronese, may be closer to Giovanni Antonio Fasolo.

Coll: H. O. Havemeyer, N.Y.

Ref: Chicago. Art Institute, Bulletin *41: 1–4, 1947; Fiocco, G.,* Paolo Veronese *,1928, p. 202*

ITALIAN SCHOOL, 17th century

PORTRAIT OF AN OFFICER Illus. p. 52

Painted about 1650. Oil on canvas, 28⅛ × 23¾ in. (71.5 × 60.5 cm.)
Mr. and Mrs. Martin A. Ryerson Collection, 33.1093

TWO MONKS IN A LANDSCAPE

Painted about 1645. Oil on canvas, 25¼ × 30⅜ in. (64.2 × 77.2 cm.)
Wentworth Greene Field Memorial Fund, 38.223

This picture, formerly attributed to Murillo, is probably Neapolitan.

Coll: Simonetti, Rome; Walter Schnackenberg, Munich

Ref: Chicago. Art Institute, Bulletin *32: 85–7, 1938*

JACKSON, John ~ *b. 1778 Lastingham, England. d. 1831 London*

Jackson studied briefly at the Royal Academy and was influenced by Reynolds.

SELF PORTRAIT

Painted about 1820 or 1830. Oil on canvas, 30 × 24¾ in. (76.3 × 63 cm.)
Gift of Mrs. G. P. A. Healy, 05.56

AN ENGLISH GENTLEMAN

Painted about 1810. Oil on canvas, 27 × 23⅜ in. (68.7 × 59.4 cm.)
Gift of Mrs. G. P. A. Healy, 05.57

JACOPO DI CIONE (called Robiccia) ~ *Active about 1365–1398 Florence*

Jacopo was the younger brother of Andrea di Cione, called Orcagna. He assisted in his brother's workshop and, after Orcagna's death in 1368, continued his style.

MADONNA OF HUMILITY WITH TWO ANGELS

Painted about 1370. Tempera on panel, 29¾×16½ in. (75.6×42 cm.)
Mr. and Mrs. Martin A. Ryerson Collection, 37.1004

The attribution to Jacopo di Cione is by Bernard Berenson.

Coll: Kerr Lawson, Florence

Ref: Berenson, B., Pitture Italiane del Rinascimento, *1936, p. 235*

JAWLENSKY, Aleksej ~ *b. 1864 Torschok, Russia. d. 1941 Wiesbaden, Germany*

After his studies at the Academy of St. Petersburg, from 1890 to 1896, Jawlensky went to live in Munich where he became much involved in the activities of a group of progressive artists. With Kandinsky and Franz Marc he formed the Blue Rider group in 1912.

GIRL WITH THE GREEN FACE

Painted 1910, signed: A. Jawlensky.
Oil on composition board, 20 15/16 × 19 9/16 in. (53.1×49.7 cm.)
Gift of Mr. and Mrs. Earle Ludgin in memory of John V. McCarthy, 53.336

JEWETT, William S. *see* WALDO and JEWETT

JOHANSEN, John Christian ~ *1876 Copenhagen*

Johansen came to America and studied at The Art Institute of Chicago. Later he joined the group of Americans at the Académie Julian in Paris, and finally settled in Chicago.

DRAWING ROOM, TOWN HOUSE

Signed and dated: John C. Johansen, 1924. Oil on canvas, 29⅝×39¾ in. (75.3×101 cm.)
Friends of American Art Collection, 25.811

PIAZZA SAN MARCO, VENICE

Signed and dated: J. C. Johansen, 1908, Venice.
Oil on canvas, 29½×39½ in. (75×100.3 cm.)
Friends of American Art Collection, 10.315

JOHN, Augustus Edwin ~ *b. 1879 Tanley, Wales*

John studied at the Slade School from 1896 to 1899. Charles Conder and James Dickenson Innes influenced his development.

A BUNDLE OF LAVENDER

Oil on panel, 12¾×9 in. (32.3×22.8 cm.)
Gift of Emily Crane Chadbourne, 26.1587

THE ROGUE

Signed and dated: John 1923. Oil on canvas, 29¼ × 24¾ in. (74.3 × 63 cm.)
Charles H. and Mary F. S. Worcester Collection, 25.728

Ref: Huxley, A., Vanity Fair *20: 46, 1923;* Vanity Fair *23: 59, November 1924;* Colour, *N.A. 1: 13, January 1925; Chicago. Art Institute,* Bulletin *20: 21, 1926; Chicago. Art Institute,* A Century of Progress Exhibition, *1933, cat. no. 266; Chicago. Art Institute,* Catalogue of the Worcester Collection, *1936, cat. no. 59*

STUDY OF A CHILD

Signed and dated: John, 1923 (twice). Oil on panel, 19¼ × 10½ in. (49 × 26.7 cm.)
Charles H. and Mary F. S. Worcester Collection, 35.444

JOHNSON, Eastman ~ *b. 1824 Lovell, Me. d. 1906 New York City*

Johnson first trained as a lithographer, later studied with an obscure portrait painter in Augusta, Maine. Abroad he worked in Düsseldorf, then spent four years in The Hague studying the Dutch masters. He settled in New York in 1860.

SELF PORTRAIT

Signed and dated: E. Johnson 1863. Oil on canvas, 15 × 11¾ in. (38.2 × 29.8 cm.)
Gift of Mrs. Arthur Meeker, 24.126

A SLY DRINK AT THE CAMP

Painted between 1865–1873, signed: E.J.
Oil on academy board, 21⅛ × 25 in. (53.8 × 63.6 cm.)
Gift of Emily Crane Chadbourne, 53.4

CORNHUSKING BEE

Signed and dated: E. Johnson, 1876. Oil on canvas, 27¼ × 54¼ in. (69.3 × 137.8 cm.)
Potter Palmer Collection, 22.444

SELF PORTRAIT

Signed and inscribed: To Geo. P. A. Healy. From his friend Eastman Johnson N.Y. May 1889.
Oil on canvas, 18 × 14 in. (45.8 × 37.7 cm.)
Gift of Mrs. G. P. A. Healy, 05.54

JOHNSON, J. Theodore ~ *b. 1902 Oregon, Ill.*

Johnson was born in the Rock River country of Illinois, went to the School of the Art Institute and worked with André Lhote and Aristide Maillol in France.

MARY

Painted about 1927, signed: J. Theo Johnson. Oil on canvas, 25¼ × 31½ in. (64.2 × 802 cm.)
Mr. and Mrs. Frank G. Logan Purchase Prize, 28.229

THE BLACK MANTILLA

Painted 1928, signed: J. Theo Johnson. Oil on canvas, 30¾ × 37¼ in. (78.1 × 94.7 cm.)
Mr. and Mrs. Frank G. Logan Purchase Prize, 29.557

BISTRO BRUEL

Painted about 1930, signed: J. Theo Johnson.
Oil on canvas, 23¼ × 31⅜ in. (59.1 × 79.7 cm.)
Mr. and Mrs. Frank G. Logan Purchase Prize, 31.66

JONGKIND, Johan-Barthold ~ *b. 1819 Latrop, Holland. d. 1891 Côte-Saint-André, France*

Jongkind studied in The Hague and later in Paris. Influenced by Corot and Bonington, he is usually considered an important forerunner of Impressionism.

THE CHURCH OF OVERSCHIE

Signed and dated: Jongkind, 1866. Oil on canvas, 12 × 20 in. (30.5 × 50.9 cm.)
Mr. and Mrs. Martin A. Ryerson Collection, 33.1129
Coll: Ditrement, Paris; Deforge, Paris; May, Paris

KANDINSKY, Wassily ~ *b. 1866 Moscow. d. 1944 Paris*

Originally trained as an economist, Kandinsky began to study painting in Munich in 1897. He traveled extensively in his youth, coming in contact with Impressionism and Fauvism; both movements, however, affected him only briefly. It is thought that it was Kandinsky who created the first abstract painting in 1911. During World War I Kandinsky taught in Moscow. From 1922 to 1934 he was a member of the faculty of the Bauhaus in Weimar and later in Dessau.

TROIKA

Painted 1911, signed: Kandinsky. Oil on canvas, 27⅜ × 38 5/16 in. (69.6 × 97.2 cm.)
Arthur Jerome Eddy Memorial Collection, 31.509

Ref: Kandinsky (Der Sturm, *Berlin, c. 1914); Chicago. Art Institute,* Catalogue of the Eddy Collection, *1922, cat. no. 39; Chicago. Art Institute,* Bulletin *16: 69, 1922*

LANDSCAPE WITH TWO POPLARS

Painted 1912, signed: Kandinsky. Oil on canvas, 30⅞ × 39½ in. (78.4 × 100.3 cm.)
Arthur Jerome Eddy Memorial Collection, 31.508

Ref: Eddy, A. J., Cubists and Post-Impressionism, *1914, pp. 116–7;* Kandinsky (Der Sturm, *Berlin, c. 1914); Chicago. Art Institute,* Catalogue of the Eddy Collection, *1922, cat. no. 42; Chicago. Art Institute,* A Century of Progress Exhibition, *1933, cat. no. 779*

IMPROVISATION WITH GREEN CENTER (no. 176)

Signed and dated: Kandinsky 1913. Oil on canvas, 43¼ × 47½ in. (109.9 × 120.6 cm.)
Arthur Jerome Eddy Memorial Collection, 31.510

Ref: Chicago. Art Institute, Catalogue of the Eddy Collection, *1922, cat. no. 44; Chicago. Art Institute,* A Century of Progress Exhibition, *1933, cat. no. 778*

IMPROVISATION NO. 30 Illus. p. 434

Signed and dated: Kandinsky 1913. Oil on canvas, $43\frac{5}{8} \times 43\frac{5}{8}$ in. (110.9×110.9 cm.)
Arthur Jerome Eddy Memorial Collection, 31.511

Ref: Eddy, A. J., Cubists and Post-Impressionism, *1914, pp. 124–5;* Kandinsky *(*Der Sturm, *Berlin, c. 1914); Chicago. Art Institute,* Catalogue of the Eddy Collection, *1922, cat. no. 36; Bulliet, C. J.,* Creative Art *10: 216, 218, 1932; Chicago. Art Institute,* A Century of Progress Exhibition, *1933, cat. no. 777; Moholy-Nagy, L.,* The New Vision, *1938, p. 81; Blanc, P.,* Magazine of Art *44: 149, April 1951; Grohmann, W.,* Wassily Kandinsky, *(*Junge Kunst, *Bd. 42, n.d.)*

ON THE GREEN LINE

Signed and dated: V K 38.
Gouache and mixed media on canvas, $9\frac{1}{4} \times 25\frac{1}{2}$ in. (23.5×64.8 cm.)
Gift of Mr. and Mrs. Hans von der Marwitz, 53.337

KANTOR, Morris ~ *b. 1896 Minsk, Russia*

Kantor came to the United States in 1909. He studied in New York and Paris.

HAUNTED HOUSE

Signed and dated: M. Kantor 1930. Oil on canvas, $37\frac{1}{8} \times 33\frac{1}{2}$ in. (94.3×85.2 cm.)
Mr. and Mrs. Frank G. Logan Purchase Prize, 31.707

KARS, George ~ *b. 1882 Kralupy, Czechoslovakia. d. 1945 Paris [?]*

Kars studied in Munich with Franz von Stuck and went to Paris in 1905.

ORIENTAL WOMAN WITH EARTHEN JAR

Signed and dated: Kars '30. Oil on canvas, $39 \times 31\frac{1}{2}$ in. (99.2×80.2 cm.)
Gift of Mr. and Mrs. Carter H. Harrison, 35.308

WOMAN VIEWED FROM THE BACK

Signed and dated: Kars '30. Oil on canvas, $25\frac{9}{16} \times 21\frac{1}{4}$ in. (65×54.1 cm.)
Gift of Mr. and Mrs. Carter H. Harrison, 37.382

KATZMAN, Herbert ~ *b. 1923 Chicago*

Katzman studied at the School of The Art Institute of Chicago.

VIEW OF PRAGUE

Signed and dated: H. Katzman, Prague '48. Oil on canvas, $63\frac{7}{8} \times 51\frac{1}{4}$ in. (162.3×130.3 cm.)
Walter M. Campana Memorial Prize, 51.246

KENSETT, John F. ~ *b. 1818 Cheshire, Conn. d. 1872 New York City*

Kensett was one of the principal members of the Hudson River School. In 1840 he went abroad with Asher B. Durand.

THIRD BEACH, NEWPORT

Signed and dated: JF. 69. Oil on canvas, 11⅝ × 24¼ in. (29.5 × 62.4 cm.)
Friends of American Art Collections, 44.686

KENT, Rockwell ~ *b. 1882 Tarrytown Heights, N.Y.*

Rockwell Kent began his art studies at the age of fifteen under William Merritt Chase, then continued under Robert Henri, Abbott Thayer, and Kenneth Hayes Miller.

ALASKA

Signed and dated: Rockwell Kent, Alaska, 1919–27.
Oil on canvas, 28 × 34 in. (71.2 × 86.4 cm.)
Gift of Mrs. John Bordon, 27.997

MOUNT EQUINOX, WINTER

Signed and dated: Rockwell Kent—Vermont—1921.
Oil on canvas, 34 3/16 × 44 3/16 in. (86.6 × 111.9 cm.)
Gift of Gertrude V. Whitney, 23.51

KLEE, Paul ~ *b. 1879 Muenchenbuchsee, Switzerland. d. 1940 Muralto, Switzerland*

Klee early showed talent as a draughtsman. After three years of academic training, he went to Italy and Paris. In 1906 he established himself in Munich were he became a member of the Blue Rider group. During the 1920's Klee taught at the Bauhaus and in 1931 at the Düsseldorf Academy.

HEAD OF AN ARCHAEOLOGIST

Signed and dated: Klee 1924/13, inscribed: *Kopf eines Archaeologen.*
Oil and mixed media on paper, 14¾ × 11⅛ in. (37.5 × 28.3 cm.)
Gift of Annie Swan Coburn in memory of Olivia Shaler Swan, 52.1008

STAKIM

Painted about 1928, signed: Klee. Tempera on paper, 8 × 12¾ in. (20.3 × 32.3 cm.)
Gift of Mrs. Gilbert W. Chapman, 48.560

Stakim, according to the artist's biographer, Will Grohmann, is an invented word which Klee used to suggest by its very sound the pointed and angular forms which appear in the picture.

DUKE LEADER (LADDER) NOT ALONE

Signed and dated: Klee 1938 N4, inscribed: Herzog Leiter Nicht Allein.
Oil on paper, 13½ × 19⅛ in. (34.4 × 48.6 cm.)
Cyrus McCormick Fund, 51.255

To understand a picture by Klee it helps to consult the title. In this case a play on words is involved, for *Leiter* means both "ladder" and "leader." With hasty calligraphic symbols and unexpected color surprises (both typical of Klee), the picture possibly suggests an ambitious "climber."

WOMEN HARVESTING

Painted about 1937, signed: Klee.
Pastel on canvas, mounted on burlap, $19\frac{1}{2} \times 21$ in. (49.7×53.5 cm.)
Gift of Mrs. Morton G. Schamberg, 59.18

THE DANCER

Painted 1940, signed: P. K. Oil on cloth, $20\frac{1}{8} \times 20\frac{1}{8}$ in. (51.2×51.2 cm.)
Gift of George B. Young, 59.172

KNATHS, Karl ~ *b. 1891 Eau Claire, Wisc.*

While Knaths was studying at The Art Institute of Chicago, he was greatly affected by the Armory Show, a part of which was exhibited there in 1913. His work shows the influence of several contemporary artists, particularly Matisse and Braque.

STORE AND GEAR

Painted 1941, signed: Karl Knaths. Oil on canvas, $40 \times 49\frac{7}{8}$ in. (101.7×126.7 cm.)
Art Institute Purchase Fund, 42.36

THE TREE OF LIFE

Painted about 1942, signed: Karl Knaths. Oil on canvas, $25\frac{3}{4} \times 21\frac{1}{2}$ in. (65.5×57.3 cm.)
Gift of Mr. and Mrs. Harry L. Winston, 54.1311

KOERBECKE, Johann ~ *Active 1446–1491 Münster, Germany*

Koerbecke was probably a native of Münster, where he was apprenticed to a local master. Later he came under the influence of Stephan Lochner and adopted the style of the School of Cologne.

THE ANNUNCIATION

Painted 1457. Oil on canvas transferred from panel, $24\frac{5}{8} \times 36\frac{1}{4}$ in. (62.7×92.1 cm.)
Mr. and Mrs. Martin A. Ryerson Collection, 33.1064
Coll: Abbey Marienfeld, Westphalia, 1457–1803; Tollin de Rivarolles, Paris

Ref: Burkhard Meier, Westfalen *4: 110, 1912; Hugelsdorfer, W.,* Zeitschrift für Bildende Kunst *60: 179–84, 1926–1927; Hugelsdorfer, W.,* Der Cicerone *22, pt. 2: 371–6, 1930; Bensing, T.,* Westfalen *18: 262, 1933; Chicago. Art Institute,* A Century of Progress Exhibition, *1933, cat. no. 21;* Ibid., *1934, cat. no. 15; Tietze, H.,* Meisterwerke Europaeischer Malerei in Amerika, *1935, pl. 196; Kuhn, C. L.,* Catalogue of German Paintings of the Middle Ages and Renaissance . . . , *1936, cat. no. 63; Sommer, J.,* Johann Koerbecke, *1937, pp. 16, 24*

KOKOSCHKA, Oskar ~ *b. 1886 Pöchlarn, Austria*

Kokoschka, who studied at the School of Decorative Arts in Vienna, first exhibited in 1908.

PORTRAIT OF EBENSTEIN

Painted 1908, signed: OK. Oil on canvas, 39 × 31 in. (99.2 × 78.8 cm.)
The Joseph Winterbotham Collection, 56.364

Ebenstein, court-tailor in Vienna, was considered a great artist in the field of fashion. Kokoschka was introduced to him by his architect friend, Adolf Loos. Ebenstein provided him with a fine suit and even taught him anatomy from a tailor's point of view. In return Kokoschka painted this likeness of him.

Coll: Private collection, Vienna; Hugo, Simon, Paris; Christophe Bernoulli, Basle, Switzerland

Ref: Biermann, O., Oskar Kokoschka, *1929, pl. 2; Heilmaier, H.,* Kokoschka, *1929, pl. 3; Hoffman, E.,* Kokoschka, Life and Work, *1947, pp. 47, 82, 89, 290; Wingler, H. M.,* Oskar Kokoschka, *1956, cat. no. 10*

ELBE RIVER NEAR DRESDEN

Painted 1919, signed: OK. Oil on canvas, 31⅝ × 44 in. (80.5 × 111.9 cm.)
The Joseph Winterbotham Collection, 39.2244
Coll: Staatliche Gemälde Galerie, Dresden

Ref: Chicago. Art Institute, Catalogue of the Winterbotham Collection, *1946, p. 26; Hoffmann, E.,* Kokoschka, Life and Work, *1947, pp. 165–6, 309, cat. no. 126; Plaut, J. S.,* Oskar Kokoschka, *Boston, 1948, pp. 20, 84*

KRAFFT, Carl R. ~ *b. 1884 Reading, Ohio. d. 1938 Oak Park, Ill.*

MISSISSIPPI RIVER

Painted in 1924, signed: Carl R. Krafft. Oil on canvas, 25 × 30 in. (63.6 × 76.3 cm.)
Mr. and Mrs. Martin A. Ryerson Collection, 33.1211

KROHG, Per Larson ~ *b. 1889 Aasgaardstrand, Norway*

The artist studied in Paris and later under his father Christian Krohg. In 1909 he was a student of Henri Matisse.

THE AMBASSADRESS—A NOUVEAU-RICHE

Painted late 1920s, signed: Per Krohg. Oil on canvas, 45 × 34 in. (114.4 × 86.4 cm.)
Gift of Mr. and Mrs. Carter Harrison, 36.9

CONVERSATION

Painted late 1920s, signed: Per Krohg. Oil on canvas, 39¼ × 32 in. (99.8 × 81.3 cm.)
Gift of Mr. and Mrs. Carter H. Harrison, 35.305

KROLL, Leon ~ *b. 1884 New York City*

Kroll's first teacher was John Twachtman, later he studied at the Art Students League, the National Academy of Design, and under Jean Paul Laurens in Paris.

LEO ORNSTEIN AT THE PIANO

Signed and dated: Kroll 1918. Oil on canvas, 34×40 in. (86.4×101.7 cm.)

Friends of American Art Collection, 19.874

PATH BY THE SEA

Painted about 1929, signed: Leon Kroll. Oil on canvas, 26×42½ in. (66.1×108 cm.)

Friends of American Art Collection, 30.1000

KRONBERG, Louis ~ *b. 1872 Boston, Mass.*

Kronberg studied at the School of the Museum of Fine Arts in Boston, the Arts Students League, and at the Académie Julian.

WATCHING THE DANCERS

Signed and dated: Louis Kronberg 1930. Oil on board, 16⅛×13 in. (41.1×33 cm.)

Charles H. and Mary F. S. Worcester Collection, 47.83

LACHMAN, Harry B. ~ *b. 1886 La Salle, Ill.*

Lachman went to Paris when he was fifteen. He studied with Charles Cottet and was very much influenced by Paul Cézanne.

SAINT NICOLAS DU CHARDONNET

Signed and dated: Harry B. Lachman '18. Oil on canvas, 36×36 in. (91.5×91.5 cm.)

Friends of American Art Collection, 19.937

THE TOWER, CORMERY

Signed and dated: Harry B. Lachman '18. Oil on canvas, 36×28½ (91.5×72.5 cm.)

Friends of American Art Collection, 20.90

LANCRET, Nicholas ~ *1690–1743 Paris*

Lancret's first teacher, Pierre Dulin, was a painter of historical scenes, and later he entered the studio of Claude Gillot, who had been Watteau's master.

THE BEAUTIFUL GREEK GIRL

Painted about 1730. Oil on canvas, 27½×20½ in. (70×52.1 cm.)

Gift of Mrs. Albert J. Beveridge in memory of her mother Abby Louise Spencer Eddy, 48.565

This painting may represent a young Parisian actress who at one time played the role of a Greek slave. The canvas was originally accompanied by a pendant, *The Amorous Turk.*

Ref: Wildenstein, G., Lancret, *1924, p. 117, cat. no. 700*

LANYON, Ellen ~ *b. 1926 Chicago*

Ellen Lanyon studied at The Art Institute of Chicago.

ELEVATED, NIGHT

Signed and dated: Lanyon 47.
Egg tempera and mixed media on board, 12¼ × 16¼ in. (32.3 × 41.5 cm.)
Town and Country Arts Club Purchase Prize, 47.403

LASCAUX, Elie ~ *b. 1888 Limoges, France*

Lascaux, who started as a designer for the Limoges china firm, reflects his early training in color, specializing in brilliant blues contrasted with porcelain white.

CHARTRES CATHEDRAL

Painted 1930, signed lower right: Lascaux. Oil on canvas, 31⅞ × 39 5/16 in. (81 × 99.8 cm.)
Gift of Joseph Winterbotham, 54.1358

LA TOUCHE, Gaston ~ *b. 1854 Saint-Cloud, France. d. 1913 Paris*

La Touche was influenced by Bracquemond and also derived a certain brilliance of technique from Manet.

PARDON IN BRITTANY

Signed and dated: G. La Touche 96. Oil on canvas, 38¾ × 42½ in. (98.5 × 108 cm.)
Mr. and Mrs. Martin A. Ryerson Collection, 33.1130

LAUFMAN, Sidney ~ *b. 1891 Cleveland, Ohio*

Laufman studied at the School of the Art Institute and the Art Students League.

LANDSCAPE—LA COLLE

Painted 1928, signed: Sidney Laufman. Oil on canvas, 28½ × 39¼ in. (72.5 × 99.8 cm.)
Friends of American Art Collection, 43.546

LAVERY, Sir John ~ *b. 1856 Belfast, Ireland. d. 1941 County Kilkenny, Ireland*

Lavery studied in Glasgow, London, and at the Académie Julian in Paris. Influenced by Bastien-Lepage, Alfred Stevens, and his friend Whistler, he collaborated with the latter to found the International Society of Sculptors, Painters and Gravers.

A GRAY DAY, TANGIER

Painted 1890–1891, signed: J. Lavery. Oil on canvas, 24½ × 29½ in. (62.4 × 75 cm.)
George F. Porter Collection, 27.307

LAWRENCE, Sir Thomas ~ *b. 1769 Bristol, England. d. 1830 London*

Lawrence painted portraits from the time he was five years of age. Except for a short period after he entered the Royal Academy in 1787, he received no formal training. As President of the Royal Academy from 1820 until he died, Lawrence was recognized as England's leading portrait painter of that time.

MRS. JENS WOLFF

Painted about 1803. Oil on canvas, 50⅜ × 40¼ in. (128 × 102.3 cm.)
Mr. and Mrs. W. W. Kimball Collection, 22.4435

In 1803 Lawrence began his portrait of Mrs. Jens Wolff, wife of the Danish consul, whose house at Sherwood Lodge, Battersea, was filled with fine antique casts. Here an interesting group of artists and writers often gathered. In 1813 Mrs. Wolff separated from her husband and the collection was sold. This perhaps explains why the portrait was not finished until 1815 when Lawrence put it on exhibition at the Royal Academy. A portrait head of Mrs. Wolff closely related to the Art Institute portrait is in the collection of Mrs. O. G. S. Croft.

Ref: Ladyard, G. S., ed., Sir Thomas Lawrence's Letter-Bag, *1906, p. 246; Armstrong, Sir W.,* Lawrence, *1913, pp. 65, 172; Chicago. Art Institute,* Bulletin *14: 73, 77, 1920; Chicago. Art Institute,* A Century of Progress Exhibition, *1933, cat. no. 198;* Ibid., *1934, cat. no. 144; Goldring, D.,* Regency Portrait Painter, The Life of Sir Thomas Lawrence, *1951, pp. 204, 205, 235, 236; Garlick, K.,* Sir Thomas Lawrence, *1954, pp. 11, 63 of cat.*

THE MARCHIONESS OF ELY

Painted about 1810. Oil on canvas, 30¾ × 25¾ in. (78.1 × 65.5 cm.)
Gift of Alice H. Brown, 51.199

The attribution of this painting to Lawrence is uncertain.

Coll: R. Hall McCormick, Chicago

Ref: Catalogue of the McCormick Collection, *Chicago, 1897, p. 88;* Library of Congress Portrait Index, *1906, p. 473*

LAWSON, Ernest ~ *b. 1873 San Francisco. d. 1939 Miami Beach, Fla.*

Ernest Lawson was a student at the Art Students League, then spent a year at Cos Cob, Conn., working with Twachtman and J. Alden Weir. This was followed by a year at the Académie Julian in Paris.

ICE BOUND FALLS

Signed and dated: E. Lawson 1919. Oil on canvas, 39½ × 50 in. (100.3 × 127 cm.)
Friends of American Art Collection, 21.97

LECHAY, James ~ *b. 1907 New York City*

Lechay studied at the University of Illinois.

PIER ON SUNDAY

Painted 1939, signed: James Lechay. Oil on canvas, 30×40¼ in. (76.3×102.2 cm.)
Gift of the Society for Contemporary American Art, 42.21

LEE, Doris ~ *b. 1905 Aledo, Ill.*

Doris Lee studied at the Kansas City Art Institute with Ernest Lawson and at the California School of Fine Arts with Arnold Blanch.

THANKSGIVING

Painted about 1935, signed: Doris Lee. Oil on canvas, 28⅛×40 in. (71.5×101.7 cm.)
Mr. and Mrs. Frank G. Logan Purchase Prize, 35.313

LEGER, Fernand ~ *b. 1881 Argentan, France. d. 1955 Gif-sur-Yvette, France*

Trained originally as an architect, Fernand Léger early turned to painting. Along with Picasso, Braque, and Juan Gris he is considered a pioneer of the Cubist movement.

FOLLOW THE ARROW Illus. p. 435

Painted 1919, signed: F. Léger. Oil on canvas, 25½×28⅛ in. (53.8×64.8 cm.)
Gift of Mrs. Patrick Hill in memory of Rue Winterbotham Carpenter to The Joseph Winterbotham Collection, 53.341

THE RED TABLE

Signed and dated: F. Léger 20. Oil on canvas, 21⅛×25⅝ in. (54.4×65.2 cm.)
Gift of Kate L. Brewster, 48.557

COMPOSITION IN BLUE

Signed and dated: F. Léger 21–27. Oil on canvas, 51⅛×38⅛ in. (129.9×96.9 cm.)
Charles H. and Mary F. S. Worcester Collection, 37.461

Ref: Tériade, E., Fernand Léger, *1928; Chicago. Art Institute,* A Century of Progress Exhibition, *1933, cat. no. 781; Chicago. Art Institute,* Catalogue of the Worcester Collection, *1938, cat. no. 89*

NATURE MORTE TRICOLORE, 1928

Signed and dated: F. Léger 28. Oil on canvas, 29⅛×36⅝ in. (74.3×93 cm.)
Gift of Mr. and Mrs. Leigh B. Block, 53.468

Ref: Cahiers d'Art, *Année 4: 156, 1929*

DIVERS ON YELLOW BACKGROUND Illus. p. 465

Signed and dated: 41 F. Léger. Oil on canvas, 75¾×87½ in. (192.5×222.3)
Gift of Mr. and Mrs. Maurice E. Culberg, 53.176
Coll: Roger Vivier, Paris; Frederick William Bradley, New York

Ref: Sweeney, J. J., Art News *41: 18, 30, October 1942;* Fernand Léger, la Forme Humaine Dans L'Espace, *Montreal, 1945, p. 51*

COMPOSITION WITH LEMON

Signed and dated: 39 F. Léger. Oil on canvas, 25⅝ × 20 in. (65.2 × 50.9 cm.)
Gift of J. W. Alsdorf, 54.1200

Ref: Cahiers d'Art, *Année 15, 1940, p. 23 (ill.)*

LENBACH, Franz von ~ *b. 1836 Schrobenhausen, Germany. d. 1904 Munich*

Son of a successful stonemason, Lenbach was first trained in the craft of his father. Later he studied painting in Munich and worked in Italy and Spain. From 1871 to 1874 Lenbach frequently lived in Vienna where he received innumerable portrait commissions. More than 4000 portraits are known to have been painted by him.

PRINCE OTTO VON BISMARCK

Painted 1896. Oil on canvas, 49½ × 37⅛ in. (125.6 × 94.3 cm.)
Gift of Mrs. and Mrs. Otto K. Eitel, 56.1205

LEPINE, Stanislas ~ *b. 1835 Caen, France. d. 1892 Paris*

Lépine was a pupil of Corot and was influenced by Jongkind. He specialized in intimate little scenes of Paris.

THE APPLE MARKET

Painted about 1880, signed: S. Lépine. Oil on canvas, 18¼ × 25¾ in. (46.5 × 65.5 cm.)
Mr. and Mrs. Martin A. Ryerson Collection, 33.1133

THE COURTYARD

Painted about 1880, signed: S. Lépine. Oil on canvas, 13¼ × 7 in. (33.7 × 17.8 cm.)
Mr. and Mrs. Martin A. Ryerson Collection, 37.1018

LE SIDANER, Henri Eugène ~ *b. 1862 Port Louis, France. d. 1939 Versailles*

Le Sidaner was academically trained under Cabanel but later came under the influence of Manet and Signac.

SEINE AND PONT ROYAL

Painted between 1905 and 1910, signed: Le Sidaner.
Oil on canvas, 32½ × 46¼ in. (82.6 × 117.5)
Mr. and Mrs. Martin A. Ryerson Collection, 33.1131

LESLIE, Charles Robert ~ *1794–1859 London*

Leslie came to America with his parents in 1800. He studied with Thomas Sully, then went back to London to work under the American painters Washington Allston and Benjamin West.

JAMES WILLIAM WALLACK

Painted about 1850. Oil on canvas, 30⅛×25⅛ in. (76.6×63.9 cm.)
Friends of American Art Collection, 23.359

LEVI, Julian Edwin ~ *b. 1900 New York City*

Levi was trained at the Pennsylvania Academy of the Fine Arts under Henry McCarter, Arthur B. Carles and Hugh Breckenridge.

WELLFLEET HARBOR

Painted 1941, signed: Julian Levi. Oil on canvas, 30×40 in. (76.3×101.7 cm.)
Gift of the Society for Contemporary American Art, 43.533

LEVINE, Jack ~ *b. 1915 Boston*

At the age of fourteen Levine became a student of Denman Ross in Cambridge. He later moved to New York.

THE TRIAL

Painted 1953–1954, signed: J. Levine. Oil on canvas, 72×63 in. (182.9×160.1 cm.)
Gift of Mr. and Mrs. Edwin E. Hokin and Goodman Fund, 54.438

Levine himself has written a full account of the two years he spent on this painting. He did no less than twenty-five preliminary drawings which he gave to The Art Institute of Chicago when the picture was purchased. In addition, he painted three oil studies. Levine wrote, "My first essay on the theme was a 30×36 inch canvas based remotely on a painting by Daumier, *Ventre Législatif.* It was an array of judges in white robes. The second study in its general layout seemed the better scaffolding for the final large version. Unlike the first version which was pyramidal this one was based on a rocking diamond, like certain Greco compositions. I have had no experience with courtrooms. The Trial is a composite of all my impressions of such things, such places and such people at one remove."

LEYDEN, Lucas van ~ *1489–1533 Leyden, Holland*

Lucas, primarily an engraver, was equally distinguished as a painter and is known to have also designed stained glass windows. Taught first by his father Huygh Jacobsz, he continued his studies under Cornelis Engelbrechtsz. In 1521 he met Dürer in Antwerp, exchanged engravings with him, and was undoubtedly influenced by him. He showed the influence of Italian Mannerism in his later work.

EPIPHANY Illus. p. 152

Painted about 1510. Oil on panel, 11¼×14 in. (28.6×35.7 cm.)
Mr. and Mrs. Martin A. Ryerson Collection, 33.1045 (Friedlaender no. 120)

The composition of this painting may have been suggested by an illuminated manuscript from the School of Bruges.

Ref: Chicago. Art Institute, Bulletin *10: 240, 1916 (ill.); Friedlaender, M. J.,* Von Eyck bis Breughel, *1921, p. 200; Conway, W. N.,* The Van Eycks and Their Followers, *1921, pp. 471–2; Baldass, L.,* Die Gemaelde des Lucas van Leyden, *1923, pp. 18–9; Winkler, F.,* Die Altniederlaendische Malerei, *1924, p. 264; Friedlaender, M. J.,* Cicerone *22, pt. 2: 495, 498, 1930; Friedlaender, M. J.,* Die Altniederlaendische Malerei, *X, 1932, cat. no. 120; Chicago. Art Institute,* A Century of Progress Exhibition, *1933, cat. no. 43; Chicago. Art Institute,* Bulletin *27: 10, 12, 59, 60, 1933; Tietze, H.,* Meisterwerke Europaeischer Malerei in Amerika, *1935; Hoogewerff, G. J.,* De Noord-Nederlandsche Schilderkunst, *III, 1939, p. 233*

LHERMITTE, Léon Augustin ~ *b. 1844 Mont-Saint-Père, France. d. 1925 Paris*

Lhermitte painted in the manner of Millet.

THE HARVESTERS

Painted about 1900, signed: L. Lhermitte. Oil on canvas, 21×30½ in. (53.5×77.5 cm.)
Mr. and Mrs. Martin A. Ryerson Collection, 33.1139

LHOTE, André ~ *b. 1885 Bordeaux, France*

Lhote began as a sculptor but learned to paint by copying the work of Rubens and Delacroix. Much impressed by both Gauguin and Cézanne, he was also influenced by the Cubists. He first exhibited at the Salon des Indépendants in 1906 and with the Cubists in their famous show of 1911.

THE LADIES OF AVIGNON

Painted about 1923, signed: A. Lhote. Oil on canvas, 43⅜×33 in. (110.3×83.9 cm.)
Helen Birch Bartlett Memorial Collection, 26.215

PORTRAIT OF A LADY

Painted 1927, signed: A. Lhote. Oil on canvas, 35¾×28 in. (101×71.2 cm.)
Gift of Mr. and Mrs. Carter H. Harrison, 37.383

MADAME LHOTE AT THE PIANO

Painted 1927, signed: A. Lhote. Oil on canvas, 31⅜×22¾ in. (79.7×57.9 cm.)
Gift of Mr. and Mrs. Carter H. Harrison, 35.306

SAILOR AND WOMAN FROM MARTINIQUE

Signed and dated: A. Lhote 30. Oil on canvas, 36½×29 in. (92.8×73.7 cm.)
Gift of Mr. and Mrs. Carter H. Harrison, 36.10

OLD MARSEILLES HARBOR

Signed and dated: A. Lhote. 30. Oil on canvas, $23\frac{1}{2}\times 36\frac{1}{2}$ in. (59.6×92.8 cm.)
Gift of Mr. and Mrs. Carter H. Harrison, 37.384

LIE, Jonas ~ *b. 1880 Moss, Norway. d. 1940 New York City*

Lie came to America at the age of thirteen, studied at the National Academy of Design and the Art Students League. In 1934 he was elected President of the National Academy of Design.

AFTERGLOW

Painted about 1913, signed: Jonas Lie. Oil on canvas, $50\frac{1}{4}\times 60\frac{3}{8}$ in. (127.7×153.4 cm.)
Friends of American Art Collection, 14.389

LIOTARD, Jean Etienne (attributed to) ~ *1701–1789 Geneva, Switzerland*

Liotard, born of French parents in Geneva, studied with the miniature painter, Jean-Baptiste Massé in Paris. Shortly after 1736 he went to Rome and then to Constantinople where he remained for five years. Returning to Europe in 1743, he traveled widely, earning commissions and honors in many capitals. After his marriage in 1756, Liotard settled in Geneva.

PORTRAIT OF THE ARTIST'S MOTHER

Painted about 1730. Oil on canvas, $31\frac{7}{8}\times 25\frac{3}{4}$ in. (81×64.5 cm.)
Simeon B. William Fund, 35.299

The attribution to Liotard is by no means certain. Hermann Voss has suggested that the picture may be by Subleyras.

Coll: Jean Liotard-Crommelin; Liotard Pallard; Johanna Victoire Liotard; Professor J. W. R. Tilanus; Dr. C. B. Tilanus, Amsterdam

Ref: Humbart, E., A. Revilliod and J. W. R. Tilanus, La Vie et les Oeuvres de Jean Etienne Liotard, *Amsterdam, 1897, p. 141, no. 118; Chicago. Art Institute,* Annual Report, *1935, p. 24; Chicago. Art Institute,* Bulletin *30: 74–6, 1936*

LIPPI, Filippino (attributed to) ~ *b. 1457/8 Spoleto. d. 1504 Florence*

MADONNA AND CHILD

Painted about 1490. Oil on panel, $20\frac{1}{2}\times 18\frac{3}{8}$ in. (52.1×46.8 cm.)
Max and Leola Epstein Collection, 54.289

LOISEAU, Gustave ~ *1865–1936 Paris*

Loiseau studied at the School of Decorative Arts in Paris.

ORCHARD IN BLOOM

Painted about 1900, signed: G. Loiseau. Oil on canvas, 23 × 28¼ in. (58.6 × 71.7 cm.)
Mr. and Mrs. Martin A. Ryerson Collection, 33.1141

LONGHI, Pietro ~ *1702–1785 Venice*

Pietro Longhi, who studied with Crespi, was also influenced by Piazzetta.

CHILD WITH DOG

Painted about 1740. Oil on canvas, 25½ × 19½ in. (64.8 × 49.4 cm.)
Charles H. and Mary F. S. Worcester Collection, 47.84

The attribution to Longhi is not certain.

Coll: Francesco Zanetti, Venice

Ref: Chicago. Art Institute, Bulletin *25: 37, 1931; Ojetti, U.,* Il Settecento Italiano, *I, 1932, cat. no. 72; Chicago. Art Institute,* Catalogue of the Worcester Collection, *1937, cat. no. 26*

LADY AT HER TOILET

Painted about 1740. Oil on canvas, 22⅜ × 17¼ in. (56.9 × 43.9 cm.)
Flora Erskine Miles Fund, 47.433
Coll: Dr. Max Emden, Switzerland

THE DANCE

Painted about 1745. Oil on canvas, 24¼ × 19½ in. (61.7 × 49.7 cm.)
Charles H. and Mary F. S. Worcester Collection, 32.52
Coll: John Wanamaker, Philadelphia

Ref: Ravà, A., Pietro Longhi, *1909, p. 149;* Parnassus *3: 36, December 1931; Chicago. Art Institute,* Annual Report, *1932, p. 19; Chicago. Art Institute,* A Century of Progress Exhibition, *1933, cat. no. 147; Chicago. Art Institute,* Catalogue of the Worcester Collection, *1937, cat. no. 25*

LUKS, George Benjamin ~ *b. 1867 Williamsport, Pa. d. 1933 New York City*

After studying at the Pennsylvania Academy of the Fine Arts, Luks went abroad, first to the Düsseldorf Academy, then to Munich, London, and Paris.

THE BUTCHER CART

Signed and dated: Geo. B. Luks, 1901. Oil on canvas, 22 × 27 in. (56 × 68.7 cm.)
Friends of American Art Collection, 41.825

LUNGREN, Ferdinand ~ *1859 Hagerstown, Md. d. 1932 Santa Barbara, Calif.*

Lungren studied in Cincinnati and New York and was for a brief time a pupil of Thomas Eakins. After a trip to Paris he returned to New York.

SARAH BERNHARDT AT THE CAFE DE LA PAIX

Painted probably 1882, signed: Lungren. Oil on canvas, 31⅜ × 41¼ in. (79.7 × 104.8 cm.)
Charles H. and Mary F. S. Worcester Collection, 47.85

LURÇAT, Jean ~ *b. 1892 Brueres, France*

Lurçat originally studied medicine, then turned to art.

DELPHI

Signed and dated: Lurçat 28. Oil on canvas, 35 × 45¾ in. (88.9 × 116.2 cm.)
Gift of Joseph Winterbotham, 29.768

Ref: Chicago. Art Institute, Bulletin *24: 3, 1930; Heilmaier, H.,* Deutsche Kunst und Dekoration *68: 156–7, 1931; Kunstler, C.,* Art et Décoration *59: 132, 1931; Chicago. Art Institute,* A Century of Progress Exhibition, *1933, cat. no. 782; Chicago. Art Institute,* Catalogue of the Winterbotham Collection, *1947, p. 27*

MC EWEN, Walter ~ *b. 1860 Chicago. d. 1943 New York City*

Walter McEwen was a Chicago painter who went to Paris in the eighties and remained there most of his life. In 1893, he was commissioned to do murals for the World's Columbian Exposition.

BOY'S HEAD (studies)

Painted about 1890 [?], signed: W. McEwen. Oil on canvas, 13¾ × 19⅜ in. (35 × 49.4 cm.)
Gift of Mrs. W. J. Calhoun, 45.211

MACIVER, Loren ~ *b. 1909 New York City*

Loren MacIver studied at the Art Students League in New York.

LES BAUX

Painted 1952, signed: MacIver. Oil on canvas, 47¾ × 40 in. (121.3 × 101.7 cm.)
Gift of the Claire and Albert Arenberg Fund, 53.465

MACLANE, Jean ~ *b. 1878 Chicago*

Jean MacLane studied with Frank Duveneck and John Vanderpoel and graduated from the School of the Art Institute.

VIRGINIA AND STANTON

Painted about 1913, signed: M. Jean MacLane.
Oil on canvas, 49½ × 40 in. (125.8 × 110.7 cm.)
Friends of American Art Collection, 14.819

MC LAUGHLIN, Gerald ~ *b. 1925 Sacramento, Calif.*

The artist studied at the Chouinard Art Institute in Los Angeles from 1940 to 1944.

THE HOST

Painted 1955. Oil on masonite, 45×99 in. (114.4×251.6 cm.)
Mr. and Mrs. Seymour Oppenheimer Purchase Prize and Goodman Fund, 56.8

McLaughlin states that this painting is concerned with man's relationship to his environment. According to him, the picture is identified with creative evolution.

THE ORATOR AND THE LADIES

Painted 1955, signed: McLaughlin. Oil on canvas, 28⅛×48 in. (71.5×122 cm.)
Mr. and Mrs. Frank G. Logan Purchase Prize, 55.649

MACRINO D'ALBA (Gian Giacomo de Alladio) ~ *Before 1470– before 1525 Alba, Italy*

Macrino imitated the styles of both Pinturicchio and Botticelli.

MADONNA AND CHILD ENTHRONED WITH ANGELS

Painted after 1500. Tempera on panel, 42×18 in. (106.7×45.8 cm.)
Mr. and Mrs. Martin A. Ryerson Collection, 33.1016
Coll: Volpi, Florence (sale May 1910, cat. no. 376)

Ref: Berenson, B., Italian Paintings of the Renaissance, *1932, p. 320; Berenson, B.,* Pitture Italiane del Rinascimento, *1936, p. 275*

MAES, Nicholas ~ *b. 1632 Dordrecht, Holland. d. 1693 Amsterdam*

Maes was a pupil of Rembrandt. After Maes moved to Antwerp in 1666, he adopted characteristics of the Flemish manner.

PORTRAIT OF A GENTLEMAN

Painted between 1650 and 1660. Oil on panel, 12×10½ in. (30.5×26.7 cm.)
Gift of Charles L. Hutchinson, 25.716 (HdG no. 389 [?])
Coll: G. Rothan, Paris

Ref: Valentiner, M. R., Nicolaes Maes, *1924, p. 60; Chicago. Art Institute,* Bulletin *19: 102, 103, 1925; Chicago. Art Institute,* A Century of Progress Exhibition, *1934, cat. no. 96*

PORTRAIT OF A LADY

Painted between 1650 and 1660. Oil on panel, 12×10½ in. (30.5×26.7 cm.)
Gift of Charles L. Hutchinson, 25.715 (HdG no. 440)

Pendant to the preceding portrait.

Coll: G. Rothan, Paris

Ref: Valentiner, M. R., op. cit., *p. 60; Chicago. Art Institute,* Bulletin *19: 102, 103, 1925; Chicago. Art Institute,* A Century of Progress Exhibition, *1934, cat. no. 97*

PORTRAIT OF A MAN

Oil on canvas, 40½ × 31 in. (102.9 × 78.8 cm.)
Gift of Kate S. Buckingham, 23.47

MAGGIOTTO, Domenico (attributed to) ~ *1713–1794 Venice*

Maggiotto, a student of Piazzetta, was active during the last phase of 18th century Venetian painting. He worked both in Germany and Italy, where he was noted for his large allegorical and historical pictures.

RAPE OF THE SABINES

Probably painted about 1760. Oil on canvas, 100¼ × 114¼ in. (254.7 × 264.9 cm.)
Gift of Mrs. Richard E. Danielson and Mrs. Chauncey McCormick, 45.288

MAGNASCO, Alessandro ~ *1667–1749 Genoa*

Magnasco, apprenticed to Filippo Abbiati, was also influenced by Mola, Salvator Rosa, and Tintoretto.

ARCADIAN LANDSCAPE

Painted about 1700. Oil on canvas, 28 × 37¼ in. (71.2 × 94.7 cm.)
Charles H. and Mary F. S. Worcester Collection, 29.915

Ref: Chicago. Art Institute, Annual Report, *1929, p. 22; Chicago. Art Institute,* Bulletin *23: 42–3, 1929; Chicago. Art Institute,* A Century of Progress Exhibition, *1933, cat. no. 150; Chicago. Art Institute,* Catalogue of the Worcester Collection, *1937, cat. no. 17; Scheyer, E.,* Apollo *28: 66–71, 1938; Geiger, B.,* Magnasco, *1949, cat. no. 11*

MONKS AT SUPPER

Probably painted between 1700 and 1725. Oil on canvas, 26¾ × 32¼ in. (68 × 82 cm.)
Mr. and Mrs. Martin A. Ryerson Collection, 33.1085

Ref: Chicago. Art Institute, Bulletin *23: 42–3, 1929; Geiger, B.,* Magnasco, *1949, cat. no. 405*

THE SYNAGOGUE Illus. p. 55

Probably painted between 1734 and 1749. Oil on canvas, 47 × 58¾ in. (119.4 × 149.3 cm.)
Gift of Annie Swan Coburn to the Mr. and Mrs. Lewis L. Coburn Memorial Collection, 49.586

Magnasco's biographer, Ratti, mentions that the synagogue was his favorite subject. He painted this subject at least four different times, with considerable variation. The earliest version is in the Uffizi, the second in Seitenstetten (Austria), while the two latest are in the Cleveland Museum of Art and the Art Institute.

Ref: Nicodemi, G., Emporium, *1922, p. 333; Bernard, E.,* L'Amour de l'Art *10: 345–50, October 1929; Delogu, G.,* Pittori Minori Liguri; *Lombardi,* Piedmontesi del Seicento e del Settecento, *1931, cat. no. 123; Posposil, M.,* Magnasco, *Florence, 1945, pl. 154–7; Geiger, B.,* Magnasco, *1949, pp. 146, 147, 188, cat. no. 199; Chicago. Art Institute,* Bulletin *44, no. 4: 2, 1950*

MAGNASCO, School of

THE WITCH

Probably painted between 1700 and 1725. Oil on panel, 12⅜ × 8¾ in. (31.5 × 22.3 cm.)
Charles H. and Mary F. S. Worcester Collection, 29.916

Ref: Chicago. Art Institute, Bulletin *23: 43, 48, 1929; Chicago. Art Institute,* Catalogue of the Worcester Collection, *1937, cat. no. 18; Geiger, B.,* Magnasco, *1949, cat. no. 328*

MAINARDI, Sebastiano di Bartolo ~ *b. about 1460 S. Gimignano. d. 1513 Florence*

Mainardi was first a pupil, then collaborator, of his brother-in-law Domenico Ghirlandajo. He worked closely in the manner of this master.

MADONNA ADORING THE CHILD

Painted about 1500. Tempera on panel, 38¼ in. diameter (97.2 cm.)
Mr. and Mrs. Martin A. Ryerson Collection, 37.1005
Coll: Louis Ehrich

Ref: Van Marle, The Development of the Italian Schools of Painting, *XIII, 1931, pp. 223–4*

MAKART, Hans ~ *b. 1840 Salzburg. d. 1884 Vienna*

Makart studied in Vienna, under Carl von Piloty in Munich, then returned to Vienna in 1869.

TREASURES OF THE SEA

Painted about 1870–1875. Oil on canvas, 15⅞ × 41⅝ in. (40.4 × 105.8 cm.)
A. A. Munger Collection, 01.440

MALER ZU SCHWAZ, Hans (attributed to) ~ *b. c. 1479/80 Ulm [?]. d. c. 1530 Schwaz*

Hans Maler was influenced by the Swabian masters, Bernard Strigel and Bartholomäus Zeitblom. He worked mainly in Schwaz in the Tyrol.

CHRIST BEARING THE CROSS

Painted about 1515. Tempera and oil on panel, 13¼ × 22$\frac{11}{16}$ in. (33.7 × 57.6 cm.)
Charles H. and Mary F. S. Worcester Collection, 47.87

Maler made free use of an engraving by Schongauer.

Coll: Private collection, France; Galerie St. Lucas, Vienna; Anonymous (probably Baron Eugen von Kohne)

Ref: Baldass, L., Oberrheinische Kunst, *II, 1926–1927, p. 185; Saxl, F.,* Belvedere *9, pt. 1: 205–15, 1930; Chicago. Art Institute,* Bulletin *24: 82, 1930; Chicago. Art Institute,* A Century of Progress Exhibition, *1933, cat. no. 24; Kuhn, C. L.,* A Catalogue of German Paintings of the Middle Ages and Renaissance in American Collections, *1936, p. 64, cat. no. 262; Chicago. Art Institute,* Catalogue of the Worcester Collection, *1937, cat. no. 36*

PORTRAIT OF A YOUNG MAN

Painted about 1520. Oil on panel, 16⅝ × 13 in. (42.3 × 33 cm.)
Charles H. and Mary F. S. Worcester Collection, 47.89
Coll: Colonel Vombwell, London

Ref: Freund, F. E. W., Belvedere *8, pt. 2: 286, 1929; Chicago. Art Institute,* A Century of Progress Exhibition, *1933, cat. no. 25; Kuhn, C. L.,* op. cit., *p. 65, cat. no. 269; Chicago. Art Institute,* Catalogue of the Worcester Collection, *1937, cat. no. 38*

MANE-KATZ ~ *b. 1894 Kremtchoug, Russia*

First trained in Kiev, Mané-Katz came to Paris in 1913 where he met his countrymen, Chagall and Soutine. Forced to return to Russia during World War I, he worked with the Russian Ballet and taught at various art schools. Since 1921, Mané-Katz has lived in Paris.

FLOWERS OF SHARON

Signed: Mané-Katz. Oil on canvas, 35⅛ × 27¼ in. (89.3 × 69.3 cm.)
Gift of Mr. and Mrs. Herman Spertus, 57.163

MANET, Edouard ~ *1832–1883 Paris*

Manet was a pupil of Couture and was greatly influenced by the work of Velázquez, Goya, Hals, Delacroix and Courbet.

STILL LIFE WITH CARP

Painted 1864, signed: Manet. Oil on canvas, 28⅞ × 36¼ in. (73.4 × 92.1 cm.)
Gift of Annie Swan Coburn to the Mr. and Mrs. Lewis L. Coburn Memorial Collection, 42.331
(Jamot & Wildenstein no. 96)

Painted in the summer of 1864 at Boulogne, this still life was exhibited the following year with six other paintings by Manet at Martinet's, a cooperative exhibition gallery.

Coll: Gérard, Paris; Manzi, Paris; Alfred Chatain, Chicago; Mrs. John W. Simpson, New York

Ref: Paris. Place de l'Alma, Exposition Manet Particulière, *May 1867, cat. no. 38; Paris. Ecole des Beaux-Arts,* Exposition des oeuvres de Edouard Manet, *January 1884, cat. no. 31; Paris. Exposition Internationale Universelle de 1900,* Catalogue Général Officiel, Oeuvres d'Art, *p. 53, cat. 449; Duret, T.,* Manet and the French Impressionists, *1910, p. 220, cat. no. 70; Meier-Graefe, J.,* Edouard Manet, *1912, p. 69, fig. 38; New York. Durand-Ruel Gallery,* Exhibition, *1913, cat. no. 6; Tabarant, A.,* Manet, Histoire Catalographique, *1931, p. 131, cat. no. 90; Cleveland, Ohio. Museum of Art,* Twentieth Anniversary Exhibition . . . , *June/October 1936, cat. no. 286; New York. Wildenstein & Co.,* Edouard Manet . . . , *March/April 1937, cat. no. 7 (ill.); Duret, T.,* Manet, *1937, pl. 39; Jedlicka, G.,* Edouard Manet, *1941, p. 197; Tabarant, A.,* Manet et ses oeuvres, *1947, pp. 97, 98, 518, 535, 605, cat. no. 90*

THE OUTLET OF BOULOGNE HARBOR

Painted 1864, signed: Manet. Oil on canvas, 29⅛ × 36⅝ in. (74 × 93 cm.)
Potter Palmer Collection, 22.425 (Jamot & Wildenstein no. 92)
Coll: Clapisson, Paris; Mme A. Dureau, Paris; E. F. Millikin

Ref: Paris. Place de l'Alma, Exposition Manet Particulière, *May 1867, cat. no. 40; Zola, E.,* Edouard Manet, *1867, p. 38; New York. Durand-Ruel Galleries,* Exposition of Paintings by Edouard Manet, *1895, cat. no. 15; Paris. Exposition Internationale Universelle de 1900,* Catalogue Général Officiel, Oeuvres d'Art, *p. 53, cat. no. 442;* La Chronique des Arts et de la Curiosité, *1902, p. 136; Duret, T.,* Manet and the French Impressionists, *1910, p. 222, cat. no. 79; Proust, A.,* Edouard Manet, *1913, p. 54, no. 40; Chicago. Art Institute,* Bulletin *15: 158, 1921;* Ibid., *18: 48–9, 1924; Moreau-Nélaton, E.,* Manet, Raconté par lui-même, *I, 1926, pp. 62–3, 89; Duret, T.,* Histoire de Edouard Manet et de son Oeuvre, *1926, p. 246, cat. no. 79; Tabarant, A.,* Manet, Histoire Catalographique, *1931, p. 147, cat. no. 101; Chicago. Art Institute,* A Century of Progress Exhibition, *1933, cat. no. 323;* Ibid., *1934, cat. no. 245; Venturi, L.,* Les Archives de l'Impressionisme, *II, 1939, pp. 189, 191; Tabarant, A.,* Manet et ses Oeuvres, *1947, pp. 90, 91, 535, 604, no. 76*

THE RACES AT LONGCHAMP, PARIS Illus. p. 281

Signed and dated: Manet 1864. Oil on canvas, 17¼ × 33¼ in. (43.9 × 84.5 cm.)
Potter Palmer Collection, 22.424 (Jamot & Wildenstein no. 202)

Pictures of horse races form two distinct groups in Manet's works; those done around 1864 to which this canvas belongs, and later ones dated about 1872.

Coll: Delius, 1884; Potter Palmer

Ref: Paris. Ecole des Beaux-Arts, Exposition des Oeuvres de Edouard Manet, *January 1884, cat. no. 61; New York. Durand-Ruel Galleries,* Exposition of Paintings by Edouard Manet, *1895, cat. no. 27; Duret, T.,* Manet and the French Impressionists, *1910, p. 231, cat. no. 142;* Zeitschrift für Bildende Kunst, *April 1, 1910, p. 188; Haendcke, B.,* Die Kunst *12, pt. 1: 156, 1910–1911; Meier-Graefe, J.,* Edouard Manet, *1912, p. 220;* Cicerone, *October 1, 1913, p. 680; Proust, A.,* Kunst und Künstler *11: 211, 1913; Chicago. Art Institute,*

Bulletin *18: 49, 1924; Blanche, J.-E.,* Manet *(Masters of Modern Art), 1925, p. 41, 46; Moreau-Nélaton, E.,* Manet, Raconté par lui-même, *I, 1926, fig. 155, p. 139; Duret, T.,* Histoire de Edouard Manet et de son Oeuvre, *1926, p. 255, no. 142; Fierens, P.,* L'Art et les Artistes *21: 11, 1930; Tabarant, A.,* Manet, Histoire Catalographique, *1931, p. 136, cat. no. 96; Wilenski, R. H.,* French Painting, *1931, p. 245; Tabarant, A.,* Revue de l'Art *61: 19, 1932; Chicago. Art Institute,* A Century of Progress Exhibition, *1933, cat. no. 332;* Ibid., *1934, cat. no. 252; Duret, T.,* Manet, *1937, pl. 14; McMahon, A. P.,* Parnassus *9: 9, March 1937; New York. Wildenstein & Co.,* Edouard Manet . . . , *March/April 1937, cat. no. 18 (ill.); Cambridge, Mass. Fogg Art Museum,* The Horse, Its Significance in Art, *April/May 1938, cat. no. 14; Rey, R.,* Manet, *1938, pp. 120, 163, no. 120; Jedlicka, G.,* Edouard Manet, *1941, pp. 163, 403; New York. Wildenstein & Co.,* From Paris to the Sea Down the River Seine, *January/February 1943, cat. no. 18; Tabarant, A.,* Manet et ses Oeuvres, *1947, pp. 101, 536, cat. no. 101; Venturi, L.,* Impressionists and Symbolists, *London, 1950, fig. 11*

PHILOSOPHER (WITH HAT)

Painted 1865, signed: Manet. Oil on canvas, 73¾ × 42½ in. (187.3 × 108 cm.)
Arthur Jerome Eddy Memorial Collection, 31.504 (Jamot & Wildenstein no. 111)
Coll: Faure, Paris; Arthur Jerome Eddy

Ref: Paris. Place de l'Alma, Exposition Manet Particulière, *May 1867, cat. no. 32; Paris. Ecole des Beaux-Arts,* Exposition des Oeuvres de Edouard Manet, *January 1884, cat. no. 29; Duret, T.,* Manet and the French Impressionists, *1910, p. 219, cat. no. 65; Meier-Graefe, J.,* Edouard Manet, *1912, pp. 82, 310; Proust, A.,* Edouard Manet, *1913, p. 53, no. 31; Chicago. Art Institute,* Catalogue of the Eddy Collection, *cat. no. 52; Chicago. Art Institute,* Bulletin *18: 47, 1924; Blanche, J.-E.,* Manet *(Masters of Modern Art), 1925, p. 41; Moreau-Nélaton, E.,* Manet, Raconté par lui-même, *1926, I, pp. 76, 89, II, fig. 340; Duret, T.,* Histoire de Edouard Manet et de son Oeuvre, *1926, pp. 86, 243, no. 65; Venturi, L.,* L'Arte *32: 154, July/August 1929; Rosenthal, L.,* Gazette des Beaux-Arts *12, per. 5: 210, 212; Tabarant, A.,* Manet, Histoire Catalographique, *1931, p. 145, cat. no. 104; Chicago. Art Institute,* Catalogue of the Eddy Collection, *1931–1932, cat. no. 11; Rich, D. C.,* Parnassus *4: 4, February 1932; Chicago. Art Institute,* A Century of Progress Exhibition, *1933, cat. no. 330;* Ibid., *1934, cat. no. 251; Rey, R.,* Manet, *1938, pp. 14, 44, 162, no. 44; Venturi, L.,* Les Archives de l'Impressionisme, *II, 1939, pp. 189, 190; Huth, H.,* Gazette des Beaux-Arts *29, ser. 6: 236, 242, 1946; Detroit. Art Institute,* The Two Sides of the Medal, French Painting from Gerôme to Gauguin, *1954, cat. no. 17*

PHILOSOPHER (WITH BERET)

Painted 1865, signed: Manet. Oil on canvas, 74¼ × 43 in. (188.6 × 109.3 cm.)
A. A. Munger Collection, 10.304 (Jamot & Wildenstein no. 112)
Coll: Hoschédé, 1878; Faure, Paris

Ref: Paris. Place de l'Alma, Exposition Manet Particulière, *1867, cat. no. 31; Paris. Ecole des Beaux-Arts,* Exposition des Oeuvres de Edouard Manet, *January 1884, cat. no. 30;*

London. Grafton Galleries, A Selection from the Pictures . . . , *1905, cat. no. 97; Duret, T.,* Manet and the French Impressionists, *1910, p. 219, cat. no. 66; Chicago. Art Institute,* Bulletin *4: 62, 1911; Meier-Graefe, J.,* Edouard Manet, *1912, pp. 83, 310; Proust, A.,* Edouard Manet, *1913, p. 53, no. 32; Chicago. Art Institute,* Bulletin *18: 47–8, 1924; Blanche, J.-E.,* Manet *(Masters of Modern Art), 1925, p. 41; Moreau-Nélaton, E.,* Manet, Raconté par lui-même, *1926, I, pp. 76, 89, II, fig. 340; Duret, T.,* Histoire de Edouard Manet et de son Oeuvre, *1926, pp. 86, 244, no. 66; Tabarant, A.,* Manet, Histoire Catalographique, *1931, p. 145, cat. no. 105; Wilenski, H.,* French Painting, *1931, p. 245; Chicago. Art Institute,* A Century of Progress Exhibition, *1933, cat. no. 331;* Ibid., *1934, cat. no. 250; Rey, R.,* Manet, *1938, pp. 14, 45, 162, no. 45; Venturi, L.,* Les Archives de l'Impressionisme, *II, 1939, pp. 189–90; Jedlicka, G.,* Edouard Manet, *1941, pp. 83, 397; Huth, H.,* Gazette des Beaux-Arts *29, ser. 6: 237, 242, 1946; Tabarant, A.,* Manet et ses Oeuvres, *1947, pp. 115–6, 536; Babelon, J.,* Clavilleno *3, no. 13: 15–20, January/February 1952*

CHRIST MOCKED

Painted 1865, signed: Manet. Oil on canvas, 75⅛ × 58⅜ in. (191.5 × 148.3 cm.)
Gift of James Deering, 25.703 (Jamot & Wildenstein no. 113)
Coll: James Jackson Jarves; James Deering

Ref: Paris. Place de l'Alma, Manet Exposition Particulière, *1867, cat. no. 6; Zola, E.,* Edouard Manet, *1867, p. 34; Paris. Hotel Drouot,* Catalogue de vente Manet, *February 1884, cat. no. 17; Jarves, J. J.,* Art Thoughts, *1879, p. 269; New York. Durand-Ruel Galleries,* Exposition of Paintings by Edouard Manet, *March 1895, cat. no. 9; Gsell, P.,* Art et les Artistes *2: 43, November 1905; Duret, T.,* Manet and the French Impressionists, *1910, p. 218, no. 57; Wolf, G. J.,* Die Kunst *12, pt. 1: 150, 1910–1911; Meier-Graefe, J.,* Edouard Manet, *1912, pp. 71, 73, 318, fig. 40, no. 17; Proust, A.,* Edouard Manet, *1913, pp. 47, 52, no. 6; Chicago. Art Institute,* Annual Report, *1925, p. 32; Blanche, J.-E.,* Manet *(Masters of Modern Art), 1925, p. 35; Chicago. Art Institute,* Bulletin *20: 1, 1926; Duret, T.,* Histoire de Edouard Manet et de son Oeuvre, *1926, pp. 43, 242, no. 57; Moreau-Nélaton, E.,* Manet, Raconté par lui-même, *I, 1926, pp. 67–8, fig. 75; Jamot, P.,* Burlington Magazine *50: 28, 1927; Venturi, L.,* L'Arte *32: 154, July/August 1929; Tabarant, A.,* Manet, Histoire Catalographique, *1931, p. 141, cat. no. 101; Wilenski, R. H.,* French Painting, *1931, pp. 245, 249, 252; Rich, D. C.,* Parnassus *4: 4, February 1932; Chicago. Art Institute,* A Century of Progress Exhibition, *1933, cat. no. 327, pl. 56; Frankfurter, A. M.,* The Arts *20: 33, May 1933; Philadelphia. Museum of Art,* Bulletin *29: 17, December 1933; Chicago. Art Institute,* A Century of Progress Exhibition, *1934, cat. no. 247; Baltimore. Museum of Art,* A Survey of French Painting, *November 1934/January 1935, cat. no. 23; Tietze, H.,* Meisterwerke Europaeischer Malerei in Amerika, *1935, pl. 283; Duret, T.,* Manet, *1937, pp. 29, 35, 40; Rey, R.,* Manet, *1938, p. 14; Jedlicka, G.,* Edouard Manet, *1941, pp. 86, 87, 379; Tabarant, A.,* Manet et ses oeuvres, *1947, pp. 104, 105, 106, 113, 136, 536; Hamilton, G. H.,* Manet and his Critics, *1954, pp. 65, 66, 70–80; De Leiris, A.,* Art Bulletin *41, no. 2: 198–201, June 1959*

BULLFIGHT

Painted 1865–1866, signed: Manet. Oil on canvas, 18⅞ × 23⅞ in. (48 × 60.8 cm.)
Mr. and Mrs. Martin A. Ryerson Collection, 37.1019 (Jamot & Wildenstein no. 121)

This bullfight was one of the few pictures with Spanish subject matter which Manet painted after he returned from his trip to Spain in 1865.

Coll: Mrs. Inglis, New York, 1886; Martin A. Ryerson, 1912

Ref: Paris. Durand-Ruel, Exposition, *1886, cat. no. 190; New York. Durand-Ruel,* Exposition of Paintings by Edouard Manet, *1895, cat. no. 19; Duret, T.,* Manet and the French Impressionists, *1910, p. 221, cat. no. 74; Toledo, Ohio. Museum of Art,* Inauguaral Exhibition, *January/February 1912, cat. no. 183; Moreau-Nélaton, E.,* Manet, Raconté par lui-même, *1926, I, pp. 75 (fig. 81), 89, 107, no. 242, II, fig. 341; Duret, T.,* Histoire de Edouard Manet et de son oeuvre, *1926, p. 245, no. 74; Tabarant, A.,* Manet, Histoire Catalographique, *1931, p. 155, no. 115; Meier-Graefe, J.,* Formes *24: 252, pl. 6, April 1932; Paris. Musée de l'Orangerie,* Exposition Manet, *1932, cat. no. 24; Chicago. Art Institute,* A Century of Progress Exhibition, *1933, cat. no. 324; Philadelphia. Museum of Art,* Bulletin *26: 19, December 1933; Chicago. Art Institute,* A Century of Progress Exhibition, *1934, cat. no. 246; Chicago. Art Institute,* Bulletin *32: 4–5, 1938; Brewster, K. L.,* Magazine of Art *31: 94, February 1938; Venturi, L.,* Les Archives de l'Impressionisme, *II, 1939, pp. 189, 192; Huth, H.,* Gazette des Beaux-Arts *29, ser. 6: 235, 239 (footnote 22), 1946; Tabarant, A.,* Manet et ses oeuvres, *1947, pp. 119, 120, 536*

LE JOURNAL ILLUSTRE Illus. p. 289

Painted about 1878–1879, signed: Manet. Oil on canvas, 24¼ × 19⅞ in. (61.7 × 50.7 cm.)
Mr. and Mrs. Lewis L. Coburn Memorial Collection, 33.435 (Jamot & Wildenstein no. 334)
Coll: Faure, 1882; Mrs. Annie Swan Coburn

Ref: Paris. Ecole des Beaux-Arts, Exposition des oeuvres de Edouard Manet, *January 1884, cat. no. 92; Duret, T.,* Manet and the French Impressionists, *1910, p. 251, cat. no. 255; Pittsburgh. Carnegie Institute,* Exhibition of Paintings . . . , *October/December 1924, cat. no. 37; Moreau-Nélaton, E.,* Manet, Raconté par lui-même, *II, 1926, p. 53, figs. 241, 346; Duret, T.,* Histoire de Edouard Manet et de son oeuvre, *1926, p. 273, no. 255;* Cicerone *20: 113, 1928; Paris. Bernheim-Jeune,* Exposition des Oeuvres de Manet, *April/May 1928, cat. no. 25;* Kunst und Kuenstler *28: 82, 1929;* The Arts *16: 411, 1930; Chicago. Art Institute,* Catalogue of the Coburn Collection, *1932, cat. no. 17; Chicago. Art Institute,* Bulletin *26: 67, 1932;* Arts and Decoration *46: 19, April 1937; New York. Wildenstein & Co.,* Edouard Manet . . . , *March/April 1937, cat. no. 29; Rey, R.,* Manet, *1938, pp. 69, 162, no. 69; San Francisco, California,* Golden Gate International Exposition . . . , *1940, cat. no. 276; New York. Metropolitan Museum of Art,* French Painting from David to Toulouse-Lautrec, *February/March 1941, cat. no. 81; Tabarant, A.,* Manet et ses oeuvres, *1947, pp. 327, 328, 541, no. 297; Birmingham, Alabama. Museum of Art,* Catalogue of the Opening Exhibition, *April/June 1951, p. 29;* Apollo, *February 1953, pp. 49–52*

PORTRAIT OF A LADY WITH BLACK FICHU

Painted 1878. Oil on canvas, 24⅛ × 19⅞ in. (61.3 × 50.7 cm.)

Mr. and Mrs. Lewis L. Coburn Memorial Collection, 33.436 (Jamot & Wildenstein no. 284)

Coll: Atelier Manet, Paris (Vente, Paris 1884, no. 26); Dr. de Bellio, 1884; Donop de Monchy; Rosenberg, Paris; Mr. and Mrs. L. L. Coburn

Ref: Paris. Ecole des Beaux-Arts, Exposition des oeuvres de Edouard Manet, *January 1884, cat. no. 128; Paris. Hôtel Drouot,* Catalogue de Vente Manet, *February 1884, cat. no. 26; Duret, T.,* Manet and the French Impressionists, *1910, p. 249, cat. no. 248; Meier-Graefe, J.,* Edouard Manet, *1912, p. 320, no. 26; Zürich. Kunsthaus,* Exposition d'Art des XIXe et XXe siècles, *October/November 1917, cat. no. ?; Duret, T.,* Histoire de Edouard Manet et de son oeuvre, *1926, p. 272, cat. no. 248; Moreau-Nélaton, E.,* Manet, Raconté par lui-même, *1926, p. 130, no. 128; Tabarant, A.,* Manet, Histoire Catalographique, *1931, p. 324, cat. no. 274; Chicago. Art Institute,* Catalogue of the Coburn Collection, *1932, cat. no. 16; Chicago. Art Institute,* Bulletin *26: 68, 1932; Chicago. Art Institute,* A Century of Progress Exhibition, *1934, cat. no. 248; Tabarant, A.,* Manet et ses oeuvres, *1947, pp. 333, 541, no. 306*

THE MAN WITH THE ROUND HAT

Painted 1878 [?], signed: Manet, also stamped in red: E.M.

Mixed media on paper mounted on panel, 21½ × 17¾ in. (54.7 × 45.2 cm.)

Gift of Kate L. Brewster, 50.123 (Jamot & Wildenstein no. 528)

Coll: Atelier Manet (Vente, Paris 1884, no. 121); Marcel Bernstein, Paris; Walter S. Brewster

Ref: Gonse, L., Gazette des Beaux-Arts *29, per. 2: 149, 1884; Paris. Ecole des Beaux-Arts,* Exposition des oeuvres de Edouard Manet, *January 1884, cat. no. 154; Paris. Hôtel Drouot,* Catalogue de Vente Manet, *February 1884, cat. no. 121; Duret, T.,* Manet and the French Impressionists, *1910, p. 276, cat. no. 74; Mireur, H.,* Dictionnaire des Ventes d'Art, *V, 1911, p. 65; Meier-Graefe, J.,* Edouard Manet, *1912, p. 327, no. 121; Moreau-Nélaton, E.,* Manet, Raconté par lui-même, *1926, I, p. 108, II, p. 98; Duret, T.,* Histoire de Edouard Manet et de son oeuvre, *1926, p. 298, no. 74; Tabarant, A.,* Manet, Histoire Catalographique, *1931, p. 459, cat. no. 438; New York. Wildenstein & Co.,* Edouard Manet . . . , *March/April 1937, cat. no. 37; Rey, R.,* Manet, *1938, pp. 42, 162, no. 42; Tabarant, A.,* Manet et ses oeuvres, *1947, pp. 338, 546; Chicago. Art Institute,* Bulletin *44: 51, 52, September 1950*

YOUNG WOMAN

Painted in 1879.

Essence (thin oil) on thin canvas, 25¾ × 18 9/16 in. (65.5 × 47.25 cm.)

Gift of Joseph Winterbotham, 54.314 (Jamot & Wildenstein no. 329)

Ref: Tabarant, A., Manet et ses oeuvres, *1947 (third ed.), ill. no. 335, p. 366*

MANFREDI, Bartolomeo (attributed to) ~ *b. 1587 Ustiano. d. 1620/21 Rome*

THE CHASTISEMENT OF LOVE Illus. p. 56

Painted about 1605–1610. Oil on canvas, 69 × 51⅜ in. (175 × 130 cm.)
Charles H. and Mary F. S. Worcester Collection, 47.58

The treatment of this subject is close to Caravaggio's manner, indicating that the artist who painted this canvas belonged to the circle of the master. Longhi attributes the painting to Bartolomeo Manfredi.

Coll: Armando Brosini, Rome, 1937

Ref: Baglione, G., Le vite dei pittori, *1733, p. 129; Pevsner, N.,* Zeitschrift für Bildende Kunst *61: 390, 1927–1928; Sestieri, E.,* L'Arte *N.S. 8: 264–83, 1937 (ill. p. 276); Voss, H.,* Apollo *27: 30–2, 1938 (ill.);* Apollo *34, August 1941; Isarlov, G.,* Caravage et le Caravagisme Européen, *catalogues, Aix, 1941; San Francisco, California. Palace of the Legion of Honor,* Italian Baroque Painting, *1941, cat. no. 13; Longhi, R.,* Proporzioni, I. *1943, p. 51, no. 53, pl. 53; Chicago. Art Institute,* Bulletin *41: 59, 62, 1947 (ill.); Button, D.,* Apollo, *August 1951, pp. 45–8; Milan. Palazzo Reale,* Mostra del Caravaggio, *April/June 1951, cat. no. 62, p. 42, pl. 59; Seattle. Art Museum,* Caravaggio and the Tenebrosi, *April/May 1954, cat. no. 3; Baumgart, F.,* Caravaggio, *1955, p. 113*

MANGRAVITE, Peppino ~ *b. 1896 Lipari, Italy*

After early training in Carrara, Mangravite came to this country in 1915 and continued his studies at the Cooper Union Art School with H. P. Hansen and Robert Henri, and at the Art Students League.

THE SONG OF THE POET

Painted 1944, signed: Mangravite. Oil on canvas, 60 × 48 in. (152.5 × 122 cm.)
Friends of American Art Collection, 44.30

MARC, Franz ~ *b. 1880 Munich, Germany. d. 1916 Verdun, France*

Franz Marc's work was chiefly influenced by Cubism. A member and founder of the Expressionist group known as the Blue Rider, which included Kandinsky, Jawlensky, Campendonk, Macke, Klee, and others, Marc tended to paint with strong bright color.

THE BEWITCHED MILL

Painted 1913, signed: M. Oil on canvas, 51⅜ × 35¾ in. (130.6 × 90.8 cm.)
Arthur Jerome Eddy Memorial Collection, 31.522

Ref: Chicago. Art Institute, Catalogue of the Eddy Collection, *1922, cat. no. 50;* Ibid., *1931–1932, cat. no. 2; Chicago. Art Institute,* A Century of Progress Exhibition, *1933, cat. no. 757; Rich, D. C.,* American-German Review *1, no. 4: 37, June 1935; Schardt, A. J.,* Franz Marc, *1936, p. 164*

MARCA-RELLI, Corrado di ~ *b. 1913 Boston*

Living for some time in Italy, Argentina, and Mexico, Marca-Relli has now settled on Long Island. Closely associated with the Abstract Expressionist group of New York City, the artist has developed pictorial concepts of a personal character.

COLLAGE

Painted 1954. Canvas collage and oil, $73\frac{1}{4} \times 48\frac{1}{2}$ in. (186.1 × 123.2 cm.)
Mr. and Mrs. Frank G. Logan Purchase Prize, 54.271

MARCHAND, Jean Hippolyte ~ *1883–1941 Paris*

Marchand, a pupil of Luc-Olivier Merson, Léon Bonnat and Henri Martin, was influenced by Cézanne.

THE HILL NEAR CAGNES

Painted about 1920, signed: J. H. Marchand. Oil on canvas, 20 × 25 in. (50.9 × 63.6 cm.)
Mr. and Mrs. Martin A. Ryerson Collection, 33.1142

MARCKE DE LUMMEN, Emile van ~ *b. 1827 Sèvres, France. d. 1890 Hyères, France*

After studying at the Academy of Liége, Van Marcke was a decorator of porcelain at the Sèvres factory. Under the influence of Troyon, he became interested in the Barbizon School and took up landscape painting.

THE TETE-A-TETE

Painted between 1870 and 1890, signed: Em. van Marcke.
Oil on canvas, $10\frac{3}{4} \times 15\frac{7}{8}$ in. (27.3 × 40.4 cm.)
Henry Field Memorial Collection, 94.1073

DESCENT OF CATTLE FROM THE PYRENEES

Painted between 1870 and 1890, signed: Em. van Marcke.
Oil on canvas, 39 × 26 in. (99.2 × 66.1 cm.)
Mr. and Mrs. W. W. Kimball Collection, 22.4473

MARCOLA, Marco ~ *1740–1793 Verona, Italy*

Marcola came of a family of provincial painters who worked in the Venetian manner. He specialized in lively scenes of the theater, affording interesting glimpses of the 18th century Italian stage.

AN ITALIAN COMEDY IN VERONA

Signed and dated: M. M. 1772 (MDCCLXXII).
Oil on canvas, (oval) $45\frac{3}{8} \times 32\frac{5}{8}$ in. (115.3 × 83 cm.)
Gift of Emily Crane Chadbourne, 22.4790

Ref: Theatre Arts Monthly *21: 595, 1937*

FRENCH IMPRESSIONIST AND POST-IMPRESSIONIST PAINTINGS

SECTION ONE

XIXth—XXth Centuries

ILLUSTRATIONS

Renoir, Pierre Auguste, Lady at the Piano, c. 1875. Mr. & Mrs. Martin A. Ryerson Collection

Monet, Claude, Beach at Sainte-Adresse, 1867, Mr. & Mrs. Lewis L. Coburn Memorial Collection

Monet, Claude, Old St. Lazare Station, Paris, 1877. Mr. & Mrs. Martin A. Ryerson Collection

Pissarro, Camille, On the Banks of the Marne, Winter, 1866. Mr. & Mrs. Lewis L. Coburn Fund

Manet, Edouard, The Races at Longchamp, Paris, 1864. Potter Palmer Collection

Renoir, Pierre Auguste, Two Little Circus Girls, 1879. Potter Palmer Collection

Renoir, Pierre Auguste, On the Terrace, 1881. Mr. & Mrs. Lewis L. Coburn Memorial Collection

Monet, Claude, Iris by the Pond, 1919/25. Art Institute Purchase Fund

Degas, Edgar, Woman at her Toilette, c. 1903. Mr. & Mrs. Martin A. Ryerson Collection

Toulouse-Lautrec, Henri de, Woman with a Pink Bow, 1886
Gift of Annie Swan Coburn to the
Mr. & Mrs. Lewis L. Coburn Memorial Collection

Degas, Edgar, Uncle and Niece, c. 1876. Mr. & Mrs. Lewis L. Coburn Memorial Collection

Morisot, Berthe, Lady at Her Toilette, c. 1875. The Stickney Fund

Manet, Edouard, Le Journal Illustré, c. 1878/79
Mr. & Mrs. Lewis L. Coburn Memorial Collection

Sisley, Alfred, Sand Heaps, 1875. Mr. & Mrs. Martin A. Ryerson Collection

Opposite: Cézanne, Paul, The Gulf of Marseille, L'Estaque, 1886–90. Mr. & Mrs. Martin A. Ryerson Collection

Renoir, Pierre Auguste, Rowers' Lunch, c. 1879/80. Potter Palmer Collection

MARESCALCHI, Pietro (attributed to) ~ *ca. 1510–1584 Feltre*

PORTRAIT OF A GENTLEMAN

Oil on canvas, 55×45¾ in. (139.7×116.2 cm.)
Gift of Mrs. William R. Timken, 51.318

This picture, once implausibly given to Veronese, is not far in style from Marescalchi.

MARGO, Boris ~ *b. 1902 Wolotschisk, Russia*

Margo studied at the Academy in Odessa and emigrated to America in 1930. He taught at the Master Institute of United Arts in New York and later at the American University in Washington.

NUMBER 5

Signed and dated: Boris Margo 49. Oil on canvas, 50×20 in. (127×50.9 cm.)
Gift of the Society for Contemporary American Art, 50.1361

MARIESCHI, Michele ~ *1696–1743 Venice*

Like Guardi, Canaletto and Bellotto, Marieschi was a painter of Venetian life in the 18th century.

SANTA MARIA DELLA SALUTE, VENICE

Painted about 1740. Oil on canvas, 21⅞×33⅛ in. (55.7×84.2 cm.)
Charles H. and Mary F. S. Worcester Collection, 46.375

It has been suggested that the figures were painted by Antonio Guardi.

Coll: Sir A. Pilkington, Wakefield, Yorkshire

Ref: Studies in the History of Art Dedicated to William E. Suida . . . , *London, 1959, 338ff. (Morassi)*

MARIN, John ~ *b. 1870 Rutherford, N.J. d. 1953 Cape Split, Me.*

Marin worked in an architect's office, then studied at the Pennsylvania Academy of the Fine Arts, and later at the Art Students League in New York. He went to Paris in 1905 and again in 1909.

MOVEMENT: BOATS AND OBJECTS, BLUE GRAY SEA

Signed and dated: Marin '47. Oil on canvas, 29×36¼ in. (73×92.1 cm.)
Alfred Stieglitz Collection and Robert A. Waller Fund, 49.610

MARQUET, Pierre-Albert ~ *b. 1875 Bordeaux, France. d. 1947 Paris*

Marquet studied with Gustave Moreau.

PONT SAINT MICHEL, PARIS

Painted about 1910, signed: Marquet. Oil on canvas, 12½ × 15⅝ in. (31.8 × 39.8 cm.)
Mr. and Mrs. Martin A. Ryerson Collection, 33.1145

MARSH, Reginald ~ *b. 1898 Paris. d. 1954 Bennington, Vt.*

Reginald Marsh was born in Paris of American parents. At Yale he did cartoons and was editor of the *Yale Record.* He went to New York as a free-lance artist and took courses at the Art Students League under John Sloan, George Luks and Kenneth Hayes Miller.

TATTOO AND HAIRCUT

Signed and dated: Reginald Marsh 1932.
Egg tempera on canvas, 46½ × 47⅞ in. (118.2 × 121.6 cm.)
Gift of Mr. and Mrs. Earle Ludgin, 47.39

MARTIN, Homer Dodge ~ *b. 1836 Albany, N.Y. d. 1897 St. Paul, Minn.*

Martin received only scanty instruction from the brothers William and James M. Hart. In 1876 he went abroad, studied the old masters and became acquainted with Whistler.

ON THE SEINE

Painted about 1895, signed: H. D. Martin. Oil on canvas, 15¼ × 24⅛ in. (38.3 × 61.3 cm.)
Friends of American Art Collection, 43.92

MARTIN, Philip ~ *b. 1927 East Anglia, England*

In 1948 Martin entered the Franciscan Brotherhood as a lay brother but left a year later to devote his life to painting.

METRO

Painted 1952, signed lower left: Martin 5-1952.
Oil on paper, 44½ × 69¼ in. (113.4 × 175.9 cm.)
Gift of Theodore S. Gary, 55.823

MARTINELLI, Giovanni ~ *About 1610–1659 Florence*

Martinelli may have been a pupil of Matteo Rosselli.

JUDITH

Painted about 1650. Oil on canvas, 38¾ × 29¾ in. (98.5 × 75.6 cm.)
Charles H. and Mary F. S. Worcester Collection, 39.2240

A young Florentine woman is here represented as Judith.

MARTORELL, Bernardo ~ *Active 1427–1452 Barcelona*

Martorell was the leading painter of the Catalan School during the second quarter of the 15th century. He has been identified as the painter of the altarpiece of St. Peter at Púbol (1437). On the basis of stylistic similarity, the Art Institute's *St. George and the Dragon* and four related panels in the Louvre have been attributed to this artist who was formerly identified as the Master of St. George.

ST. GEORGE AND THE DRAGON Illus. p. 95

Painted c. 1438. Tempera on panel 56×38 in. (142.3×96.5 cm.)
Gift of Mrs. Richard E. Danielson and Mrs. Chauncey McCormick, 33.786

Coll: Roccabruna Family; Vidal Ferrer y Soler, Barcelona

Ref: Sanpere y Miquel, S., Los Cuatrocentistas Catalanes *I, 1906, pp. 193–5, II, p. 276; Bertaux, E.,* La Revue de l'Art *22: 255, 260–6, July/December 1907; Michel, A.,* Histoire de l'Art . . ., *III, pt. 2, 1908, pp. 772–5; Bertaux, E.,* La Revue de l'Art *23: 269–79, 341, 1908; S. de Mandach, E. Piot,* Monuments et Mémoires publiés par L'Académie des Inscriptions et Belles-Lettres, *XVI, 1909, pp. 15, 152; Dieulafoy, M. A.,* Art in Spain and Portugal, *1913, pp. 175, 179; Chicago. Art Institute,* Bulletin *16: 17–21, 1922 (ill.); King, G. Goddard,* Art Bulletin *5: 6, September 1922;* International Studio *76: 59, 1922; Richert, G.,* Mittelalterliche Malerei in Spanien, *1925, p. 60; Pope Miller, P.,* Art Bulletin *9: 161–6, September 1926; Post, C. R.,* A History of Spanish Painting *II, 1930, pp. 394–7, VII, 1938, pt. 1, pp. 60, 120, 205, pt. 9, pp. 669, 769; Rowland, B. Jr.,* Jaume Huguet, A Study of Late Gothic Painting in Catalonia, *1932, pp. 23, 24, 130, 131; Chicago. Art Institute,* A Century of Progress Exhibition, *1933, cat. no. 178;* Ibid., *1934, cat. no. 78; Tietze, H.,* Meisterwerke Europaeischer Malerei in Amerika, *1935, pl. 2; Dezarrois, A.,* La Revue de l'Art *71: 42, 43, 1937; Valentiner, W. R.,* Gazette des Beaux-Arts *18, per. 6: 23–46, July/August 1937; Gudiol, J.,* Spanish Painting, *1941, pp. 24–5*

MARTYL ~ *b. 1918 St. Louis, Mo.*

A graduate of Washington University in St. Louis, Martyl also studied with Arnold Blanch at the Colorado Springs Fine Arts Center. She now lives near Chicago.

MARKET PLACE NO. 2, BARCELONA

Signed and dated: Martyl 1954. Oil on masonite, 36×48 in. (91.5×122 cm.)
Gift of Claire and Albert Arenberg Fund, 55.644

MASSYS, Quentin ~ *b. 1465–66 Louvain, Flanders. d. 1530 Antwerp*

Little is known of Massys' life. Records show that he worked in Antwerp after 1491. He was influenced by Leonardo, particularly by his drawings, and among his countrymen Memling and Dirk Bouts played a role in the development of his style.

MAN WITH A PINK

Painted between 1510 and 1520. Oil on panel, 17¼ × 11½ in. (43.9 × 29.2 cm.)

Gift of John J. Glessner, 94.1025 (Friedlaender no. 47)

Coll: de Beurnonville, Paris; Rothan, Paris; M. E. May, Paris; Prince Demidoff, Pratolino, 1890

Ref: Chicago. Art Institute, Catalogue of Works of Old Dutch Masters and Other Pictures, *1890, cat. no. 1 (as Hans Holbein the Younger); D'Unger, G.,* Fine Arts Journal *30: 301, 1914; Conway, M.,* The Van Eycks and Their Followers, *1921, pp. 319, 327; Friedlaender, M.,* Von Eyck bis Breughel, *1921, p. 95, pl. 13; Friedlaender, M. J.,* Pantheon *1: 22, January/June 1928; Friedlaender, M. J.,* Die Altniederlaendische Malerei, *VII, 1929, pp. 65, 122, cat. no. 47, pl. 44; Comette, A. H.,* La Peinture à l'Exposition d'Art Flamand ancien à Anvers, *1930, p. 9, no. 197;* Oud-Vlaamsche Kunst, *Antwerp, 1930, cat. no. 197;* Trésor de l'Art Flamand du moyen âge au XVIII siècle . . ., *I, 1932, pp. 58, 59, 122, cat. no. 197, pl. 24; Lambotte, P.,* Apollo *12: 16, 1930; Chicago. Art Institute,* A Century of Progress Exhibition, *1933, cat. no. 45;* Ibid., *1934, cat. no. 122; Tietze, H.,* Meisterwerke Europaeischer Malerei in Amerika, *1935, pl. 141*

MASTER OF AMIENS

The School of Amiens was oriented towards Burgundy. Around 1475 Amiens developed a more indigenous style of painting which was in itself a variation of the Franco-Flemish manner prevalent in the border areas of both France and Flanders.

AMIENS ALTARPIECE: SCENES FROM THE LIFE OF CHRIST AND PATRON SAINTS

Painted about 1480. Oil on panel, each, 46⅛ × 20 in. (117.2 × 50.9 cm.)

Mr. and Mrs. Martin A. Ryerson Collection, 33.1054, 33.1055, 33.1056, 33.1057, 33.1058, 33,1059, 33.1060 Illus. p. 138

These seven panels were once part of an altarpiece in the Carthusian monastery of Thuison near Abbéville. There were originally eight panels forming four movable wings, painted on both sides, flanking a carved and gilded central group showing the Passion of Christ. During the French Revolution in 1795 the altarpiece was dismantled but the wings were saved. In 1860 each panel was split in two, so that all eight could be seen at once. One section was lost at that time.

(a) The Last Supper. The composition is adapted from an engraving dating from about 1475 by the Dutch Master of Zwolle. The next sequence in the story, the Resurrection, is presumably lost.
(b) The Ascension.
(c) Pentecost.
(d) St. Honoré. While the inside panels of the altar depicted scenes from the life of Christ, the outside wings were devoted to patron saints.
(e) Madonna and Child.
(f) St. Hugh of Lincoln.
(g) St. John the Baptist.

Coll: St. Honoré, Thuison-les-Abbéville; Church of the Holy Sepulchre, Abbéville, 1795; Soyez, Amiens, 1904; Kraemer, Paris

Ref: Delignières, E., Réunion des Sociétés des Beaux-Arts des Départments *(22me Session), Paris, 1898, pp. 305, 343; Reinach, S.,* Répertoire de Peintures du Moyen Age et de la Renaissance, *V, 1922, p. 266; Hausenstein, W.,* Tafelmalerei der Alten Franzosen, *VII, 1923, pp. 43, 44; Mather, F. J., Jr.,* The Arts *12: 246, 247, November 1927; Heil, W.,* Pantheon *3: 76, 78, January/June 1929; Barnes, A. C. and V. de Mazia,* The French Primitives and their Forms, *1931, pp. 378–81; Lemoisne, P. A.,* Gothic Painting in France, XIV and XV Centuries, *c. 1931, p. 138; Chicago. Art Institute,* Bulletin *27: 9, 12, 1933; Chicago. Art Institute,* A Century of Progress Exhibition, *1933, cat. no. 3;* Ibid., *1934, cat. no. 3; Dupont, J.,* Les Primitifs Français, *1937, p. 36; Evans, J.,* Art in Mediaeval France, *987–1498, 1948, figs. 141, 142; Ring, G.,* A Century of French Painting, *1400–1500, c. 1949, cat. no. 169*

MASTER OF ASTORGA

The painter is so designated on the basis of an altarpiece he executed for the cathedral of Astorga in the province of León in northwest Spain.

SALOME PRESENTS THE HEAD OF THE BAPTIST TO HERODIAS

Painted about 1530. Oil on panel, 33¼ × 31¾ in. (84.2 × 81.7 cm.)
Gift of Mr. and Mrs. Chauncey McCormick, 48.564

Ref: Post, C. R., A History of Spanish Painting, *IX, pt. 2, 1947, pp. 563, 564 (ill. fig. 218); Thieme-Becker, XXXVII, 1950, p. 26*

MASTER OF THE BAMBINO VISPO

The artist was influenced by Florentine painters of the late 14th century, especially by Lorenzo Monaco.

DEATH OF THE VIRGIN

Painted early 15th century. Tempera on panel, 17 9/16 × 26¾ in. (44.7 × 68 cm.)
Mr. and Mrs. Martin A. Ryerson Collection, 33.1017

Coll: Sellar, London; Dolfus, Paris; Marcel Nicolle

Ref: Siren, O., Burlington Magazine *25: 16–17, April/September 1914; Reinach, S.,* Répertoire de Peintures du Moyen Age et de la Renaissance, *V, 1922, p. 442; Van Marle, R.,* The Development of the Italian Schools of Painting, *IX, 1927, p. 200; Chicago. Art Institute,* A Century of Progress Exhibition, *1933, cat. no. 90; Berenson, B.,* Pitture Italiane del Rinascimento, *c. 1936, p. 277; Pudelko, G.,* Art in America *26: 54, 55, April 1938*

MASTER OF THE BIGALLO CRUCIFIX

The Master of the Bigallo is the name given to the painter of a cross in the Bigallo, the orphanage of a confraternity in Florence. The style is closely related to that of the Master Berlinghieri of Lucca in its coloristic quality and purity of line. The "Bigallo" Crucifix, however, has been ascribed by certain scholars to the School of Florence on the basis of its affinity to an altar frontal in San Zenobio and other Florentine works of the period.

CRUCIFIX

Illus. p. 35

Painted about 1240–1270. Tempera on panel, 75⅜ × 50¼ in. (190.5 × 127.7 cm.)
A. A. Munger Collection, 36.120

Coll: Austrian private collection

Ref: Sandberg-Vavalá, E., La Croce Dipinta Italiana e L'Iconografia della Passione, *1929, pp. 112, 394, no. 120*

MASTER OF THE CHANJENKO ADORATION

This master, a follower of Hugo van der Goes, was named after a diptych once in the Chanjenko (Khanenko) Collection in Kiev. He is supposed to have been active in Brussels around 1500.

THE ANNUNCIATION

Painted about 1500. Oil on panel, 16½ × 11 in. (42 × 28 cm.)
Mr. and Mrs. Martin A. Ryerson Collection, 33.1043

Ref: Pantheon *21: 34–5, 1938*

MASTER OF THE DIDO PANELS

The master was influenced by Pesellino.

ADVENTURES OF ULYSSES

Painted mid 15th century. Tempera on panel, 16½ × 65⅝ in. (42 × 166.7 cm.)
Mr. and Mrs. Martin A. Ryerson Collection, 37.1006

Ref: Schubring, P., Cassoni, *I, 1915, p. 276, cat. no. 253; Mather, F. J.,* A History of Italian Painting, *1923, pp. 182–3; Van Marle, R.,* The Development of the Italian Schools of Painting, *X, 1928, p. 554; Berenson, B.,* Pitture Italiane del Rinascimento, *1936, p. 283*

MASTER OF THE FEMALE HALF FIGURES

Presumably active in Antwerp, this master imitates Gerard David, but more often he comes close to Adriaen Isenbrant's style, gradually incorporating some of the progressive concepts of Bernard van Orley's new Roman manner.

SAINT MARY MAGDALEN

Painted around 1525. Oil on panel, 20½ × 14¾ in. (52.1 × 37.5 cm.)
Max and Leola Epstein Collection, 54.290 (Friedlaender no. 89)

Ref: Friedlaender, M. J., Die Altniederlaendische Malerei, *XII, 1924, p. 174, no. 89*

MASTER OF FRANKFORT

Although a Flemish painter, this master was named on the basis of an altarpiece he painted for the city of Frankfurt. He presumably worked in Antwerp, largely for the export trade, frequently copying earlier compositions.

SAINT JAMES OF COMPOSTELA WITH DONOR
SAINT ELIZABETH WITH DONOR

Painted about 1510.
Oil on panel, (a) 29⅜ × 17⅜ in. (74.6 × 44.2 cm.) (b) 29⅛ × 17 15/16 in. (74 × 43.9 cm.)
Mr. and Mrs. Martin A. Ryerson Collection, 33.1046, 33.1047

These are the two wings of a triptych. The central panel depicting the Madonna is now lost.

Coll: Martin A. Ryerson, 1913

Ref: Friedlaender, M. J., Jahrbuch der Preussischen Kunstsammlungen *38: 149, 1917, no. 40; Friedlaender, M. J.,* Die Altniederlaendische Malerei, *VII, 1929, p. 139, cat. no. 135; Chicago. Art Institute,* A Century of Progress Exhibition, *1933, cat. nos. 47a, b*

MASTER OF THE GROOTE ADORATION

Though this master was Flemish he was named after an altarpiece owned by Baron von Groote of Kitzburg, Germany. Active in Antwerp after the beginning of the 16th century, he was one of the so-called Mannerists.

DAVID AND HIS WARRIORS
SOLOMON AND THE QUEEN OF SHEBA

Painted about 1510 or 1520. Oil on panel, each 28⅞ × 10⅞ in. (73.4 × 27.6 cm.)
Gift of Mrs. Charles L. Hutchinson, 36.126, 36.127

Coll: Van Groote, Kitzburg

Ref: Reinach, S., Répertoire des Peintures du Moyen Age et de la Renaissance, *II, 1907, p. 13; Friedlaender, M. J.,* Die Altniederlaendische Malerei, *XI, 1933, pp. 35, 36, no. 27*

MASTER OF THE KRAINBURG ALTAR

Probably trained in the Salzburg area, the artist worked in the Duchy of Carniola.

THE FUNERAL OF SAINT FLORIAN

Probably painted at the end of the 15th century.
Tempera on panel, 32½×33 in. (80.2×83.9 cm.)
Charles H. and Mary F. S. Worcester Collection, 47.82

Coll: Wickenburg, Gleichenberg; Roerich Museum, New York

Ref: Paecht, O., Oesterreichische Tafelmalerei der Gotik, *1929, p. 83; Chicago. Art Institute,* A Century of Progress Exhibition, *1933, cat. no. 27;* Ibid., *1934, cat. no. 16; Kuhn, C. L.,* A Catalogue of German Paintings of the Middle Ages and Renaissance in American Collections, *1936, cat. no. 333; Chicago. Art Institute,* Catalogue of the Worcester Collection, *1938, cat. no. 30; Ring, G.,* Art Bulletin *26: 51, 52, 1944*

MASTER OF MOULINS

With Jean Fouquet, the Master of Moulins is considered the most important representative of the French School around 1500. Attempts have been made to identify this artist with either Jean Perréal or Jean Hay of Antwerp. Strongly influenced by Flemish painting, mainly by Hugo van der Goes, the Master of Moulins shows certain characteristics from the Loire region. All that is definitely known is that he painted the altar piece in the cathedral of Amiens and that he was chiefly employed by the Bourbon family.

THE ANNUNCIATION Illus. p. 140

Painted about 1490 or 1500. Oil on panel, 29×20 in. (73.7×50.9 cm.)
Mr. and Mrs. Martin A. Ryerson Collection, 33.1062

This panel was probably the right wing of an altarpiece; the left wing has been identified as the Meeting of Anna and Joachim at the Golden Gate, a panel now in the National Gallery of London.

Coll: Lévêque [?], Paris

Ref: Fry, R. E., Burlington Magazine *9: 331, 1906; London. Grafton Galleries,* National Exhibition of Old Masters, *1909, cat. no. 76; Nicolle, M.,* La Revue de l'Art *27: 54, 1910; Monod, F.,* Gazette des Beaux-Arts *N.S. 3, per. 4: 243–4, January/June 1910; Guiffrey, J. and P. Marcel,* La Peinture Française, Les Primitifs, *1913, I, pp. 18–9, cat. no. 53; II, pl. 53; Conway, M.,* The Van Eycks and their Followers, *1921, p. 187; Friedlaender, M. J.,* Burlington Magazine *47: 187–91, 1925; Mather, F. J., Jr.,* The Arts *12: 240, 248, July / December 1927; New York. F. Kleinberger Galleries,* Catalogue of a Loan Exhibition of French Primitives . . ., *October 1927, cat. no. 35; Detroit, Institute of Arts,* Seventh Loan Exhibition, *November/December 1928, cat. no. 9; Heil, W.,* Pantheon *3: 76, 1929; Barnes, A. C. and V. de Mazia,* The French Primitives and Their Forms, *1931, pp. 431–2; Lemoisne, P. A.,* Gothic Painting in France, XIV and XV Centuries, *1931, p. 98; London. Royal Academy of Arts,* Exhibition of French Art, 1200–1900, *1932, cat. no. 63; Chicago.*

Art Institute, Bulletin *27: 8, 12, 1933; Chicago. Art Institute,* A Century of Progress Exhibition, *1933, cat. no. 28;* Ibid., *1934, cat. no. 17; Sterling, C.,* La Peinture Française, Les Primitifs, *1938, p. 127, no. 159; Jacques, C., (pseud.),* La Peinture Française, Les Peintres du Moyen Age, *1941, pp. 22–3, cat. no. 30; Goldblatt, C.,* Connoisseur *122: 4–5, September 1948 (ill.); Ring, G.,* A Century of French Painting, *1400–1500, 1949, cat. no. 297; London. National Gallery,* French School, *1957, cf. cat. no. 4092*

MASTER OF THE PIETA OF SAINT GERMAIN

The work of this master, who was probably trained in Cologne, shows a peculiar synthesis of styles. Though much influenced by Rogier van der Weyden and Hugo van der Goes, he adopted the softer modeling, delicate forms and lyrical expression of the School of Paris.

THE ENTOMBMENT

Illus. p. 141

Painted about 1500. Tempera on panel, 18 15/16 × 27 5/8 in. (48 × 70.3 cm.)
A. A. Munger Collection, 26.570

Coll: Lamponi, Florence; Rodolphe Kann, Paris. Achillito Chiesa, Milan

Ref: Reinach, S., Répertoire de Peintures du Moyen Age et de la Renaissance, *II, 1907, p. 454, no. 1; Chicago. Art Institute,* Bulletin *20: 73, 1926;* The Arts *9: 284, 1926; Heil, W.,* Pantheon *3: 78, 1929; Chicago. Art Institute,* Bulletin *32: 52, 1938; Chicago. Art Institute,* A Century of Progress Exhibition, *1933, cat. no. 33, pl. 7;* Ibid., *1934, cat. no. 21; Jacques, C. (pseud.),* La Peinture Française: Les Peintres du Moyen Age, *1941, Répertoire B, 15e siècle, no. 52, p. 63 of cat.; Ring, G.,* A Century of French Painting, *1400–1500, 1949, p. 232, no. 255*

MASTER OF PULKAU

This master, a follower of Altdorfer, shows the qualities of the Danube style.

THE NATIVITY

Painted about 1510 or 1520. Oil and tempera on panel, 46 3/4 × 29 1/4 in. (118.8 × 74.3 cm.)
Wilson L. Mead Fund, 33.799

Coll: Leo Blumenreich, Berlin

Ref: Chicago. Art Institute, A Century of Progress Exhibition, *1934, cat. no. 1; Kuhn, C. L.,* A Catalogue of German Paintings of the Middle Ages and Renaissance in American Collections, *1936, p. 72, cat. no. 310; Munich, Neue Staatsgalerie,* Albrecht Altdorfer und sein Kreis . . . , *1938, p. 148; Benesch, O.,* Oesterreichische Kunst *9, no. 5: 22, 23, May 1938; Chicago. Art Institute,* Bulletin *34: 2–3, 1940; Panofsky, E.,* Early Netherlandish Painting, *I, 1953, p. 470, note 1*

MASTER OF SAINT VERONICA

see

GERMAN SCHOOL, 15th century

MASTER OF THE URSULA LEGEND

see

FLEMISH SCHOOL, 15th century

MASTER OF THE VIERZIGER JAHRE

Exclusively a portrait painter, this artist has been identified by the dates which appear in his work always in the same manner, almost like a trade mark. A contemporary of Antonis Mor, he never deviated from the older Franco-Flemish tradition.

PORTRAIT OF A LADY

Dated 1544. Oil on panel, 16×12 in. (40.8×30.5 cm.)
Gift of Adolph Caspar Miller, 53.471

Coll: Dr. Benedict & Co., Berlin

Ref: Pantheon *6: 342, December 1930*

MASTER OF THE VIRGO INTER VIRGINES

This painter's designation comes from a painting in the Rijksmuseum in Amsterdam showing Mary among four holy virgins. Since some of the artist's wood engravings were published in Delft, it is presumed that he was active there. His work also shows Italian influences.

ECCE HOMO

Painted about 1480. Oil on panel, 20 7/16×13 5/8 in. (51.5×34.7 cm.)
Mr. and Mrs. Martin A. Ryerson Collection, 33.1049

Coll: Convent of San Luca, Rome; Roerich Museum, New York

Ref: Friedlaender, M. J., Jahrbuch der Preussischen Kunstsamlungen *31: 64–72, 1910; Friedlaender, M. J.,* Die Altniederlaendische Malerei, *V, 1927, pp. 72–4, cat. no. 53; Chicago. Art Institute,* Bulletin *25: 33, 34–6, 1931; Chicago. Art Institute,* A Century of Progress Exhibition, *1933, cat. no. 49;* Ibid., *1934, cat. no. 124*

MASTER OF THE WORCESTER PANEL

The origin of this artist is most obscure but he obviously came out of the tradition of the Upper Rhine region and was active in Austria and Bavaria.

CHRIST CARRYING THE CROSS Illus. p. 142

Painted about 1430. Tempera on panel, 9⅛×7⅛ in. (23.2×18.1 cm.)
Charles H. and Mary F. S. Worcester Collection, 47.79

Coll: Swiss Collection (probably Lévêque)

Ref: Washburn Freund, E. E., Belvedere *8, pt. 2: 285, 1929; Zimmermann, H.,* Nürnberger Malerei, *1932, p. 41; Chicago. Art Institute,* A Century of Progress Exhibition, *1933, cat. no. 26; Frankfurter, A. M.,* The Fine Arts *20: 18, May 1933; Kuhn, C. L.,* A Catalogue of German Paintings of the Middle Ages and Renaissance in American Collections, *1936, cat. no. 185; Chicago. Art Institute,* Catalogue of the Worcester Collection, *1938, cat. no. 27*

MATHIEU, Georges ~ *b. 1921 Boulogne-sur-Mer, France*

Mathieu has frequently exhibited at the Salon des Surindépendants and the Réalités Nouvelles.

MATITE

Signed and dated: Mathieu '51. Oil on canvas, 51⅜×63¾ in. (130.6×159.5 cm.)
Gift of Mr. and Mrs. Maurice E. Culberg, 52.998

MATISSE, Henri ~ *b. 1869 Le Cateau, France. d. 1954 Nice, France*

Matisse, who was originally trained as a lawyer, turned to painting and in 1892 enrolled as one of Gustave Moreau's many students.

STILL LIFE WITH GERANIUM PLANT AND FRUIT

Painted 1906, signed: Henri-Matisse. Oil on canvas, 38½×31½ in. (97.9×80.2 cm.)
The Joseph Winterbotham Collection, 32.1342

Coll: Frederic C. Bartlett; Joseph Winterbotham

Ref: Barnes, A. and V. de Mazia, The Art of Henri Matisse, *1933, pp. 73, 244, no. 30; Chicago. Art Institute,* Catalogue of the Winterbotham Collection, *1947, p. 30; Barr, A.,* Matisse, His Art and His Public, *1951, pp. 92, 110, 533, 558*

APPLES Illus. p. 466

Painted 1916, signed: Henri-Matisse. Oil on canvas, 46×35 in. (116.9×88.9 cm.)
Gift of Mr. and Mrs. Samuel A. Marx, 48.563

Ref: Barr, A. H., Matisse, His Art and His Public, *1951, pp. 180, 181, 194, 263, 529*

BATHERS BY A RIVER (Women at a Spring) Illus. p. 468

Begun earlier, finished 1916–1917, signed: Henri-Matisse.
Oil on canvas, (8 ft. 7 in. × 12 ft. 10 in.) 103×154 in. (261.8×391.4 cm.)
Charles H. and Mary F. S. Worcester Collection, 53.158

Coll: Paul Guillaume, Paris; Mme Jean Walter, Paris; Henry Pearlman, New York

Ref: Bonmariage, S., Cahiers d'Art, *I, 1926, pp. 239, 240; Fry, R.,* Henri-Matisse, *1930, pl. 10; Zervos, C.,* Cahiers d'Art, *nos, 5–6, 6e année, 1931, pp. 249, 294; Read, H.,* Studio *124: 179, December 1942; Barr, A. H.,* Matisse, His Art and His Public, *1951, pp. 98, 181, 183, 190, 408, no. 4; Diehl, G.,* H. Matisse, *1954, pp. 65, 66, 141, no. 74*

THE GREEN SASH

Painted 1919, signed: Henri-Matisse. Oil on canvas, 19 × 16¾ in. (48.3 × 42.6 cm.)
Charles H. and Mary F. S. Worcester Collection, 47.91

Coll: B. H. Brandon-Davis, London

Ref: Chicago. Art Institute, Catalogue of the Worcester Collection, *1937, cat. no. 92*

WOMAN BEFORE AN AQUARIUM Illus. p. 475

Painted 1921, signed: Henri-Matisse. Oil on canvas, 32 × 39½ in. (81.3 × 100.3 cm.)
Helen Birch Bartlett Memorial Collection, 26.220

Ref: Chicago. Art Institute, Catalogue of the Birch Bartlett Collection, *1926, pp. 26, 27; Chicago. Art Institute,* Bulletin *20: 44, 1926; Watson, F.,* The Arts *9: 308, 1926; Zabel, M. D.,* Art and Archaeology *26: 229, 1928; McBride, H.,* Modern Art—Matisse, *1932, pl. 22; Sweeney, J. J.,* Cahiers d'Art *7: 335, 1932; Chicago. Art Institute,* A Century of Progress Exhibition, *1933, cat. no. 398;* Formes *33: 383, 1933; Chicago. Art Institute,* A Century of Progress Exhibition, *1934, cat. no. 352; Severini, G.,* Matisse, *1944, p. 26; Chicago. Art Institute,* Catalogue of the Birch Bartlett Collection, *1946, pp. 32–3; Fremantle, C. W.,* The Studio *136: 94–5, September 1948; Barr, A. H.,* Matisse, His Art and His Public, *New York, 1951, pp. 164, 209, 210, 436*

WOMAN ON ROSE DIVAN

Painted 1921, signed: Henri-Matisse. Oil on canvas, 14⅞ × 18 in. (37.8 × 45.8 cm.)
Helen Birch Bartlett Memorial Collection, 26.219

Ref: Chicago. Art Institute, Catalogue of the Birch Bartlett Collection, *1926, pp. 24, 25; Watson, F.,* The Arts *9: 310, 1926; Zabel, M. D.,* Art and Archaeology *26: 233, 1928; Chicago. Art Institute,* Catalogue of the Birch Bartlett Collection, *1946, pp. 34–5*

INTERIOR AT NICE

Painted 1921, signed: Henri-Matisse.
Oil on canvas, 52 × 35 in. (132.2 × 88.9 cm.) (1.30 × 89 cm.)
Gift of Mrs. Gilbert W. Chapman, 56.339

Ref: Chicago. Art Institute, A Century of Progress Exhibition, *1933, cat. no. 394; Barnes, A. C. and V. de Mazia,* The Art of Henri Matisse, *1933, pp. 195, 196, 197, 307, no. 118; Escholier, R.,* Henri Matisse, *1937, p. 64; Barr, A. H.,* Matisse, His Art and His Public, *1952, pp. 209, 210, 435*

FLOWERS

Painted ca. 1906, signed: Henri-Matisse. Oil on canvas, 7½ × 9⅝ in. (19.1 × 24.5 cm.)
Gift of Emily Crane Chadbourne, 53.5

MATTA (Roberto Matta Echaurren) ~ *b. 1912 Santiago, Chile*

The artist was taken to Paris as a child. There he later studied architecture and worked with Le Corbusier. He came to New York in the late 1930's, but returned to Europe in 1950. Much influenced by Duchamp and Picabia, Matta has for years been concerned with ironic interpretations of the machine.

YO+U

Painted 1950. Oil on canvas, $49\frac{1}{4} \times 50\frac{3}{4}$ in. (125.1×128.9 cm.)
Gift of the Society for Contemporary American Art, 51.71

The title expresses Matta's belief that the universe is a manifestation of eternal laws. The Spanish "Yo" stands for "I" and the "U" for the English "you". The unification of both, as implied by the title of the picture, symbolizes a term Matta calls "Youniverse." This play on words recalls Duchamp and Picabia, as do also the forms.

GLITTERING THE BEING

Oil on canvas, $44\frac{1}{2} \times 56$ in. (113.1×142.3 cm.)
Gift of Grant J. Pick, 59.213

MATTEO DI GIOVANNI ~ *b. about 1430 Borgo-San Sepolcro. d. 1495 Siena*

Matteo di Giovanni learned the Sienese manner from Domenico di Bartolo and Vecchietta, but because of Florentine influence achieved greater solidity with his figures.

EPISODES FROM THE LIFE OF SAINT JEROME

Painted about 1482.
Tempera on panel, (a) $14\frac{3}{4} \times 25\frac{3}{4}$ in. (37.5×65.5 cm.) (b) $14\frac{3}{4} \times 26$ in. (37.5×66.1 cm.)
Mr. and Mrs. Martin A. Ryerson Collection, 33.1018, 33.1019
(a) Dream of Saint Jerome.
(b) Saint Augustine's vision of Saint Jerome and Saint John.

Coll: Lord Brownlow, Ashridge Park, England

Ref: Berenson, B., The Central Italian Painters of the Renaissance, *1909, p. 194; Hartlaub, C. F.,* Matteo da Siena und seine Zeit, *1910, p. 78; Crowe and Cavalcaselle,* A History of Painting in Italy, *V, 1914, p. 184; Cambridge, Mass. Fogg Art Museum,* Collection of Medieval and Renaissance Paintings, *1919, p. 128; Chicago. Art Institute,* Bulletin *20: 30–2, 1926; Venturi, L.,* Pitture Italiane in America, *1931, no. 227; Berenson, B.,* Italian Pictures of the Renaissance, *1932, p. 350; Chicago. Art Institute,* A Century of Progress Exhibition, *1934, cat. no. 32; Van Marle, R.,* The Development of the Italian Schools of Painting, *XVI, 1937, pp. 342–3*

MAUFRA, Maxime ~ *b. 1861 Nantes, France. d. 1918 Poncé, France*

Maufra, who spent some time in England because of business, was much impressed with the work of Constable and Turner. His early pictures also show the influence of Monet.

DOUARNENEZ IN SUNSHINE

Signed and dated: Maufra '97. Oil on canvas, $23\frac{1}{2} \times 29$ in. (59.6×73.7 cm.)
Gift of Durand-Ruel, 05.335

MAZZA, Damiano (attributed to)

This painter was active in Venice during the last third of the 16th century.

ALLEGORY

Painted after 1560. Oil on canvas, $51\frac{3}{16} \times 61\frac{1}{8}$ in. (129.9×155.3 cm.)
Charles H. and Mary F. S. Worcester Collection, 43.90

An attribution to Titian was proposed by L. Venturi and accepted by Berenson, but rejected by Panofsky and, much earlier, by Crowe and Cavalcaselle. E. Tietze-Conrat proposed an attribution to Mazza, largely on literary evidence. (Her theory that the picture was largely overpainted was false; the painting was obscured mostly by discolored varnish, but by few retouches). The picture is probably by the same hand as that given to Titian in the National Gallery, Washington, D.C., in the Kress Collection: *Portrait of a Young Lady as Venus Binding the Eyes of Cupid.* On the basis of what little is known of Mazza's work, the attribution to him seems more plausible than to Titian. The picture is unfinished, a fact revealed by recent cleaning.

Coll: Earl of Wemyss, Gosford House; German private collection; Baron von Thyssen, Lugano; Mr. and Mrs. Worcester, 1936

Ref: Chicago. Art Institute, Catalogue of the Worcester Collection, *1937, cat. no. 12; Chicago. Art Institute,* Bulletin *37: 66–8, 1943; Crowe and Cavalcaselle,* The Life and Times of Titian, *London, 1881, II, p. 468; Graves,* A Century of Loan Exhibitions, *London, 1914, pp. 1318, 1319; Valentiner, W. R.,* Das Unbekannte Meisterwerk, *1930, pl. 25; Panofsky, E.,* Studies in Iconology, *1939, p. 165, note 27; Venturi, L.,* L'Arte, *n.s. 3, November 1932, pp. 489–91; Tietze-Conrat, E.,* Art Bulletin *27: 269–71, 1945;* Paintings and Sculpture from the Kress Collection, *Washington, D.C., 1951, cf. no. 48*

MAZZANOVICH, Lawrence ~ *b. 1872 California*

Mazzanovich attended art schools in Chicago and New York and also studied at Fontainebleau.

APRIL TWENTIETH

Painted about 1910, signed: Mazzanovich. Oil on canvas, 30×30 in. (76.3×76.3 cm.)
Friends of American Art Collection, 11.139

MEIDNER, Ludwig ~ *b. 1884 Bernstadt, Germany*

PORTRAIT OF MAX HERMANN-NEISSE

Painted 1913, signed: L Meidner/Jan [?] 1913. Oil on canvas, 35¼ × 29¾ in. (89.5 × 74.6 cm.)
Gift of Mr. and Mrs. Harold Weinstein, 59.215

MEISSONIER, Jean-Louis Ernest ~ *b. 1815 Lyon, France. d. 1891 Paris*

Meissonier specialized in both miniature-like genre paintings and historical canvases.

THE OUT-POST

Painted about 1880, signed: E. Meissonier. Oil on canvas, 41½ × 35⅞ in. (105.4 × 91.2 cm.)
A. A. Munger Collection, 01.446

MELCHERS, Gari ~ *b. 1860 Detroit. d. 1932 Falmouth, Va.*

Melchers studied in Düsseldorf and at the Ecole des Beaux-Arts in Paris. In 1884 he settled in Holland where he painted mostly Dutch genre scenes. From 1909 to 1914 he taught at the Academy in Weimar, Germany, but returned to America at the outbreak of the war.

CHARLES L. HUTCHINSON

Painted about 1902, signed: Gari Melchers. Oil on canvas, 40 × 39 in. (101.7 × 99.2 cm.)
Gift of Charles L. Hutchinson, 02.105

One of the founders of the Art Institute and its President from 1882–1924, this portrait of Mr. Hutchinson shows him holding Legros' portrait of the British painter, Watts.

MRS. ALBERT ARNOLD SPRAGUE (née Nancy Atwood)

Painted about 1905, signed: G. Melchers. Oil on canvas, 40½ × 32⅜ in. (102.9 × 82.3 cm.)
Gift of Elizabeth Sprague Coolidge, 49.521

ALBERT ARNOLD SPRAGUE

Painted about 1905, signed: G. Melchers. Oil on canvas, 40⅞ × 32¼ in. (103.9 × 82 cm.)
Gift of Elizabeth Sprague Coolidge, 49.520

Mr. Sprague came to Chicago in 1862 and founded the wholesale grocery firm of Sprague, Warner & Co. He was a Trustee of the Art Institute for twenty-four years.

MOTHER AND CHILD

Painted about 1906, signed: Gari Melchers. Oil on canvas, 25 × 21⅜ in. (63.6 × 54.4 cm.)
Gift of James Deering, 25.704

EARLY MORNING, NORTH RIVER

Painted about 1915, signed: G. Melchers. Oil on canvas, 18 × 22 in. (45.8 × 56 cm.)
Gift of Mr. and Mrs. Carter H. Harrison, 37.385

AN OLD SALT

Painted in 1920s. Inscribed: To my dear Friend J. Deering, signed: G. Melchers.
Oil on canvas, 22 × 16 in. (56 × 40.8 cm.)
Gift of James Deering, 27.834

PORTRAIT OF DAVID B. JONES

Signed: Gari Melchers. Oil on canvas, 46⅛×27 in. (117.2×68.7 cm.)
Gift of Owen Barton Jones, 59.513

MELDOLLA, Andrea (called Schiavone) (attributed to) ~ *b. 1505 [?] Zara, Yugoslavia. d. 1563 Venice*

Meldolla came from the Venetian provinces on the Dalmatian coast and was active in Venice and other parts of north Italy.

THE FLIGHT INTO EGYPT

Painted middle of 16th century. Oil on canvas, 16¼×38⅛ in. (41.5×96.9 cm.)
Charles H. and Mary F. S. Worcester Collection, 47.111

Ref: Chicago. Art Institute, A Century of Progress Exhibition, *1933, cat. no. 133; Chicago. Art Institute,* Bulletin *27: 39, 44, 1933; Chicago. Art Institute,* Catalogue of the Worcester Collection, *1937, cat. no. 9 (ill. pl. 8)*

MELIORE TOSCANO

An altarpiece in the Gallery of Parma, signed "Meliore 1271", is considered the key picture by this artist about whom nothing is known. He is thought to have worked in Pistoia and in his early work shows the influence of the Berlinghieri and the School of Lucca; later he worked more closely in the Florentine tradition.

MADONNA AND CHILD ENTHRONED Illus. p. 34

Painted about 1270. Tempera on panel, 32¼×18¾ in. (82×47.7 cm.)
Mr. and Mrs. Martin A. Ryerson Collection, 33.1034

Coll: Achille Clemente

Ref: Chicago. Art Institute, Bulletin *20: 77, 1926; Weigelt, C. H.,* Art Studies *6: 215, 1928; Sandberg-Vavalà, E.,* La Croce Dipinta Italiana, *1929, p. 708; Venturi, L.,* Pitture Italiane in America, *1931, pl. 3; Chicago. Art Institute,* Bulletin *27: 3, 7, 1933; Offner, R.,* Burlington Magazine *63: 80, 1933; Chicago. Art Institute,* A Century of Progress Exhibition, *1933, cat. no. 99;* Ibid., *1934, cat. no. 33*

MEMLING, Hans ~ *b. about 1433 Seligenstadt, Germany. d. 1494 Bruges*

Memling may have served his early apprenticeship in Cologne but later worked in Roger van der Weyden's studio. Having settled in Bruges in about 1465, he became the leading master in that town.

MADONNA AND CHILD Illus. p. 144

Painted about 1485. Oil and tempera on panel, 13½×10½ in. (33.4×26.7 cm.)
Mr. and Mrs. Martin A. Ryerson Collection, 33.1050 (Friedlaender no. 50)

Coll: Unknown Spanish collection

Ref: Friedlaender, M. J., Art in America *8: 111, 115, fig. 4, April 1920; Friedlaender, M. J.,* Von Eyck bis Breughel, *1921, p. 188; Friedlaender, M. J.,* Die Altniederlaendische Malerei, *VI, 1928, cat. no. 50; Frankfurter, A. M.,* Fine Arts *18: 22, March 1932; Chicago. Art Institute,* Bulletin *27: 60, 61, 1933; Chicago. Art Institute,* A Century of Progress Exhibition, *1933, cat. no. 50;* Beaux-Arts *N.S., p. 6, June 9, 1933; Chicago. Art Institute,* A Century of Progress Exhibition, *1934, cat. no. 125; Tietze, H.,* Meisterwerke Europaeischer Malerei in Amerika, *VI, 1928, cat. no. 50; Held, J.,* Burlington Magazine *68: 176–9, 1936; Chicago. Art Institute,* Bulletin *35: 105, 116, December 1941; Bodkin, T.,* Dismembered Masterpieces, *1945, p. 49;* Connoisseur *134, no. 539: 73, August 1954*

PORTRAIT OF A DONOR — Illus. p. 145

Painted about 1485. Oil and tempera on panel, 13¾ × 10⅝ in. (35 × 27 cm.)
Gift of Arthur Sachs, 53.467 (Friedlaender no. 92)

Coll: Arthur Sachs, Paris

Ref: Friedlaender, M. J., Die Altniederlaendische Malerei, *VI, 1928, no. 92*

This devotional diptych (a painting composed of two sections framed separately and hinged together) was only recently joined after being separated for many years.

KING DAVID AND A BOY (fragment)

Painted about 1485. Oil on panel, 10 × 7¾ in. (25.5 × 19.7 cm.)
Max and Leola Epstein Collection, 54.219 (Friedlaender no. 97)

MERIDA, Carlos ~ *b. 1891 Guatemala City*

PLASTIC INVENTION ON THE THEME OF LOVE

Signed and dated: Carlos Merida 1939.
Casein and water color on paper, 29⅜ × 21¾ in. (74.6 × 55.4 cm.)
Gift of Mrs. Katharine Kuh, 55.818

MERRILD, Knud ~ *b. 1894 Jutland, Denmark. d. 1954 Copenhagen*

Merrild, after studying at the Royal Academy in Copenhagen, came to the United States in 1921. He lived for many years in Los Angeles, only returning to Denmark a short time before his death.

VOLCANIC ISLES OF ESCAPE

Signed and dated: Knud Merrild 1944. Flux on canvas, 18⅜ × 14½ in. (46.8 × 36.9 cm.)
Gift of Alexander M. Bing, 51.16

METCALF, Willard Leroy ~ *b. 1858 Lowell, Mass. d. 1925 New York City*

Metcalf was trained in Boston and at the Académie Julian in Paris.

ICEBOUND

Signed and dated: W. L. Metcalf 1909. Oil on canvas, 29×26⅛ in. (73.7×66.4 cm.)
Walter H. Schulze Memorial Collection, 10.311

METZINGER, Jean ~ *b. 1883 Nantes, France*

Metzinger studied at several fashionable academies in Paris and was influenced briefly by the Fauves. He is best known as a member of the Cubist movement.

WOMAN WITH FAN

Painted 1913, signed: Metzinger. Oil on canvas, 36½×25⅝ in. (92.8×65.2 cm.)
Gift of Mr. and Mrs. Sigmund Kunstadter, 59.10

STILL LIFE

Painted 1918, signed: J. Metzinger. Oil on canvas, 28⅜×21¼ in. (73×54.4 cm.)
Gift of Mr. and Mrs. Harry L. Winston, 54.1312

MICHEL, Georges ~ *1763–1843 Paris*

A pupil of Leduc, Michel was also influenced by Dutch 17th century landscape painting.

THE STORM

Probably painted between 1814 and 1830. Oil on panel, 23⅛×28¾ in. (58.7×73 cm.)
Wilson L. Mead Fund, 35.374

MICHETTI, Francesco Paolo ~ *b. 1851 Tocco di Casauria. d. 1929 Francavilla a Mare*

Michietti studied in Naples and was influenced by the elegance and realism of Mariano Fortuny's style. In his early years he was also much impressed by Meissonier's work.

SPRINGTIME AND LOVE

Signed and dated: Michetti 78. Oil on canvas, 37½×72¾ in. (95.3×184.8 cm.)
A. A. Munger Collection, 01.429

MIERIS, Willem van ~ *1662–1747 Leyden, Holland*

Willem van Mieris, who was greatly influenced by his father, Frans van Mieris, carried on the meticulous style of the School of Leyden.

THE HAPPY MOTHER

Painted early in the 18th century. Oil on panel, 22 5/16×18⅞ in. (56.7×48 cm.)
Gift of Edson Keith, 90.42 (HdG. no. 233)

Coll: D. Grenier, Middleburg; J. Clemens, Gent; E. A. J. van den Meersche, Gent; Count Lichtervelde; Countess Vilain XIV, Castle Wetteren, 1827; Marquis de Rhodes; Prince A. Demidoff, San Donato

MILLER, Kenneth Hayes ~ *b. 1876 Oneida, N.Y. d. 1951 New York City*

A student of William Merritt Chase, Miller was also influenced in his earlier work by Albert Pinkham Ryder and Auguste Renoir.

THE RIVER

Painted 1919, signed: Hayes Miller. Oil on canvas, $20\frac{3}{16}\times 17$ in. (51.5×43.3 cm.)
Mr. and Mrs. Martin A. Ryerson Collection, 37.1040

MILLER, Richard E. ~ *b. 1875 St. Louis, Mo. d. 1943 Provincetown, Mass.*

Miller was a student at the St. Louis School of Fine Arts and worked in Paris under Benjamin Constant and J. P. Laurens until 1918.

SUNLIGHT

Painted about 1913, signed: Miller. Oil on canvas, $45\times 57\frac{1}{2}$ in. (114.4×146.7 cm.)
Friends of American Art Collection, 15.557

MILLET, Jean François ~ *b. 1814 Gruchy, France. d. 1875 Barbizon, France*

Millet, a pupil of Paul Delaroche, established his studio in Paris in 1844. Five years later he went to Barbizon, a village on the outskirts of the forest of Fontainebleau where Théodore Rousseau had already settled. Here the artist remained for the rest of his life.

YOUNG WOMAN Illus. p. 235

Painted about 1844–1845. Oil on canvas, $20\frac{1}{2}\times 24\frac{1}{2}$ in. (52.1×62.4 cm.)
Potter Palmer Collection, 22.415

Ref: Chicago. Art Institute, Bulletin *18: 87, 1924; Chicago. Art Institute,* A Century of Progress Exhibition, *1933, cat. no. 251;* Ibid., *1934, cat. no. 197*

THE WOODCHOPPER

Painted 1858. Oil on canvas, $31\frac{1}{2}\times 25$ in. (80.2×63.6 cm.)
Potter Palmer Collection, 22.416

This canvas, well documented with several drawings, was started in 1858, but never completed.

Ref: Ady, M., Portfolio *21: 193, 1890; Soullié, L.,* Jean-François Millet, *1900, p. 49; Chicago. Art Institute,* Catalogue of the Potter Palmer Collection, *1910, cat. no. 32; Moreau-Nelaton, E.,* Millet, Raconté par lui-même, *II, 1921, pp. 46, 74, III, p. 4; Chicago. Art Institute,* Bulletin *18: 88, 89, 1924; Chicago. Art Institute,* A Century of Progress Exhibition, *1933, cat. no. 255;* Ibid., *1934, cat. no. 199B*

THE LITTLE SHEPHERDESS

Painted about 1862. Oil on canvas, 14×10 in. (35.7×25.5 cm.)
Potter Palmer Collection, 22.413

The subject, similar to an etching Millet made in 1862, was probably painted at about the same time he was preparing his large *Shepherdess* (now in the Louvre), which was exhibited in 1864.

Coll: Albert Spencer, New York

Ref: Sensier, A., Jean-François Millet, *1896, p. 195; Ady, M.,* Portfolio *21: 195, 1890;* Masters in Art *1, no. 8: 35, 1900; Chicago. Art Institute,* Annual Report, *1921; Chicago. Art Institute,* Bulletin *15: 157, 1921; Chicago. Art Institute,* A Century of Progress Exhibition, *1933, cat. no. 254;* Ibid., *1934, cat. no. 199A*

THE SHEEPSHEARERS

Probably painted between 1862 and 1864, signed: J. F. Millet.
Oil on canvas, 16×12¾ in. (40.8×32.3 cm.)
Potter Palmer Collection, 22.417

Ref: Soullié, L., Jean-François Millet, *1900, p. 25; Rolland, R.,* Millet, *1902, p. 83; Gensel, W.,* Millet und Rousseau, *1902, p. 25; Moreau-Nelaton, E.,* Millet, Raconté par lui-même, *1921, I, fig. 85, II, fig. 133; Chicago. Art Institute,* Bulletin *18: 88, 89, 1924; Gsell, P.,* Millet *(Masters of Modern Art), 1928, pl. 14; Chicago. Art Institute,* A Century of Progress Exhibition, *1933, cat. no. 256; Chicago. Art Institute,* Bulletin *27: 114, 1933; Chicago. Art Institute,* A Century of Progress Exhibition, *1934, cat. no. 199C*

BRINGING HOME THE NEW-BORN CALF

Painted between 1862 and 1864, signed: J. F. Millet.
Oil on canvas, 32⅛×39⅜ in. (81.6×100 cm.)
Henry Field Memorial Collection, 94.1063

This picture, exhibited for the first time at the Salon of 1864, was started in 1862.

Coll: Duz; Mrs. Thomas N. Page, 1894

Ref: Sensier, A., Jean-François Millet, *1896, pp. 170–1;* Masters in Art *1, no. 8: 35, 1900; Rolland, R.,* Millet, *1902, p. 4; Cartwright, J.,* Jean-François Millet, His Life and Letters, *1902, pp. 251, 264, 370; Moreau-Nelaton, E.,* Millet, Raconté par lui-même, *II, 1921, p. 195, fig. 190; Chicago. Art Institute,* Bulletin *18: 88, 89, 1924; Chicago. Art Institute,* A Century of Progress Exhibition, *1933, cat. no. 250;* Ibid., *1934, cat. no. 196*

THE OLD MILL

Painted between 1865 and 1870, signed: J. F. Millet.
Pastel on paper, 19×16 in. (48.3×40.8 cm.)
Gift of John Wentworth, 42.307

IN AUVERGNE

Painted between 1866 and 1867, signed: J. F. Millet.
Oil on canvas, 31¼×38½ in. (79.3×97.9 cm.)
Potter Palmer Collection, 22.414

Ref: Chicago. Art Institute, Bulletin *18: 89, 1924; Chicago. Art Institute,* A Century of Progress Exhibition, *1933, cat. no. 253;* Ibid., *1934, cat. no. 189; New York. Marie Harriman Gallery,* Constable and the Landscape, *November 1937, cat. no. 8*

THE KEEPER OF THE HERD

Painted between 1871 and 1874, signed: J. F. Millet.
Oil on canvas, 28×36 in. (71.7×91.5 cm.)
Mr. and Mrs. W. W. Kimball Collection, 22.4462

This unfinished canvas is supposed to have been painted in 1861. It bears the stamp of the sale of Millet's estate in 1875.

Ref: Soullié, L., Jean-François Millet, *1900, p. 45; Arsène, A.,* Corot and Millet, *1903, p. M59; Chicago. Art Institute,* Bulletin *14: 68, 1920; Chicago. Art Institute,* Bulletin *18: 89, 1924; Chicago. Art Institute,* A Century of Progress Exhibition, *1933, cat. no. 252;* Ibid., *1934, cat. no. 199*

MINTZ, Harry ~ *b. 1907 Ostrowiec, Poland*

Mintz studied at the Warsaw Academy and at the Art Institute of Chicago.

THE BROODING CITY

Signed and dated: Harry Mintz 53. Oil on canvas, 25½×33½ in. (64.8×85.2 cm.)
Gift of Claire and Albert Arenberg Fund, 53.464

MIRO, Joán ~ *b. 1893 Montroig, Spain*

Miró's early training in Barcelona was completely conventional until he met the painter and art dealer, Refel Josep Dalmau, who introduced him to the work of Picasso and Juan Gris.

PORTRAIT OF A WOMEN (Juanita Obrador) Illus. p. 430

Signed and dated: Miró 1918. Oil on canvas, 27½×24½ in. (69.5×62 cm.)
The Joseph Winterbotham Collection, 57.78

PERSONAGES WITH STAR

Painted in 1933. Oil on canvas, 78¼×97½ in. (196.3×247.9 cm.)
Gift of Mr. and Mrs. Maurice E. Culberg, 52.512

Ref: Chicago. Art Institute, Quarterly *46, no. 4: 68, November 15, 1952*

PAINTING

Signed, dated and inscribed on back: Joan Miró, "Peinture" été 1936.
Oil on masonite, 31×42⅝ in. (78.8×108.3 cm.)
Gift of Mr. and Mrs. Samuel A. Marx, 50.1518

WOMAN AND BIRDS IN FRONT OF THE SUN

Painted 1942, signed: Miró.
Pastel and mixed media on paper, 43⅜ × 31¼ in. (110.3 × 79.3 cm.)
Wirt D. Walker Fund, 48.453

Ref: Greenberg, C., Joan Miró, *1948, pl. 66*

SYMBOLS AND LOVE CONSTELLATIONS OF A WOMAN

Signed and dated on back: Joan Miro-/Palma de Mallorca/Décembre 6, 1941 [?].
Gouache on paper, 18 × 15 in. (45.8 × 38.2 cm.)
Gift of Mrs. Gilbert W. Chapman, 53.338

Ref: New York. Pierre Matisse Galleries, Joan Miró . . . , *January/February 1945, cat. no. 19*

MITCHELL, Joan ~ *b. 1926 Chicago*

Joan Mitchell studied at the Art Institute of Chicago and in 1948 spent a year in France.

CITY LANDSCAPE

Painted 1955, signed: J. Mitchell. Oil on canvas, 80 × 80 in. (203.2 × 203.2 cm.)
Gift of the Society for Contemporary American Art, 58.193

MODIGLIANI, Amedeo ~ *b. 1884 Leghorn, Italy. d. 1920 Paris*

Modigliani came to Paris at the age of twenty-two, and, until his death from tuberculosis fourteen years later, managed to eke out a poverty-ridden existence. In his early years he started as a sculptor but turned to painting when he realized that the physical exertion of carving was bad for his health. The greatest single influence on Modigliani's work was African sculpture.

MADAM POMPADOUR

Signed, dated and inscribed: Madam Pompadour 1915 Modigliani.
Oil on canvas, 24 × 19¾ in. (61 × 50.4 cm.)
The Joseph Winterbotham Collection, 38.217

Coll: Paul Guillaume, Paris

Ref: Pfannstiel, A., Modigliani, *1929, p. 7; Chicago. Art Institute,* Bulletin *33: 90, 91, 1939; Chicago. Art Institute,* Catalogue of the Winterbotham Collection, *1947, p. 31*

JACQUES LIPCHITZ AND HIS WIFE Illus. p. 431

Painted 1916, signed and inscribed: Lipchitz Modigliani.
Oil on canvas, 31½ × 21 in. (80.2 × 53.5 cm.)
Helen Birch Bartlett Memorial Collection, 26.221

This double portrait of the artist and his wife was painted just after their marriage and, as Lipchitz once wrote, was done "in the manner of a typical photographer's wedding portrait." (J. Lipchitz, "I Remember Modigliani," *Art News,* vol. 49, 1951, pp. 25–9). The price was $10 and the sitting took place in Lipchitz' studio because Modigliani had none. The painting, as far as Modigliani was concerned, was finished in one afternoon. However since Lipchitz wished to have a more substantial painting, Modigliani worked on it for two more weeks, protesting all the while that this might ruin it.

Coll: Galerie Percier, Paris

Ref: Chicago. Art Institute, Birch Bartlett Handbook, *1926, pp. 44, 45;* Ibid., *1929, pp. 50, 51; Chicago. Art Institute,* A Century of Progress Exhibition, *1933, cat. no. 702;* Ibid., *1934, cat. no. 356; Chicago. Art Institute,* Catalogue of the Birch Bartlett Collection, *1946, pp. 36, 37*

WOMAN WITH NECKLACE

Painted 1917, signed: Modigliani. Oil on canvas, 36×23⅞ in. (91.5×60.8 cm.)
Charles H. and Mary F. S. Worcester Collection, 47.93

Coll: C. Zamaron, Paris; Stephen C. Clark, New York

Ref: Carstairs, C., International Studio *93: 71, 72, August 1929;* Art News *29, pt. 1: 5, March 28, 1931; Chicago. Art Institute,* Catalogue of the Worcester Collection, *1936, cat. no. 94; Worcester, Mass. Art Museum,* News Bulletin and Calendar *8, no. 7, April 1943;* Magazine of Art *36: 17, 1943*

MOHOLY-NAGY, László ~ *b. 1895 Bacsbarsod, Hungary. d. 1946 Chicago*

Influenced by the Russian constructivists, Malevich and Lissitsky, Moholy-Nagy's consuming interest was directed toward light in all its manifestations. The artist was invited to teach at the Bauhaus where he worked under Gropius from 1923 to 1928. He moved to London in 1935 and two years later came to Chicago where he founded the New Bauhaus. Later he opened the Institute of Design in Chicago.

NUCLEAR I, CH

Painted 1946. Oil on canvas, 38$\frac{1}{16}$×30⅛ in. (96.5×76.6 cm.)
Gift of Mr. and Mrs. Leigh B. Block, 47.40

The CH identifies the painting as one of a series executed in Chicago.

MOILLON, Louise ~ *1615/16– about 1675 Paris*

Louise Moillon probably received training from her father who, like her brother, was one of the King's painters, chiefly known for landscapes and engravings. Except for the fact that she married a Parisian named Etienne Girardot, little is known of the artist's life.

STILL LIFE

Signed and dated: Louise Moillon 1630. Oil on panel, 21×28 in. (53.5×71.2 cm.)
Wirt D. Walker Fund, 48.78

Coll: Mrs. Gertrude D. Webster, Mass.

MOLA, Pier Francesco ~ *b. 1612 Coldrerio, Italy. d. 1666 Rome*

Mola, a pupil of Giuseppe Cesari (Cavaliere d'Arpino) in Rome, later studied in Venice. He was also influenced by Francesco Albani, and was active in Rome and at the French court.

HOMER DICTATING

Painted probably about 1650. Oil on canvas, 28 × 38 in. (71.2 × 96.5 cm.)
Charles H. and Mary F. S. Worcester Collection, 30.337

Ref: Chicago. Art Institute, Annual Report, *1930, p. 9; Chicago. Art Institute,* Bulletin *24: 69, 70, 71, 1930; Chicago. Art Institute,* A Century of Progress Exhibition, *1933, cat. no. 151;* Ibid., *1934, cat. no. 49; Chicago. Art Institute,* Catalogue of the Worcester Collection, *1936, cat. no. 19*

MOMPER II, Joos de ~ *1564–1635 Antwerp*

Joos de Momper studied under his father Bartholomeus de Momper, and was influenced by Pieter Brueghel the Elder.

MOUNTAIN LANDSCAPE

Painted about first quarter 17th century. Oil on panel, 19½ × 36 in. (49.7 × 91.5 cm.)
Gift of Mrs. Perry H. Smith, 35.157

Ref: Chicago. Art Institute, Bulletin *30: 38–9, 1936; Burkham, F. McPherson,* Allen Memorial Art Museum Bulletin *8: 4–16, Fall 1950*

MOUNTAIN ROAD

Painted about first quarter of 17th century. Oil on panel, 19½ × 31 in. (49.7 × 78.8 cm.)
Mr. and Mrs. Martin A. Ryerson Collection, 33.1067

Coll: A. Imbert, Rome, 1910

Ref: Chicago. Art Institute, A Century of Progress Exhibition, *1934, cat. no. 86*

MONDRIAN, Piet ~ *b. 1872 Amersfoort, Holland. d. 1944 New York City*

Mondrian studied at the Amsterdam Academy of Arts, then went to Paris in 1910 where he came in contact with Cubism. With Theo van Doesburg, he was one of the founders of the Dutch de Stijl group, and a prime influence in the development of the modern art. He came to America in 1940.

DIAGONAL COMPOSITION Illus. p. 432

Signed and dated: PM 21. Oil on canvas, 23⅝ × 23⅝ in. (60.1 × 60.1 cm.)
Gift of Edgar Kaufmann, Jr., 57.307

COMPOSITION—GRAY RED

Signed and dated: PM 35. Oil on canvas, 21⅝ × 22⅜ in. (55 × 56.9 cm.)
Gift of Mrs. Gilbert W. Chapman, 49.518

MONET, Claude ~ *b. 1840 Paris. d. 1926 Giverny, France*

Early influenced by Boudin (his first teacher) and Jongkind, Monet was also much interested in the work of Courbet and Manet. In 1863 he became a pupil of Gleyre, in whose studio he met Renoir, Sisley and Bazille. He became a leading Impressionist, who along with his colleagues arranged the famous Impressionist exhibitions starting in 1874.

THE BEACH AT SAINTE ADRESSE Illus. p. 278

Signed and dated: Claude Monet 67. Oil on canvas, 29½ × 39¾ in. (75 × 101 cm.)
Mr. and Mrs. Lewis L. Coburn Memorial Collection, 33.439

Ref: Geffroy, G., L'Art et les Artistes *n.s. 2: 64, November 1920; Geffroy, G.,* Claude Monet, *1922, p. 40; Mauclair, C.,* Claude Monet, *1927, pp. 36, 60; Lathom, X.,* Claude Monet, *1931, pl. 6; Chicago. Art Institute,* Catalogue of the Coburn Collection, *1932, cat. no. 19; Chicago. Art Institute,* Bulletin *26: 66, 67, 1932;* The Fine Arts *19: 22, June 1932; Chicago. Art Institute,* A Century of Progress Exhibition, *1933, cat. no. 292;* Ibid., *1934, cat. no. 210; Brielle, R.,* L'Art et les Artistes *28: 129, 1934; Venturi, L.,* Les Archives de l'Impressionisme, *II, 1939, p. 257; Rewald, J.,* The History of Impressionism, *New York, 1946, p. 137; Clark, Kenneth,* Landscape into Art, *1948, pp. 88, 89*

THE RIVER

Signed and dated: Monet 1868. Oil on canvas, 31⅞ × 39½ in. (81.7 × 100.3 cm.)
Potter Palmer Collection, 22.427

Ref: Chicago. Art Institute, Catalogue of the Potter Palmer Collection, *1910, cat. no. 40; Chicago. Art Institute,* Bulletin *15: 160, 1921; Chicago. Art Institute,* Bulletin *19: 18, 1925; Chicago. Art Institute,* A Century of Progress Exhibition, *1933, cat. no. 291;* Ibid., *1934, cat. no. 208; Venturi, L.,* Les Archives de l'Impressionisme, *II, 1939, p. 257; Scheyer, E.,* The Art Quarterly *5: 123, 125, 1942; Chicago. Art Institute,* Bulletin *37: 86, 1943; Rewald, J.,* The History of Impressionism, *New York, 1946, p. 188*

THE ARTIST'S GARDEN AT ARGENTEUIL

Painted 1872, signed: Claude Monet. Oil on canvas, 23⅞ × 29⅛ in. (60.8 × 74 cm.)
Mr. and Mrs. Martin A. Ryerson Collection, 33.1153

Ref: Chicago. Art Institute, Bulletin *19: 19, 1925; Chicago. Art Institute,* A Century of Progress Exhibition, *1933, cat. no. 298;* Ibid., *1934, cat. no. 209; Huth, H.,* Gazette des Beaux-Arts *29, ser. 6: 225–52, April 1946*

OLD ST. LAZARE STATION, PARIS Ill. p. 279

Signed and dated: Claude Monet 77. Oil on canvas, 31½ × 23½ in. (80.2 × 59.6 cm.)
Mr. and Mrs. Martin A. Ryerson Collection, 33.1158

Ref: Geffroy, G., Claude Monet, *1922, p. 136; Chicago. Art Institute,* Bulletin *19: 19, 1925; Fels, F.,* Claude Monet *(Les Peintres Français Nouveaux, no. 22), 1925, p. 45; Mauclair, C.,* Claude Monet, *1927, pl. 20; Lathom, X.,* Claude Monet, *1931, pl. 16;*

Chicago. Art Institute, Bulletin *27: 11, 1933; Chicago. Art Institute,* A Century of Progress Exhibition, *1933, cat. no. 299;* Ibid., *1934, cat. no. 219; Tietze, H.,* Meisterwerke Europaeischer Malerei in Amerika, *1935, pl. 289; Huth, H.,* Gazette des Beaux-Arts *29, ser. 6: 225–52, April 1946; Clark, Kenneth,* Landscape into Art, *1949, p. 102*

STILL LIFE: APPLES AND GRAPES

Signed and dated: Claude Monet 1880. Oil on canvas, $25\frac{3}{4} \times 32\frac{1}{8}$ in. (65.5 × 81.6 cm.)
Mr. and Mrs. Martin A. Ryerson Collection, 33.1152

Ref: Chicago. Art Institute, Bulletin *19: 19, 1925; Chicago. Art Institute,* A Century of Progress Exhibition, *1933, cat. no. 297;* Ibid., *1934, cat. no. 217*

PORTRAIT OF M. COQUERET, FILS

Signed and dated: Claude Monet, Janvier 1881.
Oil on canvas, $17\frac{7}{8} \times 14\frac{7}{8}$ in. (45.5 × 37.8 cm.)
Gift of Mrs. Leigh B. Block, 56.1204

THE CLIFF WALK, (ETRETAT)

Signed and dated: Claude Monet 82. Oil on canvas, $25\frac{3}{4} \times 32$ in. (65.5 × 81.3 cm.)
Mr. and Mrs. Lewis L. Coburn Memorial Collection, 33.443

Ref: Borgmeyer, C. L., Fine Arts Journal *28: 328, 1913; Chicago. Art Institute,* Bulletin *26: 66, 1932; Chicago. Art Institute,* Catalogue of the Coburn Collection, *1932, cat. no. 22; Chicago. Art Institute,* A Century of Progress Exhibition, *1933, cat. no. 295;* Ibid., *1934, cat. no. 214*

ETRETAT, MORNING

Signed and dated: Claude Monet 83. Oil on canvas, $25\frac{3}{4} \times 32\frac{1}{4}$ in. (65.5 × 82.3 cm.)
Potter Palmer Collection, 22.429

Ref: Chicago. Art Institute, Catalogue of the Potter Palmer Collection, *1910, cat. no. 38; Chicago. Art Institute,* Bulletin *19: 19, 1925; Chicago. Art Institute,* A Century of Progress Exhibition, *1934, cat. no. 216*

BORDIGHERA

Signed and dated: Claude Monet 84. Oil on canvas, $25\frac{1}{2} \times 32$ in. (64.8 × 81.3 cm.)
Potter Palmer Collection, 22.426

Ref: Chicago. Art Institute, Catalogue of the Potter Palmer Collection, *1910, cat. no. 33; Chicago. Art Institute,* Bulletin *19: 19, 1925; Fels, F.,* Claude Monet, *1925, p. 51; Chicago. Art Institute,* A Century of Progress Exhibition, *1933, cat. no. 290A; Chicago. Art Institute,* A Century of Progress Exhibition, *1934, cat. no. 207; Clark, Kenneth,* Landscape into Art, *1949, pp. 93, 94*

VIEW FROM CAP MARTIN

Signed and dated: Claude Monet 84. Oil on canvas, 26 × 32 in. (66.1 × 81.3 cm.)
Mr. and Mrs. Martin A. Ryerson Collection, 33.1162

Ref: Geffroy, G., Claude Monet, *1922, p. 109; Chicago. Art Institute,* Bulletin *19: 19, 1925; Chicago. Art Institute,* A Century of Progress Exhibition, *1934, cat. no. 224*

BOATS IN WINTER QUARTERS

Signed and dated: Claude Monet 85. Oil on canvas, 29⅛ × 36½ in. (74 × 92.8 cm.)
Potter Palmer Collection, 22.428

Ref: Chicago. Art Institute, Bulletin *19: 19, 1925; Rich, D. C.,* Pantheon *11: 77, March 1933; Chicago. Art Institute,* A Century of Progress Exhibition, *1933, cat. no. 293;* Ibid,, *1934, cat. no. 211*

BOATS IN WINTER QUARTERS: ETRETAT

Painted 1885, signed: Claude Monet. Oil on canvas, 25¾ × 32 in. (65.5 × 81.3 cm.)
Charles H. and Mary F. S. Worcester Collection, 47.95

Coll: Georges Bernheim, Paris, c. 1907; Marczell von Nemes, Budapest, 1911; Worcester, 1922

Ref: Chicago. Art Institute, Bulletin *17: 70, 1923; Chicago. Art Institute,* Catalogue of the Worcester Collection, *1937, cat. no. 77*

TORRENT, DAUPHINE

Painted about 1888–1889, signed: Claude Monet.
Oil on canvas, 25⅞ × 36½ in. (65.8 × 92.8 cm.)
Potter Palmer Collection, 22.432

Ref: Chicago. Art Institute, Bulletin *19: 19, 1925; Chicago. Art Institute,* A Century of Progress Exhibition, *1934, cat. no. 220*

POOL OF WATER LILIES

Signed and dated: Claude Monet 1900. Oil on canvas, 35⅛ × 39½ in. (89.3 × 100.3 cm.)
Mr. and Mrs. Lewis L. Coburn Memorial Collection, 33.441

Ref: Chicago. Art Institute, Bulletin *19: 20, 21, 1925; Fels, F.,* Claude Monet, *1925, p. 63; Mauclair, C.,* Claude Monet, *1927, pl. 39; Chicago. Art Institute,* Catalogue of the Coburn Collection, *1932, cat. no. 25*

HAYSTACK, WINTER, GIVERNY

Signed and dated: Claude Monet 91. Oil on canvas, 25¾ × 36½ in. (65.5 × 92.8 cm.)
Mr. and Mrs. Martin A. Ryerson Collection, 33.1155

HAYSTACKS, SETTING SUN

Signed and dated: Claude Monet 91. Oil on canvas, 25½ × 39½ in. (64.8 × 100.3 cm.)
Potter Palmer Collection, 22.431

Ref: Chicago. Art Institute, Catalogue of the Potter Palmer Collection, *1910, cat. no. 36; Chicago. Art Institute,* Bulletin *19: 20, 1925*

TWO HAYSTACKS

Signed and dated: Claude Monet 91. Oil on canvas, 25½×39¼ in. (64.8×99.8 cm.)
Mr. and Mrs. Lewis L. Coburn Memorial Collection, 33.444
Coll: Pottter Palmer, Chicago

Ref: Chicago. Art Institute, Catalogue of the Coburn Collection, *1932, cat. no. 24*

A FIELD OF FLOWERS IN FRANCE

Signed and dated: Claude Monet 91. Oil on canvas, 24×38 in. (61×96.5 cm.)
Mr. and Mrs. W. W. Kimball Collection, 22.4465

Ref: Chicago. Art Institute, Bulletin *19: 19, 1925*

MORNING ON THE SEINE

Signed and dated: Claude Monet '97. Oil on canvas, 34½×35½ in. (87.6×89.5 cm.)
Mr. and Mrs. Martin A. Ryerson Collection, 33.1156

COAST GUARD SHACK

Signed and dated: Claude Monet 97. Oil on canvas, 26×36½ in. (66.1×92.8 cm.)
Mr. and Mrs. Martin A. Ryerson Collection, 33.1149

Ref: Chicago. Art Institute, Bulletin *19: 20, 1925; Chicago. Art Institute,* A Century of Progress Exhibition, *1933, cat. no. 296;* Ibid., *1934, cat. no. 215*

VETHEUIL

Signed and dated: Claude Monet 1901. Oil on canvas, 35¼×36⅝ in. (89.5×93 cm.)
Mr. and Mrs. Lewis L. Coburn Memorial Collection, 33.447

Ref: Chicago. Art Institute, Bulletin *19: 18, 1925; Chicago. Art Institute,* A Century of Progress Exhibition, *1934, cat. no. 222*

VETHEUIL AT SUNSET

Signed and dated: Claude Monet 1901. Oil on canvas, 34¾×36 in. (88.3×91.5 cm.)
Mr. and Mrs. Martin A. Ryerson, 33.1161

Ref: Chicago. Art Institute, A Century of Progress Exhibition, *1934, cat. no. 223*

CHARING CROSS BRIDGE, LONDON

Signed and dated: Claude Monet 1901. Oil on canvas, 25×36 in. (63.6×91.5 cm.)
Mr. and Mrs. Martin A. Ryerson Collection, 33.1150

Ref: Chicago. Art Institute, Bulletin *19: 20, 1925; Chicago. Art Institute,* A Century of Progress Exhibition, *1933, cat. no. 294;* Ibid., *1934, cat. no. 212*

HOUSES OF PARLIAMENT, WESTMINSTER

Painted 1903, signed: Claude Monet. Oil on canvas, 31⅞×36¼ in. (81×92.1 cm.)
Mr. and Mrs. Martin A. Ryerson Collection, 33.1164

Ref: Chicago. Art Institute, Bulletin *19: 20, 1925; Pickens, B. L.*, The Art Quarterly *3: 275, 277, 1940*

WATERLOO BRIDGE

Signed and dated: Claude Monet 1903. Oil on canvas, 25¾×39⅜ in. (65.5×100 cm.)
Mr. and Mrs. Martin A. Ryerson Collection, 33.1163

Ref: Geffroy, G., Claude Monet, *1922, p. 317; Chicago. Art Institute*, Bulletin *19: 21, 1925*

WATER LILIES (I)

Signed and dated: Claude Monet 1906. Oil on canvas, 35¼×36¾ in. (89.5×93.4 cm.)
Mr. and Mrs. Martin A. Ryerson Collection, 33.1157

Ref: Geffroy, G., L'Art et les Artistes, *N.S. 2: 73, November 1920; Chicago. Art Institute*, Bulletin *19: 20, 1925; Slocombe, G.*, Coronet *3: 26, March 1938; Venturi, L.*, Impressionists and Symbolists, *London, 1950, fig. 62 (ill.)*

VENICE, SAN GIORGIO MAGGIORE

Signed and dated: Claude Monet 1908. Oil on canvas, 25¼×35¾ in. (64.2×90.8 cm.)
Mr. and Mrs. Martin A. Ryerson Collection, 33.1160

Ref: Chicago. Art Institute, Bulletin *19: 21, 1925*

VENICE, DARIO PALACE

Signed and dated: Claude Monet 1908. Oil on canvas, 25½×31 in. (64.8×78.8 cm.)
Mr. and Mrs. Lewis L. Coburn Memorial Collection, 33.446

Ref: Geffroy, G., Claude Monet, *1922, p. 312; Chicago. Art Institute*, Catalogue of the Coburn Collection, *1932, cat. no. 26; Chicago. Art Institute*, A Century of Progress Exhibition, *1934, cat. no. 221*

IRIS BY THE POND Illus. p. 284

Painted 1919–1925, stamped: Claude Monet.
Oil on canvas, 79×79½ in. (200.7×252.6 cm.)
Art Institute Purchase Fund, 56.1202

MONTICELLI, Adolphe Joseph Thomas ~ *1824–1886 Marseille, France*

Monticelli studied in Marseille and later in Paris with Paul Delaroche. He also was influenced by Diaz and Delacroix.

PORTRAIT OF A LADY Illus. p. 234

Signed and dated: Monticelli P. Mai-Septembre (and illegible date).
Painted between 1870 and 1879. Oil on panel, 51⅜×38⅜ in. (130.6×97.5 cm.)
A. A. Munger Collection, 47.25

Ref: Chicago. Art Institute, Bulletin *42: 78–81, November 1948*

FRENCH IMPRESSIONIST AND POST-IMPRESSIONIST PAINTINGS

SECTION TWO

XIXth—XXth Centuries

ILLUSTRATIONS

Seurat, Georges, La Grande Jatte, 1884–86. Helen Birch Bartlett Memorial Collection

Cézanne, Paul, Madame Cézanne in a Yellow Armchair, 1890/94. Wilson L. Mead Fund

Cézanne, Paul, Vase of Tulips, 1890-94. Mr. & Mrs. Lewis L. Coburn Memorial Collection

Above: Van Gogh, Vincent, Bedroom at Arles, 1888. Helen Birch Bartlett Collection

Toulouse-Lautrec, Henri de, In the Circus Fernando, 1888. The Joseph Winterbotham Collection

Van Gogh, Vincent, The Drinkers, 1890. The Joseph Winterbotham Collection

Van Gogh, Vincent, Self Portrait, 1886–88. The Joseph Winterbotham Collection

Gauguin, Paul, Marie Derrien, 1890. The Joseph Winterbotham Collection

Gauguin, Old Women of Arles, 1888. Gift of Annie Swan Coburn to the Mr. & Mrs. Lewis L. Coburn Memorial Collection

Toulouse-Lautrec, Henri de, At the Moulin Rouge, 1892. Helen Birch Bartlett Memorial Collection

Gauguin, Paul, The Day of the God, 1894. Helen Birch Bartlett Memorial Collection

Degas, Edgar, The Millinery Shop, c. 1885. Mr. & Mrs. Lewis L. Coburn Memorial Collection

THE PRINCESSES

Painted about 1870, signed: Monticelli. Oil on panel, 11¾ × 23⅞ in. (29.8 × 60.8 cm.)
Charles H. and Mary F. S. Worcester Collection, 47.97

Coll: Barbizon House, London

Ref: Barbizon House, 1920, An Illustrated Record, *1920, cat. no. 12; Chicago. Art Institute,* A Century of Progress Exhibition, *1933, cat. no. 258; Chicago. Art Institute,* Catalogue of the Worcester Collection, *1937, cat. no. 69*

THE FAIRIES

Painted between 1870 and 1880, signed: Monticelli.
Oil on panel, 19½ × 27¾ in. (49.7 × 70.6 cm.)
Charles H. and Mary F. S. Worcester Collection, 47.96

Coll: Baron Gourgaud, Paris; Gustave, Geoffroy, Paris

Ref: Chicago. Art Institute, Catalogue of the Worcester Collection, *1937, cat. no. 68*

PORTRAIT OF STANISLAS ROULAND

Painted 1880, signed: Monticelli. Oil on canvas, 47½ × 33½ in. (120.6 × 85.2 cm.)
Gift of Grant J. Pick, 58.117

MEDITATION (SEATED WOMAN)

Painted about 1878–1879, signed lower left: A. Monticelli.
Oil on panel, 20⅝ × 15⅞ in. (52.4 × 40.4 cm.)
Gift of Joseph Winterbotham, 54.317

MOR, Anthonis ~ *b. 1519 Utrecht. d. 1575 [?] Antwerp*

Mor, a pupil of Jan van Scorel, became a master painter in Antwerp in 1547. Soon after this he went to Rome and later worked at the Hapsburg courts in Brussels, Madrid, and Lisbon, where he was especially favored by Cardinal Granvella and the Duke of Alba.

PORTRAIT OF A COURT LADY

Painted about 1555. Oil on canvas, 37¾ × 30¼ in. (95.9 × 76.9 cm.)
Gift of Chester Dale, 51.314

Coll: Pallavicino-Grimaldi; Charles Fairfax Murray, London, 1899; Achillito Chiesa

Ref: Genoa. Sale of Collection Pallavicino-Grimaldi, *November 29 to December 2, 1899, cat. no. 276; Paris. Galerie Georges Petit,* Catalogue de . . . Collection Charles Fairfax Murray . . . , *June 15, 1914, cat. no. 21*

PORTRAIT OF A NOBLEMAN

Painted probably about 1558. Oil on panel, 44½ × 33 in. (113.1 × 83.9 cm.)
Robert Alexander Waller Fund, 31.937 (Friedlaender no. 389)

Coll: Karl von der Heydt, Berlin

Ref: Hymans, H., Antonio Moro, Son Oeuvre et Son Temps, *1910, p. 164; Chicago. Art Institute,* Annual Report, *1931, p. 18; Chicago. Art Institute,* Bulletin *26: 14–5, 1932; Chicago. Art Institute,* A Century of Progress Exhibition, *1933, cat. no. 53, pl. 34;* Ibid., *1934, cat. no. 127*

PORTRAIT OF A LADY

Painted between 1560 and 1570. Oil on panel, 48⅛ × 35⅜ in. (122.6 × 89.9 cm.)
Gift of Charles L. Hutchinson, 41.29 (Friedlaender no. 405)

Coll: Aufrère [?]; Earl of Yarborough, Brocklesby Hall, Lincolnshire, England; J. H. Harding, New York, 1924

Ref: Waagen, Treasures of Art in Great Britain, *II, 1854, p. 87; Waagen,* Galleries and Cabinets of Art in Great Britain, *IV, 1857, p. 65; Burger, W.,* Trésors d'Art, *1957, p. 172; Hymans, H.,* Antonio Moro, Son Oeuvre et Son Temps, *1910, pp. 134, 135 (footnote 1); Cust, L.,* Burlington Magazine *18: 11, 12, October 1910; Marlier, G.,* Anthonis Mor Van Dashorst, *1934, p. 103 (section III of cat. no. 51); Chicago. Art Institute,* A Century of Progress Exhibition, *1934, cat. no. 126; Chicago. Art Institute,* Bulletin *36: 1–3, 1942*

PORTRAIT OF A BOY

Painted about 1560–1570. Oil on canvas, 15½ × 10⅜ in. (39.5 × 26.4 cm.)
Max and Leola Epstein Collection, 54.293 (Friedlaender no. 393)

MOREELSE, Paulus ~ *1571–1638 Utrecht, Holland*

Chiefly a portrait painter, Moreelse studied in Utrecht with Michiel Mierevald and also in Rome.

PORTRAIT OF A LADY

Painted about 1620. Oil on panel, 28⅛ × 22⅝ in. (71.5 × 57.6 cm.)
Max and Leola Epstein Collection, 54.292 (de Jonge no. 119)

MORETTO DA BRESCIA, (Alessandro di Pietro Bonvicino) ~ *About 1498–1554 Brescia*

Moretto was trained in the tradition of Vincenzo Foppa in Milan. He worked in Brescia, Bergamo, Milan, and other towns of north Italy.

MARY MAGDALENE

Painted second quarter 16th century. Oil on canvas, 64½ × 17¾ in. (163.9 × 45.2 cm.)
Gift of William Owen Goodman, 35.161

This panel was probably once the right wing of an altarpiece and is known to have been in a private collection in Brescia in 1760.

Coll: Avogadri, Brescia; Fenaroli; Farrer, Sandhurst Lodge, England; Blakeslee, New York

Ref: Crowe and Cavalvaselle, A History of Painting in North Italy, *III, London, 1912, p. 307;* Rassegna d'Arte *15: 123, 1915; Venturi, A.,* Storia dell'Arte Italiana *IX, pt. 4, 1929, p. 203; Chicago. Art Institute,* A Century of Progress Exhibition, *1933, cat. no. 130; Chicago. Art Institute,* Annual Report, *1935, p. 25; Gombosi, G.,* Moretto da Brescia, *1943, p. 111, cat. no. 161*

MORISOT, Berthe ~ *b. 1841 Bourges, France. d. 1895 Paris*

Berthe Morisot was influenced by Corot, with whom she studied from 1860 to 1866. She made Manet's acquaintance while sketching at the Louvre in 1868, and from then on she became his constant companion. In 1874 she married Manet's brother, Eugène. Her first public exhibition was at the Salon of 1864, but later she showed with the Impressionists after their first exhibit in 1874.

LADY AT HER TOILETTE Illus. p. 288

Painted about 1875, signed: Berthe Morisot. Oil on canvas, 23¾ × 31¾ in. (60.5 × 80.8 cm).
The Stickney Fund, 24.127

Coll: Mary Cassatt, 1896

Ref: Dewhurst, W., International Studio *19: 165, 168, May 1903; Marx, R.,* Gazette des Beaux-Arts *38, per. 3: 497, 498, December 1907; Chicago. Art Institute,* Annual Report, *1924; Chicago. Art Institute,* Bulletin *18: 50, 51, 1924; Angoulvent, M.,* Berthe Morisot, *c. 1930–1933, pp. 55, 121, cat. no. 83; Chicago. Art Institute,* A Century of Progress Exhibition, *1933, cat. no. 334;* Ibid., *1934, cat. no. 257; Venturi, L.,* Les Archives de l'Impressionisme, *II, 1939, p. 257; Huth, H.,* Gazette des Beaux-Arts *29, ser. 6: 225–52, April 1946*

WOMAN COMBING HER HAIR

Painted 1894. Pastel on paper, 23 × 16 in. (58.6 × 40.8 cm.)
Gift of Kate L. Brewster, 50.125

Ref: Fourreau, A., Berthe Morisot, *1925, pp. 61, 62; Chicago. Art Institute,* Bulletin *44: 55, September 1950*

MORONI, Giovanni Battista ~ *b. about 1525 Bondo. d. 1578 Bergamo*

Moroni, a pupil of Moretto da Brescia, came under the influence of Titian and Lorenzo Lotto. He was active mainly in Bergamo.

LUDOVICO MADRUZZO Illus. p. 46

Painted about 1560. Oil on canvas, 79¾ × 46 in. (202.6 × 116.9 cm.)
Charles H. and Mary F. S. Worcester Collection, 29.912

Coll: Madruzzo Castle, Buonconsiglio, 1658; Baron de Roccabruna, 1837; Barons I. and Valentino Salvadori; James Stillman, New York, 1906; Charles Chauncey Stillman, New York

Ref: Morelli, G., Italian Painters, *II, London, 1893, p. 65 (footnote 2); Oberziner, L.,* Rassegna d'Arte *2: 88, 89, 1902; Berenson, B.,* North Italian Painters of the Renaissance, *1907, p. 272; Lafenestre, G.,* Revue de l'Art *21: 358–60, 1907; Michel, A.,* Histoire de l'Art, *V, pt. 2, 1915, p. 528; Fogolari, G.,* Trento, *1916, pp. 142, 158, 161; Locatelli-Milesi,* Emporium *44: 380, 1916; Chicago. Art Institute,* Bulletin *21: 45, 47–9, 1927; Chicago. Art Institute,* Annual Report, *1927, p. 69; Venturi, A.,* Storia dell'Arte Italiana, *IX, pt. 4, 1929, p. 277; Chicago. Art Institute,* Bulletin *24: 30, 31, 1930; Venturi, L.,* Pitture Italiane in America, *1931, pl. 398; Berenson, B.,* Italian Pictures of the Renaissance, *1932, p. 381; Chicago. Art Institute,* A Century of Progress Exhibition, *1933, cat. no. 129;* Ibid., *1934, cat. no. 50; Tietze, H.,* Meisterwerke Europaeischer Malerei in Amerika, *1935, pl. 92; Berenson, B.,* Pitture Italiane del Rinascimento, *1936, p. 327; Chicago. Art Institute,* Catalogue of the Worcester Collection, *1938, cat. no. 8, pl. 7 (ill.)*

MORSE, Samuel F. B. ~ *b. 1791 Charlestown, Mass. d. 1872 New York City*

In 1811 Morse went to England to study with Washington Allston and Benjamin West. He came back to America and worked as a portrait painter in New England and in Charleston, S.C. Morse later settled in New York, where in 1826 he became the first president of the National Academy of Design.

PORTRAIT OF A GENTLEMAN

Painted about 1815. Oil on canvas, $30\frac{1}{4} \times 25$ in. (76.9×63.6 cm.)
Cyrus Hall McCormick Fund, 43.99

MOUNT, William Sidney ~ *1807–1868 Setauket, N.Y.*

Mount was America's most important early genre painter. He received art instruction from his brother Henry S. Mount, and was one of the early students of the National Academy of Design.

THE BREAKDOWN

Signed and dated: W. S. Mount 1835. Oil on canvas, $22\frac{3}{8} \times 27\frac{1}{2}$ in. (56.9×70 cm.)
The William Owen and Erna Sawyer Goodman Collection, 39.392

MUELLER, George ~ *b. 1929 Newark, N.J.*

George Mueller studied at the Newark School of Fine and Industrial Art and at Cooper Union.

BLACK CHART

Signed and dated on back of painting: Mueller '55.
Oil on pressed board, $60 \times 46\frac{1}{4}$ in. (152.5×117.5 cm.)
Gift of the Society for Contemporary American Art, 56.61

MÜNTER, Gabriele ~ *b. 1877 Berlin*

Gabriele Münter, early an Impressionist, later turned to Expressionism. Occasionally she exhibited with the Blue Rider group. Her work was influenced by Kandinsky.

STILL LIFE WITH QUEEN

Painted in 1912. Oil on canvas, 31 × 22⅛ in. (78.8 × 56.3 cm.)
Arthur Jerome Eddy Memorial Collection, 31.521

MUNKACSY, Mihaly de ~ *b. 1844 Munkacs, Hungary. d. 1909 Endenich, Germany*

THE WRESTLER'S CHALLENGE

Painted 1875, signed: Munkacsy, M. Oil on panel, 34¾ × 51¼ in. (88.3 × 130.3 cm.)
A. A. Munger Collection, 01.435

MURILLO, Bartolomé Esteban, Follower of,
see
ITALIAN SCHOOL, 17th century

TWO MONKS IN A LANDSCAPE

MURPHY, Hermann Dudley ~ *b. 1867 Marlboro, Mass. d. 1945 Lexington, Mass.*

Murphy studied at the School of the Museum of Fine Arts in Boston and with Jean Paul Laurens in Paris.

HENRY OSSAWA TANNER

Painted probably between 1890 and 1895, signed with initial.
Oil on canvas, 37 × 28 in. (94 × 71.2 cm.)
Friends of American Art Collection, 24.37

CHARLES H. WOODBURY

Signed with initial, dated: 1906. Oil on canvas, 29½ × 24½ in. (75 × 62.4 cm.)
Charles S. Peterson Purchase Prize, 22.4452

MURPHY, John Francis ~ *b. 1853 Oswego, N.Y. d. 1921 New York City*

Murphy was a largely self-taught painter who gained a reputation for his landscapes.

HILL TOP

Signed and dated: J. Francis Murphy, 1910. Oil on canvas, 24½ × 36 in. (62.4 × 91.5 cm.)
Friends of American Art Collection, 10.306

MYERS, Jerome ~ *b. 1867 Petersburg, Va. d. 1940 New York City*

Myers studied in night classes at Cooper Union and the Art Students League. He was mainly self-taught.

THE END OF THE STREET

Signed and dated: Jerome Myers 1922. Oil on canvas, 24½×29½ in. (62.4×75 cm.)
Friends of American Art Collection, 23.974

NEAGLE, John ~ *b. 1796 Boston. d. 1865 Philadelphia*

For a brief period Neagle was a pupil of Bass Otis in Philadelphia. His early ventures as a portrait painter in Lexington, Ky., and in New Orleans proved unsuccessful, but after settling in Philadelphia he was soon able to establish himself.

VIEW OF THE SCHUYLKILL

Signed, inscribed and dated on back: View of the Schuylkill looking up towards the falls, embracing Peter's Island, painted from nature, John Neagle 1827.
Oil on canvas, 25×30 in. (63.6×76.3 cm.)
Friends of American Art Collection, 34.388

NEAL, David ~ *b. 1837 Lowell, Mass. d. 1915 Munich*

Neal went to Munich in 1861 to study with Piloty. He was one of the first Americans to work in Munich.

INTERIOR OF ST. MARK'S, VENICE

Signed and dated: David Neal München, 1869.
Oil on canvas, 72½×58½ in. (184.2×148.7 cm.)
Nickerson Collection, 87.232

NEER, Eglon van der ~ *b. 1634 Amsterdam. d. 1703 Düsseldorf, Germany*

Eglon van der Neer was a pupil of his father, Aert van der Neer the Elder, and of Jacob van Loo. In 1690 he became court painter in Düsseldorf.

DOMESTIC SCENE

Painted end of 17th century. Oil on canvas, 19×15 in. (48.3×38.2 cm.)
Gift of Honoré Palmer, 43.1183 (HdG no. 104)

Coll: O. Pein, Cologne; Rümerskirch, Munich

NETSCHER, Caspar ~ *b. 1639 Heidelberg, Germany. d. 1684 The Hague*

Netscher, a pupil of Gerard Terborch, traveled in Italy and France and finally settled at the Hague in 1662. Influenced by Terborch and Gabriel Metsu, Netscher later turned to the French manner of artists like Mignard.

PORTRAIT OF A LADY BEFORE A MIRROR

Signed and dated: C. Netscher 1680. Oil on panel, 14⅛×11⅞ in. (36×30.2 cm.)
Gift of Charles L. Hutchinson, 25.718 (HdG no. 55)

Coll: G. J. Vernon; Miss Davison; Smith, 1848

Ref: Redford, G., Art Sales, . . . *II, 1888, p. 311; Graves,* Art Sales, . . . *II, 1921, p. 281; Chicago. Art Institute,* Bulletin *19: 103, 1925; Chicago. Art Institute,* A Century of Progress Exhibition, *1933, cat. no. 68;* Ibid., *1934, cat. no. 100*

PORTRAIT OF A GENTLEMAN

Signed and dated: C. Netscher 1680. Oil on canvas, 18½ × 15 in. (47.1 × 38.2 cm.)
Mr. and Mrs. Martin A. Ryerson Collection, 33.1087 (HdG no. 347)

Coll: G. Rothan, Paris (sale May 29, 1890, no. 79, p. 58)

NEWMAN, Robert Loftin ~ *b. 1827 Richmond, Va. d. 1912 New York City*

Newman studied with Couture in Paris, was also influenced by Millet, and owed some of his color to Delacroix.

MOTHER AND CHILD

Signed and dated: R. L. Newman 1900. Oil on canvas, 17 × 14 in. (43.3 × 35.1 cm.)
Charles H. and Mary F. S. Worcester Collection, 47.98

NORTON, John Warner ~ *b. 1876 Lockport, Ill. d. 1934 Charleston, S.C.*

Norton began his studies at the School of the Art Institute in 1899. He later taught there.

LIGHT AND SHADOW

Painted about 1924, signed: Norton. Oil on canvas, 35½ × 41½ in. (90.2 × 105.4 cm.)
Friends of American Art Collection, 24.953

NUZI, Allegretto ~ *about 1315–1385 Fabriano, Italy*

Although first mentioned in Florence in 1346, most of Nuzi's activities were concentrated in the towns of Fabriano and Macerata.

CRUCIFIXION

Painted about 1365–1370. Tempera on panel, 28½ × 19⅞ in. (72.5 × 50.7 cm.)
Mr. and Mrs. Martin A. Ryerson Collection, 37.1006

This was the central panel of an altarpiece, the wings of which are in the Kress Collection at the National Gallery in Washington, D.C.

Ref: Berenson, B., Italian Pictures of the Renaissance, *1932, p. 399; Chicago. Art Institute,* A Century of Progress Exhibition, *1933, cat. no. 92; Berenson, B.,* Pitture Italiane del Rinascimento, *1936, p. 343; Zeri, F.,* Bolletino d'Arte *34: 21–30, 1949*

EPISCOPAL SAINT ENTHRONED

Painted about 1370. Tempera on panel, 34 × 26 in. (86.4 × 66.1 cm.)
Mr. and Mrs. Martin A. Ryerson Collection, 33.1022

Coll: Horace Morison, Boston

Ref: Crowe and Cavalcaselle, A History of Painting in Italy, *III, p. 181 (note 1); Van Marle,* The Development of the Italian Schools of Painting, *V, pp. 160, 163, (ill. fig. 101); Berenson, B.,* Italian Pictures of the Renaissance, *1932, p. 399; Berenson, B.,* Pitture Italiane del Rinascimento, *1936, p. 343; Post, C. R.,* Art in America *3: 214–22, 1915; Edgell, G. H.,* Art and Archaeology *2: 17, 19, 20. 1915*

OBERTEUFFER, George ~ *b. 1878 Philadelphia. d. 1940 Gloucester, Mass.*
Oberteuffer was a pupil of William Merritt Chase and Thomas Anshutz.

VIOLIN STILL LIFE
Painted about 1925, signed: Oberteuffer. Oil on canvas, 20$\frac{7}{8}$ × 35$\frac{3}{4}$ in. (53.1 × 90.8 cm.)
Charles H. and Mary F. S. Worcester Collection, 30.992

OCHTERVELT, Jacob ~ *b. 1634–35 Rotterdam. d. 1708–10 Amsterdam*
Ochtervelt, together with Pieter de Hooch, was a pupil of Nicolas Bercham. Like Terborch he painted interiors; but whereas Terborch depended chiefly on sharp contours and cool light, Ochtervelt adopted Vermeer's dispersed luminosity.

THE MUSICIANS Illus. p. 196
Painted about 1670, signed: Jac. Ochtervelt. Oil on panel, 31$\frac{1}{2}$ × 25$\frac{3}{4}$ in. (80.2 × 65.5 cm.)
Mr. and Mrs. Martin A. Ryerson Collection, 33.1088

Coll: Prince Demidoff, Pratolino, Italy

Ref: Valentiner, W. R., Art in America *12: 269–84, 1924; Freund, F. E. W.,* Cicerone *21, pt. 2: 705, 1929; Chicago. Art Institute,* A Century of Progress Exhibition, *1933, cat. no. 70;* Ibid., *1934, cat. no. 102; Plietzsch, E.,* Pantheon *20: 364, 371, 1937*

OKADA, Kenzo ~ *b. 1902 Yokahama*
Okada studied at the Tokyo Academy of Fine Arts and worked in Paris from 1924 to 1927. Influenced by American Abstract Expressionism, which he saw in 1950 when he came to the United States, his work is a combination of Japanese restraint and modern freedom.

RETURNING LIFE
Painted in 1955, signed: Kenzo Okada. Oil on canvas, 80 × 70 in. (203 × 177.9 cm.)
Gift of Mr. and Mrs. Arnold H. Maremont through the Kate Maremont Foundation, 56.337

O'KEEFFE, Georgia ~ *b. 1887 Sun Prairie, Wis.*
Georgia O'Keeffe's first instructor was John Vanderpoel at The Art Institute of Chicago; later she studied with William Merritt Chase and F. Luis Mora. After a short career as a

commercial artist, Miss O'Keeffe left New York for Texas, where she taught. In 1916, Alfred Stieglitz, whom she later married, became interested in her work. Georgia O'Keeffe is a painter of precise style, who reduces landscapes, flowers, and New York views to simple forms.

EAST RIVER FROM SHELTON (30TH STORY)
Painted 1926. Oil on canvas, 12×32 in. (30.5×81.3 cm.)
Gift of Georgia O'Keeffe, 55.1222
Georgia O'Keeffe painted several versions of the East River.

BLACK CROSS, NEW MEXICO Illus. p. 383
Painted 1929. Oil on canvas, 39×30 1/16 in. (99.2×76.3 cm.)
Art Institute Purchase Fund, 43.95

COW'S SKULL WITH CALICO ROSES
Painted 1931. Oil on canvas, 35 7/8×24 in. (91.2×61 cm.)
Gift of Georgia O'Keeffe, 47.712

Ref: Rich, D. C., Georgia O'Keeffe, *1948, cat. no. 45*

GREEN MOUNTAINS—CANADA
Painted 1932. Oil on canvas, 12×36 in. (30.5×91.5 cm.)
Gift of Georgia O'Keeffe to the Alfred Stieglitz Collection, 56.356

RED AND PINK ROCKS AND TEETH
Painted 1938. Oil on canvas, 21×13 in. (53.5×33 cm.)
Gift of Georgia O'Keeffe, 55.1223

Ref: Rich, D. C., Georgia O'Keeffe, *1943, pp. 33, 35; Chicago. Art Institute,* Georgia O'Keeffe, *1943, cat. no. 55 (ill. p. 37)*

OLINSKY, Ivan G. ~ *b. 1878 Elizabethgrad, Russia*

Olinsky, who studied at the National Academy in New York, often assisted in the execution of the murals of John La Farge.

QUIET HOUR
Signed and dated: Ivan G. Olinsky 1911. Oil on canvas, 25×30 in. (63.6×76.3 cm.)
Gift of Mr. and Mrs. Charles S. Dewey, Jr., 44.211

OROZCO, José Clemente ~ *b. 1883 Zapotlan. d. 1949 Mexico City*

Orozco, with Rivera and Siqueiros, was one of the leaders of the Artists' Syndicate, a cooperative organized in 1922 to engage painters in the service of the revolution.

ZAPATA Illus. p. 472

Signed and dated: J. C. Orozco, S. F. Julio 1930.
Oil on canvas, $78\frac{1}{4} \times 48\frac{1}{8}$ in. (198.8 × 122.3 cm.)
The Joseph Winterbotham Collection, 41.35

Coll: Vincent Price, Hollywood

Ref: Reed, A., José Clemente Orozco, *1932, pl. 192; Chicago. Art Institute,* Bulletin *35: 89, 90, 91, 1941; Helm, MacKinley,* Modern Mexican Painters, *1941, pp. 15, 16, 17; Chicago. Art Institute,* Catalogue of the Winterbotham Collection, *1947, pp. 32–3; Gamboa, F.,* José Clemente Orozco *(Colección Anahuac De Arte Mexicano, III), 1948, p. 25; Chicago. Art Institute,* Bulletin *45: 62–5, November 15, 1951*

ORPEN, Sir William ~ *b. Stillorgan, Ireland. d. 1931 London*

Orpen studied in Dublin and at the Slade School of Art in London.

THE OLD CABMAN

Painted 1907, signed: William Orpen. Oil on canvas, 30 × 25 in. (76.3 × 63.6 cm.)
Charles H. and Mary F. S. Worcester Collection, 29.918
Coll: J. Audley Harvey, 1924; Lord Leverhulme, 1926

Ref: Chicago. Art Institute, Annual Report, *1929, p. 21; Chicago. Art Institute,* Bulletin *24: 30, 1930; Konody, P. G. and S. Dark,* Sir William Orpen, Artist and Man, *1932, p. 267; Chicago. Art Institute,* A Century of Progress Exhibition, *1933, cat. no. 270; Chicago. Art Institute,* Catalogue of the Worcester Collection, *1937, cat. no. 61, pl. 40*

WOMAN IN GRAY

Painted 1908, signed: Orpen. Oil on canvas, 74 × 49 in. (188 × 124.5 cm.)
Samuel P. Avery Fund, 12.1627

Ref: Chicago. Art Institute, Bulletin *6: 9, July 1912; Konody and Dark,* op. cit., *p. 267; Chicago. Art Institute,* A Century of Progress Exhibition, *1933, cat. no. 272*

OSTADE, Adriaen van ~ *1610–1685 Haarlem*

Although a pupil of Frans Hals, Ostade was mainly influenced by Rembrandt. He is best remembered for his genre paintings dealing with realistic scenes of peasant life in Haarlem.

THE FLEMISH JESTER AT THE WINDOW

Painted probably between 1650 and 1660. Oil on panel, $11\frac{1}{16} \times 9\frac{1}{16}$ in. (28.2 × 23 cm.)
Mr. and Mrs. Martin A. Ryerson Collection, 33.1089 (HdG no. 52)

Coll: G. Rothan, Paris

THE GOLDEN WEDDING Illus. p. 194

Signed and dated: A. Ostade 1674. Oil on panel, 17½×15⅛ in. (44.5×38.5 cm.)
George B. and Mary R. Harris Fund, 94.1028 (HdG no. 542)

Coll: Calonne, 1789; Edward Coxe, London, 1807; John Dent, London, 1827; C. J. Niewenhuys; Richard Foster, Clewer Manor, 1876; Prince A. Demidoff, San Donato (sale March 1880, cat. no. 1109); Prince P. Demidoff, Pratolino

Ref: Waagen, Treasures of Art in Great Britain, *II, 1854, p. 451; Chicago. Art Institute,* Annual Report, *1920 (ill.); Chicago. Art Institute,* A Century of Progress Exhibition, *1933, cat. no. 71*

OWEN, William ~ *b. 1769 Ludlow, England. d. 1825 London*

Owen studied at the Royal Academy and received private instruction from Sir Joshua Reynolds. After 1793 he exhibited regularly at the Royal Academy and was made an Associate in 1804.

PORTRAIT OF A LADY

Painted about 1810. Oil on canvas, 30×25 in. (76.3×63.6 cm.)
Max and Leola Epstein Collection, 54.959

OZENFANT, Amédée ~ *b. 1886 Saint-Quentin, France*

Ozenfant studied in Saint-Quentin and at the "Palette" in Paris. He was the founder of the Purist movement (an off-shoot of Cubism) which developed in France between 1918 and 1925.

LANDSCAPE

Signed and dated: A. Ozenfant 1918. Oil on canvas, 21½×17½ in. (54.7×44.5 cm.)
Gift of Kate L. Brewster, 50.126

Ref: Chicago. Art Institute, Bulletin *44, no. 3: 54, September 15, 1950*

PALMA GIOVANE ~ *1544–1628 Venice* (attributed to)

MADONNA, SAINTS JOHN THE BAPTIST AND ANTHONY ABBOT

Probably painted between 1575 and 1585. Oil on canvas, 63×77 in. (160.1×95.7 cm.)
Charles H. and Mary F. S. Worcester Collection, 29.913
This painting has also been attributed to Veronese.

Coll: Hohenzollern, Berlin

Ref: Chicago. Art Institute, Catalogue of the Worcester Collection, *1937, cat. no. 14; Chicago. Art Institute,* Bulletin *22: 29–31, 1928; Berenson,* Italian Pictures of the Renaissance, *1932, p. 420; Cortissoz, R.,* Scribner's Magazine *83: 370, 1928*

PALMER, Pauline ~ *b. 1865 McHenry, Ill. d. 1938 Trondheim, Norway*

Mrs. Palmer was a portrait painter, particularly of children. She left a bequest to the Art Institute, the income from which is given as prizes in the Annual Exhibition by Artists of Chicago and Vicinity.

AFTER THE RAIN

Painted about 1910, signed: Pauline Palmer.
Oil on paper board, 15⅞×19⅞ in. (40.4×50.7 cm.)
Gift of Mary F. Lennard, 38.1324

PROVINCETOWN

Signed and dated: Pauline Palmer 1926.
Oil on paper board, 26×32 in. (66.1×81.3 cm.)
Gift of Pauline Palmer, 38.1323

PANINI, Giovanni Paolo ~ *b. 1691 Piacenza. d. 1765 Rome*

Trained as a stage designer, Panini became the leader in Rome of a group that specialized in architectural panoramas of classical remains.

FESTIVAL ON PIAZZA NAVONA (Sketch for a detail)

Painted 1729. Oil on canvas, 10⅝×18 in. (27×45.8 cm.)
Simeon B. Williams Fund, 33.914

This small sketch was a detail for the painting of a fête given on November 20, 1729 by Cardinal de Polignac, French ambassador to the Pope, to celebrate the birth of the Dauphin, son of Louis XV. The final version of the scene is in the National Gallery of Ireland; another version is in the Louvre.

Ref: Rocheblave, S., Charles-Nicolas Cochin, *1927, p. 11, pl. 4; Tietze, H.,* Meisterwerke Europaeischer Malerei in Amerika, *1935, pl. 117*

PAOLO VENEZIANO ~ *Active 1333–1358 Venice*

TWO PANELS WITH SAINTS

These two panels were sections of a large altarpiece.
(a) St. John the Baptist and St. Catherine of Alexandria.
Painted c. 1450. Tempera on panel, 30×19¼ in. (76.3×49 cm.)
Charles H. and Mary F. S. Worcester Collection, 47.116

Ref: Vavalà, E. S., Burlington Magazine *57: 171, 177, 1930; Chicago. Art Institute,* Bulletin *24: 86–9, 1930; Chicago. Art Institute,* A Century of Progress Exhibition, *1933, cat. no. 87;* Ibid., *1934, cat. no. 35; Berenson, B.,* Pitture Italiane del Rinascimento, *1936, p. 359; Chicago. Art Institute,* Catalogue of the Worcester Collection, *1938, cat. no. 1 (ill.)*

(b) St. Augustine and St. Peter.
Painted c. 1450. Tempera on panel, 30×19¼ in. (76.3×49 cm.)
Gift of Mrs. Charles V. Hickox, 58.304

Coll: Grimaldi, Venice; Roerich Museum, New York

Ref: Chicago. Art Institute, Bulletin *24: 86–9, 1930; Chicago. Art Institute,* A Century of Progress Exhibition, *1933, cat. no. 88;* Ibid., *1934, cat. no. 36; Berenson, B.,* Pitture Italiane del Rinascimento, *1936, p. 359*

PASCIN, Jules ~ *b. 1885 Vidin, Bulgaria. d. 1930 Paris*

After studying at the Academy of Vienna, Pascin worked in Munich for *Simplizissimus.* In 1905 he went to Paris, but during World War I moved to the United States, where he became a citizen in 1915. Two years before his death he returned to Paris.

HERMINE DAVID

Signed and dated: Pascin 1907. Oil on canvas, 26×21½ in. (66.1×54.7 cm.)
Gift of Mr. and Mrs. Carter H. Harrison, 36.12

HERMINE DAVID WITH VIOLIN

Painted 1907. Oil on canvas, 25½×21 in. (64.8×53.5 cm.)
Gift of Mr. and Mrs. Carter H. Harrison, 37.386

CLAUDINE RESTING

Painted 1923, signed: Pascin. Oil on canvas, 34¼×23¾ in. (80.2×60.5 cm.)
Gift of Mr. and Mrs. Carter H. Harrison, 36.11

Ref: Chicago. Art Institute, A Century of Progress Exhibition, *1933, cat. no. 704; Chicago. Art Institute,* Bulletin *38: 79, 1944*

LITTLE GIRL

Painted 1927, signed: Pascin. Oil on canvas, 36×28½ in. (91.5×72.5 cm.)
Gift of Mr. and Mrs. Carter H. Harrison, 35.307

Ref: Chicago. Art Institute, The Harrison Collection, *1929, cat. no. 14; Chicago. Art Institute,* Annual Report, *1935, p. 26*

PATER, Jean-Baptiste François ~ *b. 1695 Valenciennes. d. 1736 Paris*

Son of the sculptor Antoine-Joseph Pater, the young Pater was sent to Paris to study with Watteau. After Watteau's death in 1721, Pater was called upon to finish many of the master's paintings, and afterwards continued to work in a similar manner.

FETE CHAMPETRE

Painted about 1725–1730. Oil on panel, 19⅛×25½ in. (48.6×64.8 cm.)
Max and Leola Epstein Collection, 54.295

Coll: Marquess of Hartford, 1857; Sir Richard Wallace, 1870; Lady Wallace, Hertford House; Sir John Murray Scott; Walter S. M. Burns, London, 1925

Ref: Waagen, Art Treasures in Great Britain, *IV, Supplement, 1857, p. 84; Manchester, England. Manchester Art Gallery,* Art Treasures Exhibition, *1857, cat. no. 29; London. Christie's,* Sale of the Sir John Murray Scott Collection, *June 27, 1913, cat. no. 134; Ingersoll-Smouse, F.,* Pater, *1921, p. 44, no. 81; Hourticq, L. (and others),* Le Paysage Français de Poussin à Corot . . . , *Paris, 1926, p. 144, no. 249*

PATINIR, Jacob (attributed to) ~ *b. 1475/80 Bouvignes. d. 1524 Antwerp*

Patinir, a master painter in Antwerp in 1515, collaborated with Quentin Massys. He was one of the earliest artists to specialize in landscape.

ST. JEROME IN A LANDSCAPE

Painted about 1520. Oil on panel, 14¾×21¼ in. (37.5×54.1 cm.)
Robert A. Waller Fund, 53.27

In the foreground is the small figure of St. Jerome. This type of landscape was equally characteristic of Henri Met de Bles, a contemporary, to whom this painting has also been attributed.

Coll: Comte de Bousies

Ref: Hoogewerff, G. J., La Revue d'Art *29: 117–34, July/December 1928; Friedlaender, M. J.,* Die Altniederlaendische Malerei, *IX, 1931, pp. 101–24, cat. nos. 239–45*

PEALE, Charles Willson ~ *b. 1741 St. Paul's Parish, Queen Anne County, Md. d. 1827 Philadelphia*

Charles Willson Peale was the most prominent member of the family of painters active in America during the late 18th and early 19th centuries. In 1767 he went to London for two years to study with Benjamin West. After serving in the Revolutionary War, he settled in Philadelphia where he painted many notables of the day, including George Washington.

JOHN NICHOLSON

Painted 1790. Oil on canvas, 36×27½ in. (91.5×70 cm.)
Gift of Mr. and Mrs. Carter H. Harrison, 52.1000

Nicholson was Comptroller-General of Pennsylvania and a business partner of Robert Morris.

MRS. JOHN NICHOLSON AND CHILD

Signed and dated: C. W. Peale painted 1790.
Oil on canvas, 36×27 5/16 in. (91.5×69.3 cm.)
Gift of Mr. and Mrs. Carter H. Harrison, 52.1001

Pendant to the preceeding portrait.

Coll: Nicholson Family

Ref: Chicago. Art Institute, Bulletin *17: 33, March 1923; Sellers, C. C.,* The Artist of the Revolution, The Early Life of Charles Willson Peale, *1939, pp. 267–81; Sellers, C. C.,* Portraits and Miniatures by Charles Willson Peale, *1952, p. 151, cat. no. 595*

PEALE, James ~ *b. 1749 Chestertown, Md. d. 1831 Philadelphia*
James Peale was a younger brother of Charles Willson Peale.

OLIVIA SIMES MORRIS
Painted about 1815. Oil on canvas, 28¾×24 in. (73×61 cm.)
Gift of the Estate of Mary Morley Sellers, 40.1324

Olivia Simes Morris was the wife of John Morris of Philadelphia, a co-founder of the short-lived Columbianum, the academy of fine arts founded by Charles Willson Peale in 1794.

PEALE, Rembrandt ~ *b. 1778 near Richboro, Bucks County, Pa. d. 1860 Philadelphia*
Rembrandt Peale was one of several children of Charles Willson Peale, all of whom were artists. He studied with his father and at seventeen helped him paint a portrait of George Washington. In 1802 he visited London to study with Benjamin West. He succeeded Trumbull as President of the American Academy of Fine Arts in 1825.

COLEMAN SELLERS
Painted about 1815. Oil on canvas, 30×25 in. (76.3×63.6 cm.)
Gift of the Estate of Mary Morley Sellers, 40.1323

In 1805 Coleman Sellers married Sophonisba Angusciola [sic] Peale, daughter of Charles Willson Peale.

PEREIRA, Irene Rice ~ *b. 1907 Boston, Mass.*
Miss Pereira studied at the Art Students League in New York and also in Paris.

QUADRANGLES IN TWO PLANES
Painted 1945, signed: I. Rice Pereira.
Oil on glass and board, 29½×19 in. (75×48.3 cm.)
Gift of the Society for Contemporary American Art, 47.432

PERRONNEAU, Jean-Baptiste ~ *b. 1715 Paris. d. 1783 Amsterdam*
Perronneau studied engraving under Laurent Cars, an engraver born in Lyons in 1693. He later studied painting with Natoire, and worked with Hubert Drouais. He became a

member of the Académie Royale in 1753. He was a portrait painter, chiefly in pastel, but did not achieve the fame of his great contemporary, Maurice Quentin de la Tour. His work was much admired by Degas and the Goncourts.

THE MARQUIS OF PUENTE-FUERTE

Painted about 1761–1762, signed: Perronneau pinx.
Pastel on paper, 27½ × 22 5/16 in. (70 × 56.2 cm.)
Robert A. Waller Fund, 51.225

Don Pablo Antonio de Barrenechea y Novia, Marquis de Puente-Fuerte, was appointed Spanish Ambassador to the Netherlands in 1761. This pastel was probably painted during Perronneau's visit to Holland in 1761–1763.

Coll: Paul Sohège, 1896; Sigismond Bardac, 1920; Jules Strauss, Paris, 1933

Ref: Tourneaux, M., Gazette des Beaux-Arts 15, *per. 3: 141–2, January/June 1896; Vaillat, L. and P. Ratouis de Limay,* J.-B. Perronneau, Sa Vie et Son Oeuvre, *1923, p. 204; Ratouis de Limay, P.,* Gazette des Beaux-Arts *15, per. 5: 333, January/June 1927; Roger-Marx, C.,* L'Art Vivant, *no. 179: 498, 499, December 1933; Rich, D. C.,* Art Quarterly *16: 268, 269, 1953*

PERUGINO, Pietro ~ *b. c. 1452 Castel della Pieve. d. 1523 Fontignano*

Though trained in Perugia, Perugino was influenced by the Florentines, especially Verrocchio. He worked in Perugia, Florence and Rome.

FOUR SCENES FROM THE LIFE OF CHRIST

Painted about 1510.
Oil on canvas, (a) 10⅝ × 18⅛ in. (27 × 46.2 cm.), (b), (c) and (d) 10½ × 16¾ in. each (26.7 × 42.6 cm.)
Mr. and Mrs. Martin A. Ryerson Collection, 33.1023–33.1026

These panels, along with one of the Resurrection now in the Metropolitan Museum of Art in New York, originally formed the predella of an unidentified altarpiece.
(a) Birth of Christ.
(b) Baptism of Christ.
(c) Christ and the Woman of Samaria.
(d) Noli me Tangere.

Coll: Alexander Barker, London, 1874; Earl of Dudley, 1892; M. A. Ryerson, Chicago, 1897

Ref: Williamson, G. C., Pietro Vannucci, called Perugino, *1903, p. 126; Berenson, B.,* Central Italian Painters, *1909, p. 218; Bombe, W.,* Perugino, *1914, p. 256; Crowe and Cavalcaselle,* A History of Painting in Italy, *V, New York, 1914, p. 356; Gnoli, U.,* Pietro Perugino, *1923, p. 58; Berenson, B.,* Italian Pictures of the Renaissance, *1932, p. 436; Van Marle,* The Development of the Italian Schools of Painting, *XIV, 1933, pp. 396, 403, 406; Chicago. Art Institute,* A Century of Progress Exhibition, *1933, cat. no. 123 a–d*

PESELLINO, Francesco (School of)

MADONNA AND CHILD

Painted ca. 1450. Tempera on panel, 27¼ × 14½ in. (70 × 36.9 cm.)
Gift of Joseph Winterbotham, 54.318

PETO, John Frederick ~ *b. 1854 Philadelphia. d. 1907 Island Heights, N.J.*

The still lifes of this painter were often confused with those of William Harnett, whose signature was forged on many canvases by John Peto.

LIGHTS OF OTHER DAYS Illus. p. 385

Signed and dated on the back: John F. Peto 1906.
Oil on canvas, 30½ × 45¼ in. (77.5 × 114.4 cm.)
Goodman Fund, 56.125

PEYRAUD, Frank C. ~ *b. 1858 Bulle, Switzerland. d. 1948 Highland Park, Ill.*

Peyraud, long associated with Chicago, was trained at the Ecole des Beaux-Arts in Paris. He was the painter of a popular cyclorama of the Chicago Fire.

AFTER RAIN

Signed and dated: F. C. Peyraud, 1911. Oil on canvas, 36⅛ × 46⅛ in. (91.8 × 117.2 cm.)
Friends of American Art Collection, 13.133

PIAZZETTA, Giovanni Battista ~ *1682–1754 Venice*

First apprenticed to the Venetian painter Antonio Molinari, and later to Giuseppi Maria Crespi of Bologna, Piazzetta was also influenced by the Bassani and Guercino.

THE ANNUNCIATION TO THE SHEPHERDS

Painted about 1710. Oil on canvas, 38 3/16 × 31⅛ in. (97 × 79 cm.)
Charles H. and Mary F. S. Worcester Collection, 35.297

This is an unfinished copy of a panel by Jacopo Bassano (in the Academy of St. Luke, Rome).

Ref: Chicago. Art Institute, Annual Report, *1935, p. 19; Chicago. Art Institute,* Bulletin *31: 98, 99, 1937; Chicago. Art Institute,* Catalogue of the Worcester Collection, *1937, cat. no. 20*

THE BEGGAR BOY

Probably painted between 1725 and 1730. Oil on canvas, 26⅝ × 21½ in. (67.7 × 54.7 cm.)
Charles H. and Mary F. S. Worcester Collection, 30.747

Ref: Fiocco, G., Rivista Città di Venezia, *VIII, 1921, p. 524; Chicago. Art Institute,* Bulletin *26: 53, 55–6, 1932; Chicago. Art Institute,* A Century of Progress Exhibition, *1933, cat. no. 152;* Ibid., *1934, cat. no. 53; Pallucchini, R.,* L'Arte di Giovanni Battista Piazzetta, *1934, pp. 30, 96, 124; Chicago. Art Institute,* Bulletin *31: 99, 1937; Chicago. Art Institute,* Catalogue of the Worcester Collection, *1938, cat. no. 21; Pallucchini, R.,* Giovanni Battista Piazzetta, *1943, p. 13*

PASTORAL SCENE Illus. p. 47

Painted about 1740. Oil on canvas, 75½×56¼ in. (191.8×143 cm.)
Charles H. and Mary F. S. Worcester Collection, 37.68

Coll: Guido da Faenza, Rome, 1902; G. H. Winterbotham, London, 1935; G. Bode

Ref: Borenius, T., Burlington Magazine *20: 15, 1917; Ravà, A.,* G. B. Piazzetta, *1921, pp. 31, 61; Pallucchini, R.,* Pantheon *18: 250, 251, 1936; Chicago. Art Institute,* Bulletin *31: 97–100, 1937; Chicago. Art Institute,* Catalogue of the Worcester Collection, *1937, cat. no. 22; Pallucchini, R.,* Giovanni Battista Piazzetta, *1943, p. 17*

PICABIA, Francis ~ *1879–1913 Paris*

Picabia was, with Marcel Duchamp, one of the principal figures of the Dada movement.

EDTAONISL Illus. p. 428

Signed and dated: Picabia 1913, inscribed: Edtaonisl.
Oil on canvas, 118¼×118⅝ in. (300.4×301.1 cm.)
Gift of Mr. and Mrs. Armand Phillip Bartos, 53.622

Edtaonisl is the second of a group of three canvases which Picabia painted in 1913. All three were inspired by impressions received by the artist during his first trip to America for the Armory Show in 1913. Edtaonisl (a word made up of several words referring to adventures on the trip) tries to recreate the sensations and emotions of a Dominican monk watching a dance performance on board ship.

Ref: Eddy, A. J., Cubists and Post-Impressionism, *1914, pp. 96–8;* Arts, *May 7, 1948, p. 5;* 491, *March 4, 1949, p. 2*

PICASSO, Pablo ~ *b. 1881 Malaga*

Picasso is not only the most famous artist of the twentieth century; he has also been its most influential one. Protean in his expression, Picasso has continuously been the master of anything he has undertaken, whether in painting, the graphic arts, or sculpture.

YOUNG WOMAN

Painted 1900. Pastel on board, 14⅛×10¼ in. (36×26 cm.)
Gift of Joseph Winterbotham, 54.319

ON THE UPPER DECK

Painted 1901, signed: Picasso. Oil on panel, 19⅜ × 25¼ in. (45.4 × 64.2 cm.)
Mr. and Mrs. Lewis L. Coburn Memorial Collection, 33.448

Ref: Chicago. Art Institute, Catalogue of the Coburn Collection, *1932, cat. no. 27; Chicago. Art Institute,* A Century of Progress Exhibition, *1933, cat. no. 403;* Ibid., *1934, cat. no. 359; Barr, A. H.,* Picasso: Fifty Years of His Art, *1946, pp. 19–20*

WOMAN WITH CATS

Painted 1901, signed: Picasso. Oil on cardboard, 17½ × 16 in. (44.5 × 40.8 cm.)
The Amy McCormick Memorial Collection, 42.464

Ref: Zervos, C., Pablo Picasso, *I, 1932, cat. no. 93, pl. 46*

THE OLD GUITARIST

Painted 1903, signed: Picasso. Oil on panel, 48⅛ × 32$\frac{7}{16}$ in. (122.3 × 82.5 cm.)

Coll: A. Vollard, Paris; John Quinn, New York

Ref: Chicago. Art Institute, Annual Report, *1926; Chicago. Art Institute,* Birch Bartlett Handbook, *1926, pp. 36, 57; Chicago. Art Institute,* Bulletin *20: 64, 1926;* John Quinn Collection . . . , *Huntington, New York, 1926, cat. no. 96; Watson, F.,* The Arts *9: 307, 312, 1926; Zervos, C.,* Cahiers d'Art *5–6: 213, 1928; Chicago. Art Institute,* Bulletin *25: 68–9, 1931; Zervos, C.,* Pablo Picasso, *I, 1932, cat. no. 96; Zervos, C.,* Cahiers d'Art *nos. 3–5, 1932 (ill. ff. p. 88); Sweeney, J. J.,* Cahiers d'Art *nos. 8–10, 1932 (ill. opp. p. 334); Chicago. Art Institute,* A Century of Progress Exhibition, *1933, cat. no. 402;* Ibid., *1934, cat. no. 358; Wilenski, R. H.,* Modern French Painters, *1940, p. 199; Chicago. Art Institute,* Catalogue of the Birch Bartlett Collection, *1946, pp. 38–9; Barr, A. H.,* Picasso: Fifty Years of his Art, *New York, 1946, p. 29; Bertram, A.,* Picasso, *1951, pl. 4*

HEAD OF THE ACROBAT'S WIFE (Woman with a Helmet of Hair) Illus. p. 427

Signed and dated: Picasso 1904. Gouache on paperboard, 16⅞ × 12¼ in. (42.9 × 31.2 cm.)
Gift of Kate L. Brewster, 50.128

This picture is related to several compositions featuring acrobats and clowns produced during 1905.

Ref: Raynal, M., Picasso, *Paris, 1922, pl. 13; Goodrich, L.,* The Arts *16: 343, September 1929 to May 1930; Williams, M. B.,* Parnassus *1: 10, 11, November 1929; George, W.,* L'Art Vivant *6, pt. 2: 596, July/December 1930; Zervos, C.,* Pablo Picasso, *I, 1932, no. 233, pl. 130; Chicago. Art Institute,* Catalogue of the Brewster Collection, *1933, cat. no. 21; Barr, A. H.,* Picasso: Forty Years of His Art, *1939, p. 36, no. 24 (ill.); Barr, A. H.,* Picasso: Fifty Years of His Art, *1946, p. 30; Cassou, J.,* Picasso, *1947, pl. 16; Chicago. Art Institute,* Bulletin *44, no. 3: 53, 54, September 15, 1950*

HEAD OF A WOMAN

Painted 1909. Oil on canvas, $23\frac{7}{8} \times 20\frac{3}{16}$ in. (60.8×51.3 cm.)
The Joseph Winterbotham Collection, 40.5

Ref: Raynal, M., Picasso, *Paris, 1922, pl. 32; Einstein, E.,* Die Kunst des 20 Jahrhunderts, *1926, pp. 71, 268; Chicago. Art Institute,* Bulletin *35: 106, 107, 1941; Zervos, C.,* Picasso, *II, 1942, no. 167; Chicago. Art Institute,* Catalogue of the Winterbotham Collection, *1947, pp. 34, 35*

DANIEL-HENRY KAHNWEILER Illus. p. 426

Painted 1910. Oil on canvas, $39\frac{5}{8} \times 28\frac{5}{8}$ in. (100.6×72.8 cm.)
Gift of Mrs. Gilbert W. Chapman, 48.561

MAN WITH A PIPE

Signed and dated: Picasso 15. Oil on canvas, $51\frac{1}{4} \times 35\frac{1}{4}$ in. (130.3×89.5 cm.)
Gift of Mrs. Leigh B. Block in Memory of Albert D. Lasker, 52.1116

MOTHER AND CHILD Illus. p. 425

Signed and dated: Picasso 21. Oil on canvas, $56\frac{1}{2} \times 64$ in. (143.6×162.6 cm.)
Gift of Mary and Leigh Block Charitable Fund, Inc., Mr. and Mrs. Edwin E. Hokin, Maymar Corporation, Mr. and Mrs. Chauncey McCormick, Mrs. Maurice L. Rothschild, and the Ada Turnbull Hertle Fund, 54.270

Coll: Dr. G. F. Reber, Lausanne

Ref: Barr, A. H., Picasso: Fifty Years of His Art, *1946, p. 124; Zervos, C.,* Pablo Picasso, *IV, Paris, 1951, p. 115, no. 311*

STILL LIFE

Dated: 4-2-22. Oil on canvas, $32\frac{1}{4} \times 39\frac{1}{2}$ in. (81.6×100.3 cm.)
Ada Turnbull Hertle Fund, 53.28

Coll: Gertrude Stein

Ref: Zervos, C., Pablo Picasso, *IV, 1951, pp. 176–7 (ill.)*

HEAD

Painted 1927. Oil and plaster on canvas, $39\frac{3}{16} \times 31\frac{3}{4}$ in. (99.4×80.8 cm.)
Gift of Mr. and Mrs. Samuel A. Marx, 51.185

Coll: André Bréton; Gordon Onslow-Ford

Ref: Zervos, C., Pablo Picasso, *VII, 1951, no. 118*

ABSTRACTION: BACKGROUND WITH BLUE CLOUDY SKY

Signed and dated: Picasso 4-1-XXX. Oil on panel, $26 \times 19\frac{3}{8}$ in. (66.1×49.4 cm.)
Gift of Mr. and Mrs. Samuel A. Marx and the Wilson L. Mead Fund, 55.748

Coll: W. Rees Jeffreys, Wivelsfield Green, Sussex

Ref: Documents, *no. 2, 1930, p. 63; Einstein, C.,* Die Kunst des 20 Jahrhunderts *(third ed.), pl. IX; Zervos VII, no. 304*

THE RED ARMCHAIR Illus. p. 436

Painted in 1931, signed: Picasso. Oil on panel, 51½ × 39 in. (130.9 × 99.2 cm.)
Gift of Mr. and Mrs. Daniel Saidenberg, 57.72

Ref: Zervos, C., Pablo Picasso, *VII, 1951, no. 334*

THE READER Illus. p. 433

Painted 1953, signed: Picasso. Oil on panel, 36¼ × 28⅝ in. (92.1 × 72.8 cm.)
Gift of Mr. and Mrs. Arnold H. Maremont through the Kate Maremont Foundation, 56.337

SYLVETTE (PORTRAIT OF MLLE. D.)

Painted 1954, signed: Picasso. Oil on canvas, 51½ × 38¼ in. (130.9 × 97.2 cm.)
Gift of Mr. and Mrs. Leigh B. Block, 55.821

FIGURE

Painted 1907–1908, signed: Picasso. Gouache on board, 24¾ × 19 in. (53 × 48.3 cm.)
Gift of Mr. and Mrs. Samuel A. Marx, 53.192

PISSARRO, Camille ~ *b. 1830 St. Thomas, West Indies. d. 1903 Paris*

Pissarro, who studied at the Académie Suisse and with his friend Anton Melbye, was also influenced by Corot, Millet and Monet. Impressed by Manet and his circle, Pissarro joined the Impressionists and exhibited with them from 1874 to 1886. For a brief period shortly after 1885, he adopted the pointillist methods of Seurat.

ON THE BANKS OF THE MARNE, WINTER Illus. p. 280

Signed and dated: C. Pissarro 1866. Oil on canvas, 36⅛ × 59⅛ in. (91.8 × 150.2 cm.)
Mr. and Mrs. Lewis L. Coburn Fund, 57.306

Coll: Camille Pissarro; S.-G. Archibald

Ref: Zola, E., Le Figaro, *1866; Rousseau, J.,* Le Salon, *July 1866; Pissarro and Venturi,* C. Pissarro, son art—son oeuvre, *1939, cat. no. 47; Bates, H. E.,* Apollo, *July 1952, p. 176 (ill.)*

THE CAFE AU LAIT

Signed and dated: C. Pissarro 1881. Oil on canvas, 25⅛ × 21⅜ in. (63.9 × 54.4 cm.)
Potter Palmer Collection, 22.433

Ref: Chicago. Art Institute, A Century of Progress Exhibition, *1933, cat. no. 301; Rich, D. C.,* Pantheon *11: 78, January/June 1933; Pissarro and Venturi,* op. cit., *I, 1939, no. 549*

WOMAN AND CHILD AT THE WELL

Signed and dated: C. Pissarro 82. Oil on canvas, 32 × 26 in. (81.3 × 66.1 cm.)
Potter Palmer Collection, 22.436

Ref: Chicago. Art Institute, A Century of Progress Exhibition, *1933, cat. no. 261; Rich, D. C.,* Pantheon *11: 78, January/June 1933; Pissarro and Venturi,* op. cit., *I, 1939, no. 574*

PLACE DU HAVRE, PARIS

Signed and dated: C. Pissarro 93. Oil on canvas, $23\frac{5}{8} \times 28\frac{13}{16}$ in. (60.1 × 73.5 cm.)
Potter Palmer Collection, 22.434

Ref: Pissarro and Venturi, op. cit., *I, 1939, no. 838*

YOUNG WOMAN MENDING

Signed and dated: C. Pissarro 1895. Oil on canvas, $25\frac{5}{8} \times 21\frac{3}{8}$ in. (65.2 × 53.8 cm.)
Gift of Mrs. Leigh B. Block, 59.636

Ref: Camille Pissarro, son art, son oeuvre, *ed. Paul Rosenberg, 1939, no. 934, p. 210, pl. 189*

POIROT, Pierre-Achille ~ *b. 1797 Alençon. d. after 1852 Paris*

Poirot, an architect and architectural painter, was a lifelong friend of Corot. Since the two artists often painted the same subjects, a number of paintings by Poirot have appeared with altered signatures indicating Corot as the painter.

ST. SALVI CHURCH, ALBI

Painted probably between 1830 and 1840. Oil on canvas, $11\frac{1}{2} \times 14$ in. (29.2 × 35.7 cm.)
Gift of Mrs. Charles V. Hickox, 31.718

Ref: Chicago. Art Institute, Bulletin *26: 30–31, 1932; Chicago. Art Institute,* A Century of Progress Exhibition, *1933, cat. no. 233;* Ibid., *1934, cat. no. 167*

POLLOCK, Jackson ~ *b. 1912 Cody, Wyo. d. 1956 Easthampton, N.Y.*

Pollock studied for two years with Thomas Hart Benton at the Art Students League in New York. Later, working with huge canvases directly on the floor, he evolved his method of dripping paint (often aluminum paint and enamel mixed with sand, glass, and other foreign matter) onto the surface of his picture.

GRAYED RAINBOW Illus. p. 391

Signed and dated: Jackson Pollock 53. Oil on canvas, 72 × 96 in. (182.9 × 244 cm.)
Gift of the Society for Contemporary American Art, 55.494

POOLE, Abram ~ *b. 1882 Chicago*

From 1905 to 1912, Poole studied at the Academy in Munich as a pupil of Karl von Marr; from 1912 to 1915 he was a pupil of Lucien Simon in Paris.

MISS MCFADDEN (Mrs. Edward Lay)

Painted about 1920. Oil on canvas, $28\frac{3}{4} \times 23\frac{5}{8}$ in. (73×60.1 cm.)
Friends of American Art Collection, 21.107

POTTHAST, Edward Henry ~ *b. 1857 Cincinnati. d. 1927 New York*

Potthast studied in Cincinnati and abroad.

A HOLIDAY

Painted about 1915, signed: E. Potthast. Oil on canvas, $30\frac{1}{2} \times 40\frac{1}{2}$ in. (77.5×102.9 cm.)
Friends of American Art Collection, 15.560

POURBUS, Frans the Younger ~ *b. 1569 Antwerp. d. 1622 Paris*

The son of the portrait painter Frans Pourbus the Elder, Pourbus the Younger became a master painter in Antwerp in 1591. He became court painter to Marie de'Medici in 1609.

MARIE DE'MEDICI

Signed and dated: F. Purbis Christianiss[imae] Ma[jestatis] Pictor Faciebat An[no] 1616.
Oil on canvas, $39\frac{1}{4} \times 30\frac{1}{2}$ in. (99.8×77.5 cm.)
Gift of Kate S. Buckingham, 20.1034

This painting is one of three family portraits done on the occasion of the wedding of Louis XIII to Anne of Austria in Bordeaux in 1615.

Coll: Princess Mathilde de Saint Alarys, Paris

POUSSIN, Nicolas ~ *b. 1594 Villers, France. d. 1665 Rome*

Poussin settled in Rome in 1624, remaining there until his death, except for a trip to Paris in 1640 to execute a commission for Louis XIII.

ST. JOHN ON PATMOS Illus. p. 231

Probably painted between 1645 and 1650. Oil on canvas, $40 \times 53\frac{1}{2}$ in. (101.7×135.9 cm.)
A. A. Munger Collection, 30.500

Coll: M. Robit; M. Bryan; Sir Simon Robert Clarke, 1802; Sir Thomas Baring, 1837

Ref: Bryan's Catalogue of Robit's Collection . . . , *1802, no. 29; Landon, C. P.,* Oeuvre Complet de Nicolas Poussin . . . , *II, Paris, 1814, pl. 224; Buchanan, W.,* Memoirs of Painting, *II, 1824, p. 59, no. 91; Smith, J.,* Catalogue Raisonné of the Works of the Most Eminent Dutch and Flemish Painters, *VIII, 1837, p. 161; Andresen, A.,* Nicolas Poussin, *Leipzig, 1863, no. 454; Grautoff, O.,* Nicolas Poussin, *II, 1914, p. 259; Chicago. Art Institute,* Bulletin *24: 113–7, 1930; Valentiner, W. R.,* Das Unbekannte Meisterwerk, *I, 1930, no. 74 (ill.); Posse, H.,* Pantheon *5: 62, 64, 1930; Chicago. Art Institute,* A Century of Progress Exhibition, *1933, cat. no. 226, pl. 45;* Ibid., *1934, cat. no. 147; Chicago. Art Institute,* Bulletin *32: 49, 1938; Blunt, A.,* French Drawings at Windsor Castle, *1945, no. 47; Worcester, Mass. Museum of Art,* News Bulletin and Calendar *13: 27, April 1948; Millet, F.,* Bulletin de la Société Poussin, *December 1948, p. 52, pl. 33*

PRESTOPINO, Gregorio ~ *b. 1907 New York City*

Prestopino studied at the National Academy of Design in New York.

THE CITY

Painted in 1948, signed: Prestopino. Oil on canvas, 32¼ × 42 in. (82 × 106.7 cm.)
Gift of the Society for Contemporary American Art, 53.196

PRUD'HON, Pierre-Paul ~ *b. 1758 Cluny, France. d. 1823 Paris*

Prud'hon was influenced during an early stay in Rome by his friend, the sculptor Canova, but the greatest impact on his work came from the paintings of Correggio. His early period, reminiscent of Boucher, gave way later to the more popular classicism of early 19th century painting.

BETWEEN LOVE AND RICHES

Painted about 1804. Oil on panel, 13 × 10¼ in. (33 × 26 cm.)
Mr. and Mrs. Martin A. Ryerson Collection, 33.1090

This oil sketch is one of several the artist made for his pupil and friend, Constance Mayer, to be used for a picture she painted and exhibited at the Paris Salon in 1804.

Coll: Camille Marcille, Paris; L. Tabourier, Paris

Ref: Guiffrey, J., P. P. Prud'hon, *(Musée du Louvre), 1924, p. 35; Bricon, E.,* Prud'hon, *n.d., pl. 2*

PRYDE, James ~ *b. 1866 Edinburgh. d. 1941 London*

Pryde first studied and exhibited at the Royal Scottish Academy, and later worked for three months under Bouguereau at the Académie Julian in Paris.

A SMALL TOWER

Probably painted between 1910 and 1920. Oil on canvas, 16 × 12¼ in. (40.8 × 31.2 cm.)
George F. Porter Collection, 27.532

PUVIS DE CHAVANNES, Pierre Cécile ~ *b. 1824 Lyons. d. 1898 Paris*

Puvis de Chavannes entered the atelier of Delacroix, but left after only five days. He studied with Couture for three months, but was essentially self-taught.

THE SACRED GROVE

Painted about 1884, signed: P. Puvis de Chavannes.
Oil on canvas, 36½×82⅞ in. (92.8×231 cm.)
Potter Palmer Collection, 22.445

This is a copy by Puvis of the center panel of a large mural decoration he was commissioned to paint in 1883 for the staircase of the Palais des Arts in Lyons. The entire cycle represented the glorification of human effort. There were four other panels, but *The Sacred Grove* was probably completed first.

Ref: Chicago. Art Institute, The Potter Palmer Collection, *1910, cat. no. 45; Chicago. Art Institute,* Annual Report, *1921; Chicago. Art Institute,* Bulletin *15: 154, 1921; Chicago. Art Institute,* Bulletin *18: 118, 1924*

THE FISHERMAN'S FAMILY

Signed and dated: P. Puvis de Chavannes 1887.
Oil on canvas, 32½×28 in. (82.6×71.2 cm.)
Mr. and Mrs. Martin A. Ryerson Collection, 15.227

The artist painted this same subject (now in Dresden) in 1875, twelve years earlier than this smaller copy.

Coll: Edouard Aynard, Lyons

Ref: Vachon, M., Puvis de Chavannes, *Paris, 1896, p. 51; Wood, T. M.,* International Studio *54: 11, 1914–1915; Chicago. Art Institute,* Bulletin *9: 61, 1915; Chicago. Art Institute,* Annual Report, *1919; Chicago. Art Institute,* Bulletin *18: 119–20, 1924; Mather, F. J., Jr.,* Modern Painting, *1927; Chicago. Art Institute,* A Century of Progress Exhibition, *1933, cat. no. 273, pl. 50;* Ibid., *1934, cat. no. 199E*

RAEBURN, Sir Henry ~ *b. 1756 Stockbridge, Scotland. d. 1823 Edinburgh*

Raeburn, who was largely self-taught, first studied under David Deuchar and then with David Martin.

LADY HELEN BOYLE

Painted about 1790. Oil on canvas, 30×25 in. (76.3×63.6 cm.)
Charles H. and Mary F. S. Worcester Collection, 47.101

Coll: Sir George Douglas, Kelso, Scotland

Ref: Chicago. Art Institute, Catalogue of the Worcester Collection, *1937, cat. no. 57, pl. 38*

DR. WELSH TENNENT

Painted probably between 1810 and 1820. Oil on canvas, 49¾×39 in. (126.4×99.2 cm.)
Gift of Mrs. Robert Hall McCormick in memory of Robert Hall McCormick, 20.35

Ref: Chicago. Art Institute, Annual Report, *1920; Chicago. Art Institute,* A Century of Progress Exhibition, *1934, cat. no. 149*

SIR FRANCIS HORNER

Painted about 1812. Oil on canvas, $30\frac{1}{8} \times 25\frac{3}{8}$ in. (76.6×64.5 cm.)
Max and Leola Epstein Collection, 54.269

Ref: Frankfurter, A. M., Antiquarian *14: 32, January 1930*

RAFFAELLI, Jean François ~ *1850–1924 Paris*

Raffaëlli was known as a painter, etcher and lithographer; occasionally he was also a sculptor. In 1896 the artist visited America and was so enthusiastic about his trip that he wrote a booklet, *Impressions of an Impressionist in America.*

PLACE DE LA TRINITÉ

Painted about 1886, signed: J. F. Raffaelli. Oil on canvas, $29 \times 28\frac{1}{4}$ in. (73.7×71.7 cm.)
Potter Palmer Collection, 22.447

NOTRE-DAME DE PARIS

Painted about 1890, signed: J. F. Raffaelli. Oil on canvas, 29×25 in. (73.7×63.6 cm.)
Potter Palmer Collection, 22.446

Ref: Coquiot, G., Gazette des Beaux-Arts *5, per. 4: 140, 1911; Chicago. Art Institute,* Bulletin *16: 40, 1922*

RANGER, Henry Ward ~ *1858–1916 New York*

BROOKLYN BRIDGE

Dated: '99. Oil on canvas, $28\frac{1}{2} \times 56$ in. (72.5×142.3 cm.)
Gift of Charles L. Hutchinson, 27.720

RAVLIN, Grace ~ *b. 1885 Kaneville, Ill. d. 1956 Plano, Ill.*

PROCESSION OF IL REDENTORE, VENICE

Signed and dated: Ravlin V/14. Oil on canvas, 23×25 in. (58.6×63.6 cm.)
Friends of American Art Collection, 14.820

REAM, Carducius Plantagenet ~ *b. 1837 Lancaster, Ohio. d. 1917 Chicago*

PURPLE PLUMS

Painted probably about 1895, signed: C. P. Ream.
Oil on canvas, 16×22 in. (40.8×56 cm.)
Gift of Catherine M. White, 99.907

REDFIELD, Edward Willis ~ *b. 1869 Bridgeville, Del.*

Redfield studied at the Pennsylvania Academy of the Fine Arts and with William Bouguereau and Tony Robert-Fleury in Paris.

HILLSIDE AT CENTER BRIDGE

Painted 1904, signed: E. W. Redfield. Oil on canvas, 36×50 in. (91.5×127 cm.)
W. Moses Willner Fund, 05.152

REDON, Odilon ~ *b. 1840 Bordeaux. d. 1916 Paris*

Though Redon worked in the studio of Gérôme, it was Corot and Delacroix who seriously influenced him. Rodolphe Bresdin not only taught Redon the art of lithography but also shaped his way of thinking.

ARI REDON

Painted about 1897, signed: Odilon Redon.
Pastel on cardboard, 17⅞×12⅜ in. (45.5×31.5 cm.)
Gift of Kate L. Brewster, 50.130

Coll: Ari Redon, Paris, 1926

Ref: Chicago. Art Institute, Redon, *December 1928 to January 1929, cat. no. 21; Chicago. Art Institute,* Bulletin *44: 55, September 1950*

EVOCATION

Probably painted between 1905 and 1910, signed: Odilon Redon.
Pastel on paper, 20½×14¼ in. (52.1×36.3 cm.)
The Joseph Winterbotham Collection, 54.320

ANDROMEDA

Painted between 1900 and 1910, signed: Odilon Redon.
Oil on canvas, 21⅛×20¼ in. (53.8×51.5 cm.)
Mr. and Mrs. Martin A. Ryerson Collection, 33.1167

Coll: Chambaudet, Paris; Joseph Hessel, Paris, 1920

STILL LIFE: VASE WITH FLOWERS

Painted about 1910, signed: Odilon Redon.
Oil on cardboard, 27×21 in. (68.7×53.5 cm.)
Mr. and Mrs. Lewis L. Coburn Memorial Collection, 33.450

Ref: Chicago. Art Institute, Redon, *December 1928 to January 1929, cat. no. 4; Chicago. Art Institute,* Catalogue of the Coburn Collection, *1932, cat. no. 28; Chicago. Art Institute,* A Century of Progress Exhibition, *1933, cat. no. 707; Milwaukee, Wisc., Art Institute,* Bulletin *18: 1, 2, September 1945*

YOUNG WOMAN

Painted 1912, signed: Odilon Redon. Pastel on paper, 25×19 in. (63.6×48.3 cm.)
Mr. and Mrs. Martin A. Ryerson Collection, 33.1169

Coll: Joseph Hessel, Paris, 1920

Ref: Chicago. Art Institute, A Century of Progress Exhibition, *1934, cat. no. 309*

REGNAULT, Henri ~ *b. 1843 Paris. d. 1871 Buzenval, Belgium*

Regnault, a pupil of Lamothe and Cabanel, studied in Rome from 1867 to 1869.

PORTRAIT OF A YOUNG WOMAN

Signed and dated: Henri Regnault 1863. Oil on canvas, $36\frac{1}{4} \times 28\frac{3}{4}$ in. (92.1 × 73 cm.)
The Stickney Fund, 21.90

Ref: Chicago. Art Institute, Annual Report, *1920; Chicago. Art Institute,* Bulletin *14: 87, 1920; Chicago. Art Institute,* A Century of Progress Exhibition, *1933, cat. no. 259*

GENERAL JUAN PRIM (1814–1870)

Painted 1868. Oil on canvas, $31\frac{11}{16} \times 25\frac{5}{16}$ in. (80.5 × 64.2 cm.)
Wentworth Greene Field Fund, 47.510

Ref: Art News (Annual Supplement) *36: 162, March 1938*

REMBRANDT VAN RIJN ~ *b. 1606 Leyden. d. 1669 Amsterdam*

Rembrandt was apprenticed for three years to the painter Jacob van Swanenburgh, but the greatest influence on his work was the short period he spent as a pupil of Pieter Lastman in Amsterdam, about 1623.

HARMEN GERRITSZ VAN RIJN [?] Illus. p. 188

Probably painted about 1631, signed with monogram.
Oil on panel, $32\frac{7}{8} \times 29\frac{3}{4}$ in. (83.5 × 75.6 cm.)
Mr. and Mrs. W. W. Kimball Collection, 22.4467

This likeness, supposedly a portrait of Rembrandt's father, was probably painted shortly after his death. Rembrandt made several pictures of this same man, who also sat for Gerard Dou. Often included was a woman's portrait as a pendant. Hence, it has been concluded that these were portraits of Rembrandt's parents. This early painting is drier and more detailed than Rembrandt's later work.

Coll: M. P. W. Boulton, Tew Park, England, 1911; Marczell von Nemes, Budapest

Ref: Bode, W. von, Zeitschrift für Bildende Kunst *23: 210, 1912; Miomandre, F. de,* L'Art et les Artistes *16: 250, 1913; Hofstede de Groot,* A Catalogue Raisonné of the Works of the Most Eminent Dutch Painters of the 17th Century, *VI, 1916, pp. 321, 322, cat. no. 675; Booth, A. L.,* Fine Arts Journal *35: 106, 110, 1917; Chicago. Art Institute,* Bulletin *14: 77, 1920; Valentiner, W. R.,* Rembrandt, Wiedergefundene Gemaelde, *1921, pp. xvi (no. 19), 17; Chicago. Art Institute,* Annual Report, *1922; Van Dyke, J. C.,* Rembrandt and His School, *1923, p. 111; Chicago. Art Institute,* Bulletin *27: 124, 1933; Chicago. Art Institute,* A Century of Progress Exhibition, *1933, cat. no. 74;* Ibid., *1934, cat. no. 104; Bredius, A.,* The Paintings of Rembrandt, *c. 1936, no. 81; Rosenberg, J.,* Rembrandt, *I, 1948, p. 43; II, pl. 60*

YOUNG GIRL AT AN OPEN HALF-DOOR Illus. p. 185

Signed and dated: Rembrandt f. 1645. Oil on canvas, 40⅛×33⅛ in. (102×84.2 cm.)
Mr. and Mrs. Martin A. Ryerson Collection, 94.1022

It may be that the girl, who also appears in several other Rembrandt canvases of the same period, is Hendrickje Stoffels. She is shown in the costume of the Municipal Orphanage in Amsterdam. The possibility of an attribution to Nicolaes Maes has been suggested.

Coll: Gueffier, Paris, 1791; Robit, Paris; George Hibbert, London; Nathaniel Hibbert, London; Prince Anatole Demidoff, San Donato; Prince P. Demidoff, Pratolino

Ref: W. von Bode, Studien zur Geschichte der Hollaendischen Malerei, *II, 1883, pp. 497, 609, no. 373; Dutuit, E.,* Tableaux et Dessins de Rembrandt, *1885, p. 11; Michel, E.,* Rembrandt, His Life, His Work, and His Time, *1894, I, p. 303, II, p. 248; Bode, W. von,* The Complete Works of Rembrandt, *IV, 1900, p. 194, cat. no. 301; Rosenberg, A.,* Rembrandt, Des Meisters Gemaelde in 643 Abbildungen, *II, ca. 1909, pp. 323, 574, 584; New York. Metropolitan Museum of Art,* Bulletin *4: 170, October 1909; Wurzbach, A.,* Niederlaendisches Kuenstler-Lexikon, *II, 1910, pp. 398, 413; Chicago. Art Institute,* Bulletin *11: 249, 250, 1917; Cox, K.,* Concerning Painting, *1917, p. 155; Chicago. Art Institute,* Annual Report, *1919; Van Dyke, J. C.,* Rembrandt and His School, *1923, p. 160, pl. 37; Valentiner, W. R.,* Rembrandt Paintings in America, *1931, pl. 90; Hind, A. M.,* Rembrandt, *1932, p. 85, pl. 61; Chicago. Art Institute,* Bulletin *27: 1, 12, 1933; Chicago. Art Institute,* A Century of Progress Exhibition, *1933, cat. no. 75, pl. 34;* Ibid., *1934, cat. no. 107; Bredius, A.,* The Paintings of Rembrandt, *1937, pl. 367, p. 15 of notes; Borenius, T.,* Rembrandt, Selected Paintings, *1942, p. 32, no. 39; Chicago. Art Institute,* Bulletin *40: 47, 1946; Rosenberg, J.,* Rembrandt, *1948, I, p. 51, II, pl. 78*

REMBRANDT, (attributed to)

YOUTH WEARING A TURBAN

Painted about 1670. Oil on panel, 22×18½ in. (56×47.1 cm.)
Max and Leola Epstein Collection, 54.297

Ref: Detroit. Institute of Arts, Paintings by Rembrandt, *May 1930, cat. no. 74 (ill.); Bredius, A.,* The Paintings of Rembrandt, *1936, cat. no. 316, fig. 16 (ill.)*

REMBRANDT, School of

CHRIST IN THE STORM

Probably painted about 1640. Oil on panel, 32¼×46¾ in. (82×118.8 cm.)
Charles H. and Mary F. S. Worcester Collection, 41.1

Ref: Hofstede de Groot, A Catalogue Raisonné of the Works of the Most Eminent Dutch Painters of the 17th Century, *VI, 1916, p. 82, cat. no. 103a or 103b; Chicago. Art Institute,* Annual Report, *1941, p. 11*

AMERICAN PAINTINGS

XIXth—XXth Centuries

ILLUSTRATIONS

Opposite: Cassatt, Mary, The Bath, c. 1891. Robert A. Waller Fund

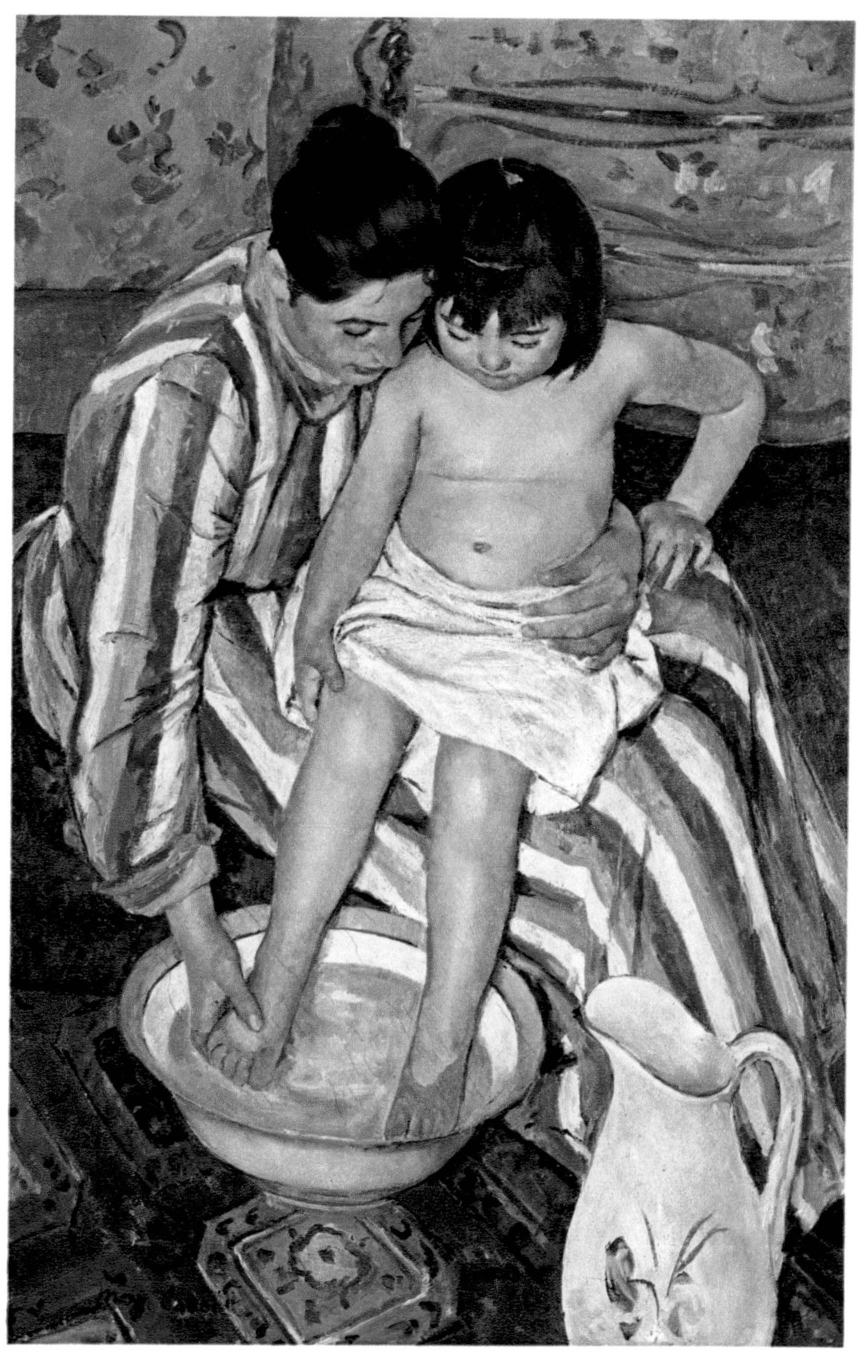

Sully, Thomas, Mrs. Joseph Klapp, 1814
Gift of Annie Swan Coburn to the Mr. & Mrs. Lewis L. Coburn Memorial Collection

Copley, John Singleton, Mrs. Daniel Hubbard, c. 1764
Art Institute Purchase Fund

Inness, George, Catskill Mountains, 1870. Edward B. Butler Collection

Bierstadt, Albert, Island in a Sound, c. 1880. Charles H. & Mary F. S. Worcester Collection

Sargent, John Singer, Mrs. Charles Gifford Dyer, 1880. Friends of American Art Collection

Whistler, James McNeill, The Artist in His Studio, c. 1864. Friends of American Art Collection

Eakins, Thomas, Addie, Woman in Black, 1899. Friends of American Art Collection

Glackens, William, Chez Mouquin, 1905. Friends of American Art Collection

Homer, Winslow, Croquet Scene, 1866. Friends of American Art Collection

Homer, Winslow, The Herring Net, 1885. Mr. & Mrs. Martin A. Ryerson Collection

Opposite: Dove, Arthur, Telegraph Pole, 1929. Alfred Stieglitz Collection

Feininger, Lyonel, Village Street, 1929. Gift of Mr. & Mrs. Sigmund Kunstadter

Wood, Grant, American Gothic, 1930. Friends of American Art Collection

O'Keeffe, Georgia, Black Cross: New Mexico, 1929. Art Institute Purchase Fund

Hopper, Edward, Nighthawks, 1942. Friends of American Art Collection

Peto, John Frederick, *Lights of Other Days*, 1906. Goodman Fund

SMYRNA

Opposite:
Harnett, William Michael, Just Dessert, 1891
Friends of American Art Collection

Sheeler, Charles, The Artist Looks at Nature, 1943
Gift of the Society for Contemporary American Art

Albright, Ivan,
That Which I Should Have Done
I Did Not Do, 1941

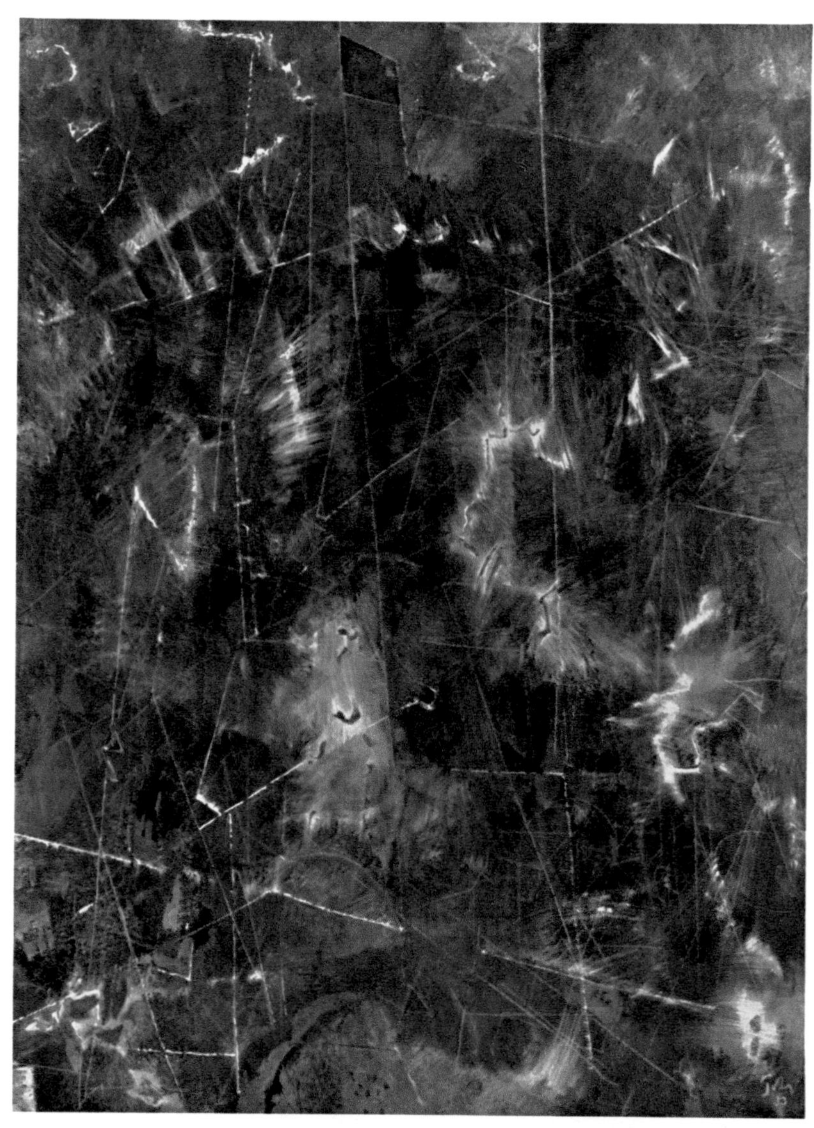

Tobey, Mark, Above the Earth, 1953. Gift of Mr. & Mrs. Sigmund Kunstadter

De Kooning, Willem, Excavation, 1950. Mr. & Mrs. Frank G. Logan Purchase Prize, Gift of Mr. Edgar Kaufmann, jr. and Mrs. Noah Goldowsky

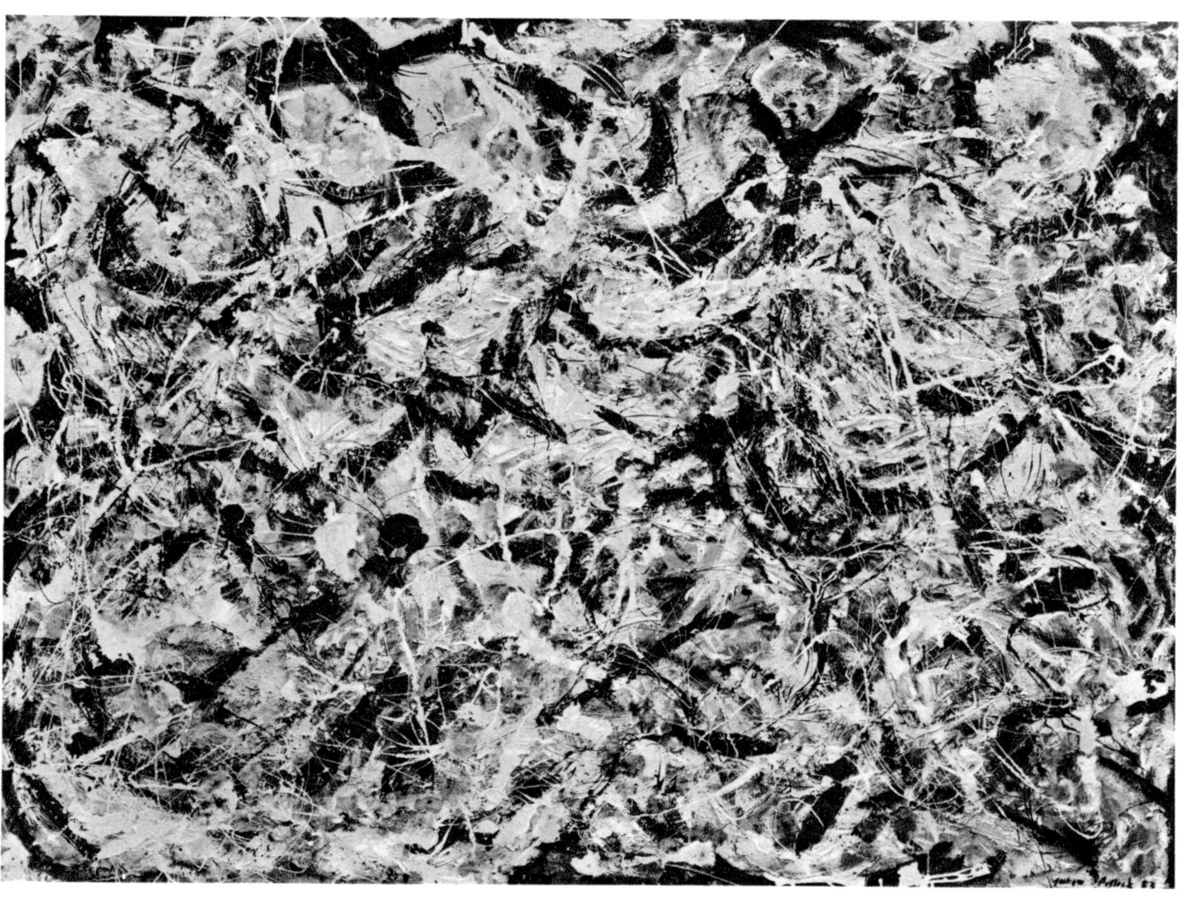

Pollock, Jackson, *Greyed Rainbow*, 1953. Gift of the Society for Contemporary American Art

Opposite: Davis, Stuart, Ready-to-Wear, 1955
Gift of Mr. & Mrs. Sigmund Kunstadter and Goodman Fund

CHRIST WASHING THE FEET OF THE DISCIPLES

Painted in the second half of the 17th century.
Oil on paper, $18 \times 23\frac{5}{16}$ in. (45.8×59.3 cm.)
Robert A. Waller Fund, 34.385

The identity of this artist is not known, though some scholars have suggested Jan Lievens or Benjamin Gerritsz Cuyp. Neither of these attributions, however, is completely convincing.

RENI, Guido ~ *1575–1642 Bologna*

Guido was the greatest Bolognese master of the *seicento*.

SALOME WITH THE HEAD OF THE BAPTIST Illus. p. 33

Painted about 1638. Oil on canvas, $97\frac{3}{4} \times 68\frac{1}{2}$ in. (248.5×173 cm.)
Frank H. and Louise B. Woods Purchase Fund, 60.3

Coll: Palazzo Colonna; Earl of Darnley, Cobham Hall

Ref: Chicago. Art Institute, Quarterly *54: 3–7, April 1960; Zeri, Federico,* Paragone *121, January 1960*

RENOIR, Pierre Auguste ~ *b. 1841 Limoges. d. 1919 Cagnes*

Renoir began his career as a decorator of porcelain. Wishing to become a painter, he studied under Gleyre and began a friendly association in the sixties with Sisley, Monet, and Bazille, the young generation of experimenters with light who were soon to be labeled Impressionists.

LADY AT THE PIANO Illus. p. 277

Painted about 1875, signed: Renoir. Oil on canvas, $36\frac{3}{4} \times 29\frac{1}{4}$ in. (93.4×74.3 cm.)
Mr. and Mrs. Martin A. Ryerson Collection, 37.1025

This painting was shown in the second Impressionist exhibition in 1875.

Ref: Chicago. Art Institute, A Century of Progress Exhibition, *1933, cat. no. 337, pl. 56;* Ibid., *1934, cat. no. 226; Barnes, A. C. and V. de Mazia,* The Art of Renoir, *1935, pp. 261, 401, 451, no. 97; Chicago. Art Institute,* Bulletin *32: 1, 4, 1938; Wilenski, R. H.,* Modern French Painters, *1940, p. 337*

TWO LITTLE CIRCUS GIRLS Illus. p. 282

Painted 1879, signed: Renoir. Oil on canvas, $51\frac{1}{4} \times 38\frac{3}{4}$ in. (130.9×98.5 cm.)
Potter Palmer Collection, 22.440

"It is your mother and myself, Francisca and Angelina Wartenberg, when we were beginning our careers as Circus Kids; the big one is of course your dear Ma, being three years my Senior—so you see, I am the greedy one, and collar most of the oranges the public pelted us with." (Original letter of Angelina Wartenberg to her niece, Marguerite W. Streckfus, December 26, 1938, Archives, The Art Institute of Chicago). These two little jugglers performed at the Cirque Fernando in Paris set up in 1875 on the Boulevard Rochechouart. This picture was shown at the first New York exhibition of the Impressionists in 1886.

Ref: Chicago. Art Institute, Annual Report, *1921; Rivière, G.,* Renoir et Ses Amis, *1921, pp. 145, 146; Chicago. Art Institute,* Bulletin *16: 37, 38, 1922; 19: 32, 33, 1925; Vollard, A.,* Renoir, An Intimate Record, *1925, p. 237; André, A.,* Renoir, *1928, pl. 36; Meier-Graefe, J.,* Renoir, *Leipzig, 1929, p. 56; Chicago. Art Institute,* A Century of Progress Exhibition, *1933, cat. no. 351, pl. 58; Rich, D.C.,* Pantheon *11:77, March 1933; Chicago. Art Institute,* A Century of Progress Exhibition, *1934, cat. no. 240; Barnes, A. C. and V. de Mazia,* The Art of Renoir, *1935, pp. 81, 72, 73, 74, 89, 262, 451, no. 99; Wilenski, R. H.,* Modern French Painters, *1940, p. 337; Drucker, M.,* Renoir, *1944, pp. 185, 201, no. 56, pl. 56; Huth, H.,* Gazette der Beaux-Arts, *29, ser. 6:240, 241, 1946; Pach, W.,* Pierre Auguste Renoir, *1950, pp. 52, 53*

ALFRED SISLEY

Painted about 1875–1876, signed: Renoir. Oil on canvas, 25¾×21⅜ in. (65.5×54.4 cm.)
Mr. and Mrs. Lewis L. Coburn Memorial Collection, 33.453

Renoir's likeness of Sisley was a token of their friendship which began in the early days of their careers when they were students in Gleyre's studio. Of the several paintings in which Sisley posed for Renoir *(Mère Anthony's Cabaret,* 1865, and *Two Portraits,* 1868), this is the latest.

Ref: Berenson, B., Gazette des Beaux-Arts *21, per. 3: 227, 1899; Lecomte, G.,* L'Art et les Artistes, *N.S. 1: 146, April 1919 to September 1920; Rivière, G.,* Renoir et Ses Amis, *1921, pl. opp. p. 50; Geffroy, G.,* Sisley *(13–14, Les Cahiers d'Aujourd'hui), 1923; Vollard, A.,* Renoir, An Intimate Record, *1925, p. 237; Meier-Graefe, J.,* Renoir, *Leipzig, 1929, p. 136; Chicago. Art Institute,* The Coburn Collection, *1932, cat. no. 31; Chicago. Art Institute,* Bulletin *26: 68, 1932; Venturi, L.,* Les Archives de l'Impressionisme, *II, 1939, pl. opp. p. 52*

LADY SEWING

Signed and dated: Renoir 79. Oil on canvas, 24¼×19⅞ in. (61.7×50.7 cm.)
Mr. and Mrs. Lewis L. Coburn Memorial Collection, 33.452

Coll: Deudon, Nice

Ref: Meier-Graefe, J., Renoir, *Leipzig, 1929, p. 122; Chicago. Art Institute,* The Coburn Collection, *cat. no. 32; Chicago. Art Institute,* A Century of Progress Exhibition, *1933, cat. no. 344;* Ibid., *1934, cat. no. 235; Wilenski, R. H.,* Modern French Painters, *1940, p. 337; Bishop, J.,* Magazine of Art *38: 172, May 1945 (ill.)*

THE WAVE

Signed and dated: Renoir 79. Oil on canvas, 25½ × 39 in. (64.8 × 99.2 cm.)
Potter Palmer Collection, 22.438

Ref: Chicago. Art Institute, Bulletin *19: 32, 47, 1925; Vollard, A.,* Renoir, An Intimate Record, *1925, p. 239; Meier-Graefe, J.,* Renoir, *Leipzig, 1929, p. 120; Rich, D. C.* Pantheon *11: 78, March 1933*

THE ROWER'S LUNCH Illus. p. 292

Painted about 1879 or 1880, signed: Renoir.
Oil on canvas, 21½ × 25¾ in. (54.7 × 65.5 cm.)
Potter Palmer Collection, 22.437

Ref: Chicago. Art Institute, The Potter Palmer Collection, *1910, cat. no. 51; Lecomte, G.,* L'Art et les Artistes, *N.S. 1: 149, April 1919 to September 1920; Chicago. Art Institute,* Bulletin *15: 161, 1921; Fosca, F.,* Renoir *(Masters of Modern Art), 1924, pl. 18; Chicago. Art Institute,* Bulletin *19: 33, 1925; Meier-Graefe, J.,* Renoir, *Leipzig, 1929, p. 124, pl. 18; Chicago. Art Institute,* A Century of Progress Exhibition, *1933, cat. no. 350; Rich, D. C.,* Pantheon *11: 77, 78, March 1933; Chicago. Art Institute,* A Century of Progress Exhibition, *1934, cat. no. 239; Wilenski, R. H.,* Modern French Painters, *1940, p. 338*

NEAR THE LAKE

Painted about 1880, signed: Renoir. Oil on canvas, 18⅛ × 21¾ in. (46.2 × 55.4 cm.)
Potter Palmer Collection, 22.439

Ref: Chicago. Art Institute, Bulletin *19: 32, 33, 1925; Chicago. Art Institute,* A Century of Progress Exhibition, *1933, cat. no. 347; Rich, D. C.,* Pantheon *11: 77, March 1933; Chicago. Art Institute,* A Century of Progress Exhibition, *1934, cat. no. 236*

THE LAUNDRESS

Painted about 1880, signed: Renoir. Oil on canvas, 32 × 22⅜ in. (81.3 × 56.9 cm.)
Charles H. and Mary F. S. Worcester Collection, 47.102

Coll: Léon Orosdi, Paris

Ref: Chicago. Art Institute, The Worcester Collection, *1923; Chicago. Art Institute,* The Worcester Collection, *1938, cat. no. 80, pl. 46*

ON THE TERRACE Illus. p. 283

Signed and dated: Renoir 81. Oil on canvas, 39½ × 31⅞ in. (100.3 × 81 cm.)
Mr. and Mrs. Lewis L. Coburn Memorial Collection, 33.455

Ref: Lecomte, G., L'Art Impressioniste, *1892, pl. opp. p. 136; Hamel, M.,* Les Arts *3, no. 35: 35, 1904; Arsène, A.,* Les Arts *11: V, XII, fig. 7, 1912; Lecomte, G.,* L'Art et les Artistes, *N.S. 1: 146–7, April 1919 to September 1920 (ill.); Rivière, G.,* Renoir et Ses Amis, *1921, pl. opp. p. 134; Jamot, P.,* Gazette des Beaux-Arts *8, per. 5: 323, 325, 1923;*

Vollard, A., Renoir, An Intimate Record, *1925, p. 240; Meier-Graefe, J.*, Renoir, *Leipzig, 1929, p. 142; Carstairs, C.*, Apollo *10: 36, July 1929; Chicago. Art Institute,* The Coburn Collection, *1932, cat. no. 33 (ill.); Chicago. Art Institute,* Bulletin *26: 67, 1932; Chicago. Art Institute,* A Century of Progress Exhibition, *1933, cat. no. 348;* Ibid., *1934, cat. no. 237; Terrasse, C.*, Cinquante Portraits de Renoir, *Paris, 1941, pl. 22; Cortissoz, R.*, Seven Paintings by Renoir, *New York, n.d., p. 7*

FRUITS FROM THE MIDI

Signed and dated: Renoir 81. Oil on canvas, 20×25⅝ in. (50.9×65.2 cm.)
Mr. and Mrs. Martin A. Ryerson Collection, 33.1176

Ref: Chicago. Art Institute, Bulletin *19: 47, 49, 1925; Vollard, A.*, Renoir, An Intimate Record, *1925, p. 240; Meier-Graefe, J.*, Renoir, *Leipzig, 1929, p. 153; Chicago. Art Institute,* A Century of Progress Exhibition, *1933, cat. no. 343; Rich, D. C.*, Pantheon *11: 78, March 1933; Chicago. Art Institute,* A Century of Progress Exhibition, *1934, cat. no. 232; Barnes, A. C. and V. de Mazia,* The Art of Renoir, *1935, p. 453; Pach, W.*, Pierre Auguste Renoir, *1950, pp. 72, 73*

CHRYSANTHEMUMS

Painted about 1882, signed: Renoir. Oil on canvas, 21½×26 in. (54.7×66.1 cm.)
Mr. and Mrs. Martin A. Ryerson Collection, 33.1173

Ref: Chicago. Art Institute, Bulletin *19: 47, 49, 1925; Chicago. Art Institute,* A Century of Progress Exhibition, *1933, cat. no. 340; Rich, D. C.*, Pantheon *11: 78, March 1933; Chicago. Art Institute,* A Century of Progress Exhibition. *1934, cat. no. 228*

CHILD IN WHITE

Signed and dated: Renoir 83. Oil on canvas, 24¼×19¾ in. (61.7×50.4 cm.)
Mr. and Mrs. Martin A. Ryerson Collection, 33.1172

A portrait of one of the Bérard children, painted at Vargemont.

Coll: Bérard, Paris

Ref: Renoir, (Témoignages), *preface by Mirbeau, Paris, 1913, pl. opp. p. 22; Chicago. Art Institute,* Bulletin *19: 48, 49, 1925; Vollard, A.*, Renoir, An Intimate Record, *1925, p. 241; Chicago. Art Institute,* A Century of Progress Exhibition, *1933, cat. no. 339; Rich, D. C.*, Pantheon *11: 78, March 1933; Chicago. Art Institute,* A Century of Progress Exhibition, *1934, cat. no. 227; Barnes, A. C. and V. de Mazia,* The Art of Renoir, *1935, pp. 271, 455, no. 134; Wilenski, R. H.*, Modern French Painters, *1940, p. 338*

MADAME CLAPISSON (Lady with a Fan)

Signed and dated: Renoir 83. Oil on canvas, 31¼×25½ in. (79.3×64.8 cm.)
Mr. and Mrs. Martin A. Ryerson Collection, 33.1174

This is one of the few commissioned portraits that Renoir painted.

Ref: Fosca, F., Renoir, *1924, pl. 24; Chicago. Art Institute,* Bulletin *19: 48, 1925; Vollard, A.,* Renoir, An Intimate Record, *1925, p. 241; André, A.,* Renoir, *1928, pl. 15; Meier-Graefe, J.,* Renoir, *Leipzig, 1929, p. 169; Rich, D. C.,* Pantheon *11: 78, March 1933; Chicago. Art Institute,* A Century of Progress Exhibition, *1934, cat. no. 229; Barnes, A. C. and V. de Mazia,* The Art of Renoir, *1935, p. 455; Wilenski, R. H.,* Modern French Painters, *1940, p. 340; Drucker, M.,* Renoir, *1944, p. 186*

HEAD OF A YOUNG GIRL

Painted about 1890–1894, signed: Renoir. Oil on canvas, $16\frac{1}{4}\times 12\frac{3}{4}$ in. (41.5×32.3 cm.)
Gift of Joseph Winterbotham, 54.322

Ref: Meier-Graefe, J., Renoir, *1929, p. 209; Drucker, M.,* Renoir, *1944, pp. 83, 84*

TWO GIRLS IN GREEN AND ROSE

Painted 1895, stamped in red: Renoir. Oil on canvas, $12\frac{5}{8}\times 13\frac{1}{8}$ in. (32.1×33.4 cm.)
Gift of Kate L. Brewster, 50.131

Ref: L'Atelier de Renoir, *preface by A. André, Paris, 1931, pl. 33*

THE ARTIST'S SON JEAN

Painted 1900, signed: Renoir. Oil on canvas, $21\frac{3}{4}\times 18\frac{1}{4}$ in. (55.4×46.5 cm.)
Mr. and Mrs. Martin A. Ryerson Collection, 37.1027

Ref: Art Digest *16: 15, June 1942; Chicago. Art Institute,* Bulletin *42: 28, 1948;* Art Digest *23: 8, 1949*

WOMAN SEWING IN A GARDEN

Painted after 1900. Oil on canvas, $11\frac{1}{2}\times 9\frac{3}{4}$ in. (29.2×24.8 cm.)
Charles H. and Mary F. S. Worcester Collection, 47.103

This sketch follows the same motif as several drawings done at this period.

Ref: Chicago. Art Institute, The Worcester Collection, *1938, cat. no. 81*

SEATED NUDE

Signed and dated: Renoir 1916. Oil on canvas, $32\frac{1}{8}\times 26\frac{5}{8}$ in. (81.6×67.7 cm.)
Gift of Annie Swan Coburn to the Mr. and Mrs. Lewis L. Coburn Memorial Collection, 45.27

Ref: Coquiot, G., Renoir, *1925, p. 234; Chicago. Art Institute,* Bulletin *39: 97–102, 1945*

FLOWERS

Painted about 1917–1918, signed: Renoir. Oil on canvas, $18\frac{1}{8}\times 16\frac{1}{4}$ in. (46.2×41.5 cm.)
Gift of Joseph Winterbotham, 54.321

Ref: L'Atelier de Renoir, *II (intro. by M. Elder), 1931, pl. 198, fig. 634 (in this photograph there appears no signature; it was probably added later when the atelier collection was sold; here dated about 1918)*

REYNOLDS, Sir Joshua ~ *b. 1723 Plympton-Earl's. d. 1792 London*

From 1740 to 1743 Reynolds was a pupil of Thomas Hudson. After that time, he traveled widely in France, the Low Countries, and the Rhineland. He was first president of the Royal Academy, from its founding in 1768 until 1790.

LADY SARAH BUNBURY SACRIFICING TO THE GRACES

Painted 1765. Oil on canvas, 94×60 in. (239×152.5 cm.)
Mr. and Mrs. W. W. Kimball Collection, 22.4468

Lady Sarah Lennox went to court in 1759 when she was scarcely fifteen. She married Sir Charles Bunbury of Barton and Milton Hall, Suffolk, but her romantic escapades led to divorce, and in 1781 she married the Hon. George Napier, a hero of the American War of Independence. Reynolds has depicted Lady Sarah as a classical matron sacrificing to the Three Graces at the altar of Apollo.

Coll: Sir Charles Bunbury; Sir Henry Bunbury and descendants, Barton Hall, London; Charles J. Wertheimer

Ref: Leslie, C. R. and Taylor, T. Life and Times of Sir Joshua Reynolds, *I, 1865, pp. 247, 248, 252; Armstrong, Sir Walter,* Sir Joshua Reynolds, *1900, pp. 167, 196; Ilchester,* The Life and Letters of Lady Sarah Lennox, *1902, ill. opp. p. 332; G. Newnes' Art Library,* Sir Joshua Reynolds, *London, ca. 1905, p. xxix, 1908, p. 110; Chicago. Art Institute,* Annual Report, *1922; Waterhouse, E. K.,* Reynolds, *1941, pp. 12, 55; Pevsner, N.,* Architectural Review *91: 37–8, London, February 1942*

MRS. GEORGE HUDDESFORD

Painted about 1776. Oil on canvas, 29⅝×25¾ in. (75.3×65.5 cm.)
Frederick T. Haskell Collection, 40.1142

Mrs. Huddesford was married to the Vicar of Loxley, son of the President of Trinity College, Cambridge. Her husband was once a pupil of Reynolds.

Coll: F. Ashcroft, London; F. Fleishman, London

Ref: Armstrong, Sir Walter, Sir Joshua Reynolds, *New York, 1900, pp. 31, 81; Chicago. Art Institute,* Bulletin *35: 111, 1941; Waterhouse, E. K.,* Reynolds, *1941, p. 67*

SIR THOMAS RUMBOLD

Painted in 1788. Oil on canvas, 50×40 in. (127×101.7 cm.)
A. A. Munger Collection, 55.1202

Rumbold, who joined the East India Company in 1752, made military service his career. This portrait is painted in Reynolds' late style when he had departed from classical poses and the grand manner. It has the clarity of tone and directness of approach which were distinguishing traits in his work after his visit to Flanders and Holland in 1781, where he became acquainted with the realism of Dutch 17th century painting.

MASTER WORSLEY, THE BOY IN RED

Painted about 1780. Oil on panel, $30\frac{1}{2} \times 24\frac{7}{8}$ in. (77.5×63.3 cm.)
Max and Leola Epstein Collection, 54.298

RIBERA, Jusepe (follower of)

HERACLITUS

Painted about 1660. Oil on canvas, $34\frac{1}{2} \times 29\frac{1}{2}$ in. (87×74.3 cm.)
Gift of the Heirs of Samuel Gans, 97.296

DEMOCRITUS

Painted about 1660. Oil on canvas, $34\frac{1}{2} \times 29\frac{1}{2}$ in. (87×74.3 cm.)
Gift of the Heirs of Samuel Gans, 97.291

Representations of Democritus and Heraclitus as beggar philosophers, with special emphasis on their contrasting expressions, were favorite subjects with Ribera and his followers in Naples. The unidentified artist may even have been a northern painter whose work shows Ribera's influence.

RIBOT, Théodule ~ *b. 1823 Saint-Nicolas-d'Attez. d. 1891 Colombes, France*

Ribot, a pupil of Auguste Glaize, turned to earlier French painters like Chardin and the brothers Le Nain. He was also interested in the type of realism advocated by Gustave Courbet.

THE SCULLION

Painted about 1860–1870, signed: T. Ribot. Oil on canvas, $36\frac{1}{4} \times 20\frac{9}{16}$ in. (92.1×52.1 cm.)
Gift of Annie Swan Coburn to the Mr. and Mrs. Lewis L. Coburn Memorial Collection, 38.1297

Coll: Baron Adolphe Kohner, Budapest

THE ARTIST'S DAUGHTER

Painted about 1860–1865, signed: T. Ribot. Oil on canvas, $11\frac{5}{8} \times 8\frac{5}{16}$ in. (29.5×21 cm.)
Gift of Kate L. Brewster, 50.132

A portrait of Ribot's daughter Louise Aimée, also a painter.

Coll: Sir James Murray

Ref: Chicago. Art Institute, Bulletin *44: 55, September 15, 1950*

RICHARDS, William Trost ~ *b. 1833 Philadelphia. d. 1905 Newport, R.I.*

Richards established a reputation for romantic seascapes done chiefly near Newport. In 1853 he went abroad to study in Paris and Italy and in 1867 settled permanently in Newport. His romantic-realist style was influenced by the Pre-Raphaelites.

THE AUGUST MOON

Signed and dated: Wm. T. Richards '89. Oil on canvas, 18×31⅞ in. (45.8×81 cm.)
Nickerson Collection, 00.599

RITSCHEL, William ~ *b. 1864 Nuremberg, Germany. d. 1949 Carmel, Calif.*

DESERT WANDERER, NAVAJO

Signed and dated: W. Ritschel 1912. Oil on canvas, 48×58 in. (122×147.7 cm.)
Friends of American Art Collection, 12.202

RIVERA, Diego ~ *b. 1886 Guanajuato. d. 1957 Mexico City*

Rivera, one of the leaders of Mexican modern art, studied at the National Academy of Fine Arts in Mexico City. During his early twenties he visited Spain and fell under the spell of Goya; from there he went to Paris, where he worked as an abstract painter under the influence of Picasso and Juan Gris.

MADAME MARCOUSSIS

Painted about 1915, signed: D M R. Oil on canvas, 57½×45½ in. (146.1×114.7 cm.)
Gift of Georgia O'Keeffe, 57.628

Coll: Alfred Stieglitz

ROBERT, Hubert ~ *1733–1808 Paris*

With Fragonard, Robert studied in Rome as a young man. At that time he was much influenced by the great architectural painters Panini and Piranesi.

FOUR DECORATIONS FROM THE CHATEAU OF MEREVILLE, FRANCE:

LANDING PLACE

Signed, dated, and inscribed: H. Robert in aedibus merevillae pro d. delaborde, pinxit A.D. 1788. Oil on canvas, 100×92 in. (254.1×233.7 cm.)
Gift of Richard T. Crane, 00.384

OLD TEMPLE

Painted 1787. Oil on canvas, 100×92 in. (254.1×233.7 cm.)
Gift of Adolphus C. Bartlett, 00.382

THE FOUNTAINS

Painted 1787 or 1788. Oil on canvas, 100×92 in. (254.1×233.7 cm.)
Gift of William C. Hibbard, 00.385

THE OBELISK

Signed and dated: H. Robert 1787. Oil on canvas, 100×92 in. (254.1×233.7 cm.)
Gift of Clarence Buckingham, 00.383

The manor house of Méréville belonged to the financier Jean-Joseph, Marquis de Laborde (1724–1794), who gave funds to Louis XVI to carry on military activities during the American War of Independence. Robert was one of the artists commissioned to transform the formal park of Méréville to suit the new romantic style. For the manor house, Robert painted six panels to decorate the drawing room. All were removed in the 19th century. The present whereabouts of the other two panels is not known.

Coll: Marquis Jean-Jacques de Labord, Château Méréville, France; Count de St. Roman; M. L. François, Paris

Ref: Paris, Galerie Georges Petit, Catalogue d'une Importante Décoration . . . Peints par Hubert-Robert . . . , *June 13, 1900, cat. no. 1–4 (ill.); de Nolhac, P.,* Hubert Robert, *1910, pp. 153, 154, cat. nos. 1–4; Leclère, T.,* Hubert Robert, *1913, p. 92; Chicago. Art Institute,* A Century of Progress Exhibition, *1933, cat. no. 227;* Ibid., *1934, cat. nos. 330–333*

ROBINSON, Theodore H. ~ *b. 1852 Irasburg, Vt. d. 1896 New York City*

Theodore Robinson, a prominent member of the American Impressionist group, spent considerable time abroad and was greatly influenced by French painting. He studied at the National Academy of Design, but in 1876 went to Paris to work with Carolus-Duran and Gérôme.

THE VALE OF ARCONVILLE

Painted about 1888, signed: Th. Robinson. Oil on canvas, 18×21⅞ in. (45.8×55.7 cm.)
Friends of American Art Collection, 41.11

Painted about a year after Robinson became a friend of Monet's.

ROMAGNOLI, Giovanni ~ *b. 1893 Faenza, Italy*

Romagnoli studied at the Institute of Fine Arts in Bologna with Domenico Ferri and Augusto Maiani.

GIRL EATING FRUIT

Painted 1923, signed: Giov. Romagnoli. Oil on canvas, 31¼×26½ in. (79.3×67.4 cm.)
Charles H. and Mary F. S. Worcester Collection, 47.106

Ref: Chicago. Art Institute, The Worcester Collection, *1937, cat. no. 98*

SUMMER (NUDE)

Painted about 1925. Oil on panel, 5⅜×12 in. (13.7×30.5 cm.)
Charles H. and Mary F. S. Worcester Collection, 47.105

Ref: Chicago. Art Institute, The Worcester Collection, *1937, cat. no. 97*

ROMNEY, George ~ *b. 1734 Dalton-in-Furness. d. 1802 Kendal, England*

Romney was a pupil of Christopher Steele in Kendal, studied in Paris and Rome, and in 1775 settled in London.

MRS. FRANCIS RUSSELL

Painted between 1765 and 1787. Oil on canvas, $50\frac{3}{16}\times 40$ in. (127.4×101.7 cm.)
Mrs. Russell was the daughter of the Vicar of Leeds and Canon of Ripon; her husband, an attorney, was a cousin of the Duke of Bedford.

Coll: C. Wertheimer

Ref: Roberts, W., Magazine of Art *21: 139, 140, 1898; Ward, H. and W. Roberts,* Romney, A Bibliographical and Critical Essay with a Catalogue Raisonné of His Works, *II, 1904, p. 137 (of cat.); Chicago. Art Institute,* Bulletin *14: 72, 1920; Chicago. Art Institute,* A Century of Progress Exhibition, *1933, cat. no. 204; Collins Baker, C. R. and M. R. James,* British Painting, *1933, p. 285; Chicago. Art Institute,* A Century of Progress Exhibition, *1934, cat. no. 152*

ROSA, Salvator ~ *b. 1615 Arenella. d. 1673 Rome*

Salvator Rosa, noted during his life as a poet, engraver, musician and painter, specialized in landscapes, portraits and battle scenes.

POLYCRATES RECEIVING FISH AND RING

Painted about 1640, signed: S.R. Oil on canvas, 29×39 in. (73.7×99.2 cm.)
Wentworth Greene Field Memorial Fund, 42.291

POLYCRATES: CRUCIFIXION

Painted about 1640. Oil on canvas, 29×39 in. (73.7×99.2 cm.)
Wentworth Greene Field Memorial Fund, 42.292

LANDSCAPE WITH ROCKS AND FORTRESS

Probably painted between 1640 and 1650, signed with monogram.
Oil on canvas, $22\frac{1}{2}\times 34\frac{7}{8}$ in. (57.3×88.6 cm.)
Cyrus McCormick Fund, 58.326

In 1640 Rosa settled in Florence, where he remained for almost a decade. This small inventive canvas may have been painted during that period. It is not certain whether the monogram is authentic. The picture is scarcely convincing as by Salvator and seems, rather, the product of a Dutch bambocciantist at work in Rome.

ROSENTHAL, Toby Edward ~ *b. 1848 New Haven, Conn. d. 1917 Munich*

Rosenthal studied art in San Francisco and in 1865 went to abroad to attend the Munich Academy under Karl von Piloty.

ELAINE

Inscribed, signed and dated: Elaine, Toby E. Rosenthal, Munich, 1874.
Oil on canvas, $38\frac{3}{4}\times 62\frac{1}{4}$ in. (98.5×158.2 cm.)
Gift of Mrs. Maurice Rosenfeld, 17.3

ROSSETTI, Dante Gabriel Charles ~ *b. 1828 London. d. Birchington-on-Sea*

Rossetti, the son of an Italian poet and professor, first studied at Cary's Drawing Academy, then at the Royal Academy, and finally with Ford Madox Brown. With Holman Hunt and J. E. Millais, he was one of the founders of the Pre-Raphaelite Brotherhood.

BEATA BEATRIX

Signed and dated: GCDR 1872.
Oil on canvas, 33¾×26½ in. (85.8×67.4 cm.) Predella 9½×26½ in. (24.2×67.4 cm.)
Gift of Charles L. Hutchinson, 25.722

Rossetti's original painting of his wife Elizabeth Siddal (1853), is now at the Tate Gallery. In 1872 he made this replica and added the predella showing Dante meeting Beatrice in Paradise. The frame was also designed by Rossetti.
Cool: William Graham

Ref: Marillier, H. C., Dante Gabriel Rossetti, An Illustrated Memorial of His Art and Life, *1899, pp. 252, 126, no. 248; Rossetti, H. M. M.,* The Life and Work of Dante Gabriel Rossetti, *c. 1902, pp. 14, 16; Knight, W.,* Nineteenth Century Artists, *1909, pl. 22; Chicago. Art Institute,* Bulletin *13: 98, 1919; 19: 102, 104, 1925; Mather, F. J.,* Modern Paintings, *1927, pp. 73, 74; Chicago. Art Institute,* A Century of Progress Exhibition, *1933, cat. no. 274*

ROTARI, Pietro Antonio ~ *b. 1707 Verona. d. 1762 Leningrad*

Rotari studied in Venice under Antonio Balestra, in Rome with Francesco Trevisani, and in Naples with Francesco Solimena. He worked at the court in Dresden and in 1756 became court painter in Russia.

THE SLEEPING GIRL

Painted about 1750. Pastel on paper, 15¾×11 13/16 in. (40.1×30 cm.)
Mr. and Mrs. Martin A. Ryerson Collection, 33.1066
The motif in this picture had been used earlier by Piazzetta.

Coll: M. L. Tabourier, Paris, 1898

ROTHKO, Mark ~ *b. 1903 Dwinsk, Russia*

Rothko came to this country at the age of ten, entered Yale in 1921, and later studied at the Art Students League.

PAINTING

Painted 1953–1954. Oil on canvas, 104½×117¼ in. (264.6×322.8 cm.)
Friends of American Art Collection, 54.1308

NUMBER 19

Signed and dated on back: Mark Rothko 1949.
Oil on canvas, 68×40 in. (172.8×101.7 cm.)
Anonymous Gift, 57.308

ROUAULT, Georges ~ *1871–1958 Paris*

Rouault started as an apprentice to a stained glass painter, an experience which strongly affected his future work. Later he studied at the Ecole des Beaux-Arts under Gustave Moreau.

THE ACADEMICIAN Illus. p. 474

Painted about 1913–1915, signed: G. Rouault.
Oil on canvas, 41⅞×29⅞ in. (106.4×76 cm.)
Gift of Mrs. Leigh B. Block in memory of her father Albert D. Lasker, 58.192

THE THREE JUDGES

Signed and dated: G. Rouault 1938.
Oil and gouache on paper, mounted on cardboard, 29 7/16×21⅝ in. (74.6×55 cm.)
Gift of Mr. and Mrs. Samuel A. Marx, 54.1309

Ref: Soby, J. T., Georges Rouault, *1947, pp. 21, 22, cat. no. 55*

THE DWARF

Painted about 1936, signed: G. Rouault. Oil on canvas, 27¼×19¾ in. (69.3×50.4 cm.)
Gift of Mr. and Mrs. Max Epstein, 46.96

Ref: Venturi, L., Georges Rouault, *New York, 1940, cat. no. 102, pl. 81;* Le Point *XXVI–XXVII, August/October 1943; Soby, J. T.,* Georges Rouault, *c. 1947, p. 15; Venturi, L.,* Georges Rouault, *Paris, 1948, pl. 95*

L'ITALIENNE

Probably painted in the late 1930's, signed: G. Rouault.
Oil on canvas, 16×11½ in. (45.8×29.2 cm.)
Gift of Mrs. Gilbert W. Chapman, 51.245

ROUSSEAU, Henri ~ *b. 1844 Laval, France. d. 1910 Paris*

Rousseau, a self-taught painter, began to exhibit his work at the Salon des Indépendents around 1866. By haunting the Louvre, by carefully observing the world around him, and by studying plant life at the botanical gardens in Paris, Rousseau prepared himself for his favorite themes—jungle scenes (inspired perhaps by his stay in Mexico) and genre.

THE SAWMILL, OUTSKIRTS OF PARIS

Painted about 1893–1895, signed: H. Rousseau.
Oil on canvas, 10 × 17⅞ in. (25.5 × 45.5 cm.)
Gift of Kate L. Brewster, 50.133

Coll: Paul Guillaume, Paris

Ref: Zervos, C., Cahiers d'Art *1: 227, 1926; Sweeney, J. J.,* Cahiers d'Art *7, nos. 1–2: 30, 1932; Huyghe, R.,* L'Amour de l'Art *14, no. 8: 192, October 1933; Zervos, C.,* Histoire de l'Art Contemporain, *1938, p. 106; Rich, D. C.,* Henri Rousseau, *1942, p. 21; Grey, R.,* Henri Rousseau, *1943, p. 85; Jakovsky, A.,* La Peinture Naïve, *1949, ill. opp. p. 43; Chicago. Art Institute,* Bulletin *44: 51, 54, September 15, 1950*

THE WATERFALL Illus. p, 476

Signed and dated: Henri Rousseau 1910. Oil on canvas, 45⅝ × 59 in. (115.9 × 149.9 cm.)
Helen Birch Bartlett Memorial Collection, 26.262

Ref: Chicago. Art Institute, The Birch Bartlett Collection, *1926, pp. 4–5; Chicago. Art Institute,* Bulletin *20: 62, 1926; Soupault, P.,* Henri Rousseau, Le Douanier, *1927, pl. 36; Chicago. Art Institute,* The Birch Bartlett Collection, *1929, pp. 10–11, 57; Chicago. Art Institute,* A Century of Progress Exhibition, *1933, cat. no. 369; Chicago. Art Institute,* Bulletin *27: 70, 1933; Chicago. Art Institute,* A Century of Progress Exhibition, *1934, cat. no. 3221 Rich, D. C.,* Henri Rousseau, *Chicago, 1942, pp. 64–5; Grey, R.,* Henri Rousseau, *1943, p. 102; Griot, A.,* Art Quarterly *7: 206, 216, 1944; Kienitz, J. F.,* Art in America *30: 122, 123, 1944; Chicago. Art Institute,* The Birch Bartlett Collection, *1946, pp. 40–1*

FLOWERS

Painted about 1905, signed: Henri Rousseau. Oil on canvas, 13 × 9½ in. (32 × 24.2 cm.)
Gift of Mrs. Emily Crane Chadbourne, 53.3

ROUSSEAU, Théodore ~ *b. 1812 Paris. d. 1867 Barbizon*

Rousseau was a pupil of his cousin, Paul de Saint-Martin, and also studied with certain other painters in Paris. He made his debut at the Salon of 1831.

LANDSCAPE

Painted about 1850. signed: Th. Rousseau. Oil on panel, 8½ × 10½ in. (21.7 × 26.7 cm.)
Henry Field Memorial Collection, 94.1065

SPRINGTIME

Painted about 1860, signed: Th. Rousseau. Oil on panel, 15⅝ × 21¼ in. (34.8 × 54.1 cm.)
Henry Field Memorial Collection, 94.1066

Coll: Saulnier, Bordeaux; M. E. Secrétan, Paris

Ref: Gensel, W., Millet and Rousseau, *1902, pp. 97, 102*

ROUSSEFF, Walter Vladimir ~ *b. 1890 Silistria, Bulgaria*

Rousseff was trained at The Art Institute of Chicago.

IN THE OPEN

Signed and dated on back: W. Vladimir Rousseff 1928.
Oil on canvas, 27¾ × 31½ in. (70.6 × 80.2 cm.)
Mr. and Mrs. Frank G. Logan Purchase Prize, 29.85

RUBENS, Peter Paul ~ *b. 1577 Siegen, Germany. d. 1640 Antwerp*

Rubens was a student of Otto van Veen and Adam van Noort. His Italian journey early in his life had a crucial effect on his art, which essentially was a Baroque development of late Venetian Mannerism done in the old Flemish medium of oil paint.

SAMSON AND DELILAH

Painted 1610/11. Oil on panel, 19¾ × 26⅛ in. (50.4 × 66.4 cm.)
Robert A. Waller Fund, 23.551

While Rubens was probably inspired by compositions of both Titian and Tintoretto, this small painting is based more directly on an engraving of Jupiter and Callisto by a minor Italian artist, Perino del Vaga. There exist two drawings and one other painting by Rubens representing various phases of the same story. Van Dyck's painting of the same subject in Vienna also shows a close relationship to Rubens' concept. For a time the Art Institute's sketch was attributed to Van Dyck, but an attribution to Rubens now seems sure.

Coll: Albert Besnard, Paris

Ref: Rooses, A., Rubens, *I, 1886, pp. 165–6; Chicago. Art Institute,* Bulletin *18: 35, 36, 37, 1924; Burchard, L.,* Sitzungsberichte der Berliner Kunstgeschichtlichen Gesellschaft, *October 8, 1926, no. 20; Chicago. Art Institute,* A Century of Progress Exhibition, *1933, cat. no. 77, pl. 38; Glück, G.,* Rubens, Van Dyck und ihr Kreis, *1933, p. 395; Chicago. Art Institute,* A Century of Progress Exhibition, *1934, cat. no. 109; Goris, J.-A. and J. S. Held,* Rubens in America, *1947, cat. no. 38, pls. 43, 44; Rotterdam, Museum Boymans,* Rubens, *December 1953 to February 1954, cat. no. 6*

THE TRIUMPH OF THE EUCHARIST

Probably painted about 1626–1627. Oil on panel, 12½ × 12½ in. (31.8 × 31.8 cm.)
Mr. and Mrs. Martin A. Ryerson Collection, 37.1012

When the Archduchess Isabella Clara Eugenia wanted to express her devotion to the Royal Convent of the Discalced Carmelites in Madrid, she dedicated to the nuns a series of tapestries exemplifying the glory of the Sacraments. Rubens was commissioned to do the designs, which he completed between 1626 and 1627. The tapestries were woven by Jacob Roes and in 1638 shipped to the convent where they are still used for high feasts.

This sketch shows five figure motifs, each of which was executed in reverse for the fabrics which were to surround the tabernacle. Though the five finished tapestries are slightly different, they indicate that this may have been the original sketch. The Fitzwilliam Museum in Cambridge, England, owns a set of seven sketches to which the Art Institute panel may be related.

Ref: Rooses, M., L'Oeuvre de P. P. Rubens, *I, 1886, pp. 53–61; Tormo, E.,* Archivo Español de Arte *15, no. 49–54: 291–315, 1942; Goris, J.-A. and J. S. Held,* Rubens in America, *ca. 1947, pp. 34–5, cat. no. 57*

THE WEDDING OF PELEUS AND THETIS

Painted about 1636–1637. Oil on panel, $10\frac{3}{4} \times 16\frac{7}{8}$ in. (27.3×42.9 cm.)
Charles H. and Mary F. S. Worcester Collection, 47.108

This is one of the sketches for a series of pictures commissioned by Philip IV of Spain for his hunting castle, Torre de la Parada, near Madrid.

Ref: Rooses, M., L'Oeuvre de P. P. Rubens, *III, Antwerp, 1890, p. 167, cat. no. 682, pl. 210; Rooses, M.,* Rubens, *II, 1904, pp. 597–604; Rosenberg, A.,* P. P. Rubens, *Stuttgart/Leipzig, 1905, pp. 409, 498; Dillon, E.,* Rubens, *1909, p. 233, pl. 399; Chicago. Art Institute,* The Worcester Collection, *1937, cat. no. 46, pl. 32; Chicago. Art Institute,* Bulletin *41: 58, 59, 1947; Goris, J.-A. and J. S. Held,* Rubens in America, *ca. 1947, p. 38, no. 76*

RUBENS, Peter Paul (attributed to)

PORTRAIT OF NICOLAS RUBENS, THE ARTIST'S SON

Painted in late 1630s. Oil on panel, $29\frac{3}{8} \times 27\frac{1}{2}$ in. (74.6×70 cm.)
Max and Leola Epstein Collection, 54.299

Ref: Bode, W. von, Zeitschrift für Bildende Kunst, *1905, p. 201; Chicago. Art Institute,* Bulletin *17: 55, 56, September 1923; Goris, J.-A. and J. S. Held,* Rubens in America, *1947, p. 46*

RUISDAEL, Jacob van ~ *1628/9–1682 Haarlem, Holland*

Jacob van Ruisdael was a pupil of his father Isaac, and probably of his uncle, Salomon van Ruisdael. His early work shows the influence of Rembrandt's landscape style.

RUINS OF EGMOND Illus. p. 193

Painted about 1650–1660, signed: v.R. Oil on canvas, $38\frac{7}{8} \times 51\frac{1}{8}$ in. (98.9×129.9 cm.)
Potter Palmer Collection, 47.475 (HdG no. 51)

Coll: Baron de Beurnonville, Paris, 1881; G. von Rath, Budapest; Oscar Huldschinsky, Berlin

Ref: Masters in Art *8: 83, 1907; Bode, W. von,* Die Sammlung Oscar Huldschinsky, *1909, cat. no. 26; Rosenberg, J.,* Jacob van Ruisdael, *ca. 1928, pp. 20, 21, 74, cat. no. 34, pl. 18, fig. 31; Cassirer, P. and H. Helbing,* Die Sammlung Oscar Huldschinsky, *1928, p. 52, cat. no. 29, pl. 25;* Pantheon *1: 128, 1929; Romdahl, A. L.,* Tidskrift för Konstvetenskap *20: 39, 40, 1927; Chicago. Art Institute,* Bulletin *42: 20, 21, 1948*

WATERFALL NEAR A CASTLE

Oil on canvas, 21⅞ × 17¾ in. (55.7 × 45.2 cm.)
W. W. Kimball Collection, 22.4470

RUTHERFORD, Alexander W.

In his *American Artist Life,* Tuckerman speaks of one Rutherford as a "genre painter of promise who died young."

INTERIOR OF A ROOM

Signed and dated: Rutherford 1845. Oil on canvas, 22 × 27 in. (56 × 68.7 cm.)
Gift of Emily Crane Chadbourne, 53.10

SAFTLEVEN, Cornelis ~ *b. 1607 Gorkum, Holland. d. 1681 Rotterdam*

Little is known about Saftleven, though he probably studied in Antwerp and spent most of his life in Rotterdam. His earliest known painting is dated 1629.

THE WITCHES' SABBATH

Painted about 1650. Oil on panel, 22 × 31 in. (56 × 78.8 cm.)
George F. Porter Collection, 45.290

Coll: Castle Dioszegh, Dioszegh, Czechoslovakia

Ref: Mireur, H., Ventes d'Art, *VI, 1912, pp. 55–70, 399*

SAGE, Kay ~ *b. 1898 Albany, N.Y.*

IN THE THIRD SLEEP

Signed and dated: Kay Sage 44. Oil on canvas, 39½ × 57 in. (100.3 × 144.9 cm.)
Watson F. Blair Purchase Prize, Goodman Fund, 45.198

SANCHEZ COTAN, Juan ~ *b. 1561 Orgaz, Spain. d. 1627 Granada*

Sánchez Cotán studied in Toledo with Blas de Prado. In 1603 he left Toledo to become a lay brother at the Charterhouse of El Paular near Segovia. After eight years he was transferred to the Charterhouse at Elvira on the outskirts of Granada. Sánchez Cotán painted Carthusian saints and other religious themes but excelled in still life paintings.

STILL LIFE

Painted about 1602. Oil on canvas, 26⅝ × 34¾ in. (67.7 × 88.3 cm.)
Gift of Mr. and Mrs. Leigh B. Block, 55.1203

A painting dated 1602 in the Hernani Collection, Madrid, may be a pendant to this picture.

SANO DI PIETRO ~ *1406–1481 Siena*

Sano di Pietro was much influenced by Sassetta.

MADONNA AND CHILD WITH SS. JEROME AND BERNARDINE

Painted between 1450 and 1475. Tempera on panel, 20¼×17 in. (51.5×43.3 cm.)
Mr. and Mrs. Martin A. Ryerson Collection, 33.1027

Coll: Jean Dollfus, Paris; Ferdinand Hermann, New York

Ref: Berenson, B., The Central Italian Painters of the Renaissance, *1909, p. 239; Gaillard, E.,* L'Antiquario, *June 1913, p. 80; Reinach, S.,* Répertoire *5: 383, 1922; Chicago. Art Institute,* Bulletin *17: 5, 1923; Gaillard, E.,* Sano di Pietro, *1923, p. 204; Trübner, J.,* Die Stilistische Entwicklung des Sano di Pietro, *1925; Van Marle, R.,* The Development of the Italian Schools of Painting, *IX, 1927, p. 494; Berenson, B.,* Italian Pictures of the Renaissance, *1932, p. 498; Chicago. Art Institute,* A Century of Progress Exhibition, *1933, cat. no. 93;* Ibid., *1934, cat. no. 34*

SANTACROCE, Girolamo da ~ *Active 1503–1566 Venice*

Girolamo may have come from the village of Santacroce near Bergamo or the one in Istria. He was a pupil and assistant of Gentile Bellini and later worked with Giovanni Bellini.

MADONNA AND CHILD

Signed, dated and inscribed: M.D.X.VI:ADI.XX IIII. OTUBRIO. IHERONIMO.DA. SANTA†. Tempera on panel, 34¼×17½ in. (87×44.5 cm.)
Mr. and Mrs. Martin A. Ryerson Collection, 33.1008

This painting, the earliest known by Girolamo, is a copy of the Giovanni Bellini *Madonna* (1505) in the church of St. Zaccaria in Venice.

Coll: Kerr Lawson, Florence, 1910

Ref: Berenson, B., Pitture Italiane del Rinascimento, *1936, p. 436*

SARGENT, John Singer ~ *b. 1856 Florence. d. 1925 London*

Sargent was born in Florence to an American family. At eighteen he entered to studio of Carolus-Duran.

MRS. CHARLES GIFFORD DYER (May Anthony) Illus. p. 374

Inscribed, signed and dated: To my friend Mrs. Dyer, John S. Sargent, Venice, 1880. Oil on canvas, 24⅝×17¼ in. (62.7×43.9 cm.)
Friends of American Art Collection, 15.592

Mrs. Dyer, wife of the American painter, lived the greater part of her life abroad. She and her husband were close friends of Sargent and spent a great deal of time with him when they were in Venice.

VENETIAN GLASS WORKERS

Painted 1882, signed: John S. Sargent. Oil on canvas, $22\frac{1}{4} \times 33\frac{3}{4}$ in. (56.6×85.8 cm.)
Mr. and Mrs. Martin A. Ryerson Collection, 33.1217

WATER CARRIERS ON THE NILE

Painted 1891, stamped on reverse: J.S.S. Oil on canvas, $21\frac{3}{8} \times 25\frac{1}{2}$ in. (54.4×64.8 cm.)
Charles H. and Mary F. S. Worcester Collection, 35.445

One of the paintings done on Sargent's trip to Egypt in 1891.

MRS. GEORGE SWINTON (Elsie Ebsworth)

Painted 1896, signed: John S. Sargent. Oil on canvas, 90×49 in. (228.7×124.5 cm.)
Wirt D. Walker Fund, 22.4450

Mrs. Swinton was a popular English singer.

THE FOUNTAIN, VILLA TORLONIA, FRASCATI

Painted 1907, signed: John S. Sargent. Oil on canvas, $28\frac{1}{2} \times 22$ in. (72.5×56 cm.)
Friends of American Art Collection, 14.57

This is one of several smaller canvases Sargent did on a visit to Italy in 1907. Shown painting in the garden is Mrs. Wilfred de Glehn (Jane Erin Emmet) and her husband, a portrait painter, pupil, and friend of Sargent.

SAVAGE, Edward ~ *1761–1817 Princeton, Mass.*

After learning engraving from a goldsmith and acquiring a knowledge of painting, Savage went abroad in 1791 and presumably studied with Benjamin West in London before continuing on to Italy. In 1801 he started the New York Museum of Paintings and Curiosities, which later moved to Boston and continued until 1825.

GEORGE WASHINGTON

Signed and dated: E. Savage 1793. Oil on canvas, $18\frac{1}{2} \times 14\frac{1}{8}$ in. (47.1×36 cm.)
Gift of Catherine Colvin, 21.88

This portrait, probably finished in London in 1793, was used as the basis for a widely circulated mezzotint.

SAVAGE, Eugene Francis ~ *b. 1883 Covington, Ind.*

Savage worked at the Corcoran School in Washington, the Art Institute, and in Munich.

ARBOR DAY

Painted 1920, signed and dated: Eugene Francis Savage xx.
Oil on panel, $45\frac{3}{8} \times 35$ in. (115.3×88.9 cm.)
Friends of American Art Collection, 21.103

SCHAFFNER, Martin ~ *c.-1479. c.1547 Ulm, Germany*

Schaffner, first pupil of Jörg Stocker of Ulm, was influenced by Hans Holbein the Elder and later by Hans Schaüffelein. He worked in the traditional manner of the Swabian School.

PORTRAIT OF A MAN

Painted about 1520. Oil on panel, 12¾ × 10⅛ in. (32.3 × 25.7 cm.)
Charles H. and Mary F. S. Worcester Collection, 47.109

Ref: Kuhn, C. L., A Catalogue of German Paintings of the Middle Ages and Renaissance in American Collections, *1936, cat. no. 273; Chicago. Art Institute,* The Worcester Collection, *1937, cat. no. 41*

SCHOFIELD, Walter Elmer ~ *b. 1867 Philadelphia. d. 1944 Cornwall, England*

Schofield studied at the Pennsylvania Academy of the Fine Arts and in Paris at the Académie Julian with William Bouguereau.

THE POWERHOUSE, FALLS VILLAGE, CONNECTICUT

Probably painted about 1914, signed: Schofield.
Oil on canvas, 40 × 49 in. (101.7 × 124.5 cm.)
Walter H. Schulze Memorial Collection, 24.915

SCHREYER, Adolf ~ *b. 1828 Frankfurt. d. 1899 Cronberg*

Schreyer, a pupil of Jakob Becker, spent many years in Paris. His participation in the Crimean War as an artist and his trips to Africa influenced his work, but it was his friendship with the French artist Decamps, one of the foremost representatives of "Orientalism," which finally determined his career as a painter of Oriental scenes.

MAN WITH LANCE RIDING THROUGH SNOW

Painted about 1880, signed: Ad. Schreyer. Oil on canvas, 6¾ × 9¼ in. (17.2 × 23.5 cm.)
Henry Field Memorial Collection, 94.1067

SCHWARTZ, William Samuel ~ *b. 1896 Smorgon, Russia*

Schwartz began his art training at the age of eleven in the Vilna Art School, and studied at the Art Institute, from 1916 to 1919.

CHICAGO HARBOR

Painted 1931, signed: William S. Schwartz. Oil on canvas, 30 × 36 in. (76.3 × 91.5 cm.)
Anonymous Gift, 51.18

READING ROOM

Painted 1943, signed: William S. Schwartz. Oil on canvas, 19⅜ × 24 in. (49.4 × 61 cm.)
Friends of American Art Collection, 44.31

SCHMIDT-ROTTLUFF, Karl ~ *b. 1884 Rottluff, Germany*

GIRLS IN A GARDEN

Signed and dated: S. Rottluff 1914. Oil on canvas, 39½ × 34 in. (100.3 × 86.4 cm.)
Gift of Mr. and Mrs. Stanley Freehling in memory of Juliet S. Freehling, 59.212

SCHWITTERS, Kurt ~ *b. 1887 Hanover. d. 1948 Ambleside, England*

Schwitters received his formal training at the Academy in Dresden. When the Dada movement began in 1916, Schwitters invented an original form of Dadaism, called MERZ (a part of the word commerziell). MERZ was a special type of collage where useless cast-off scraps were combined into witty designs. He used the same name for a magazine which he published in 1921.

AUFRUF

Painted 1919. Collage, 7 × 5½ in. (17.8 × 14 cm.)
Gift of Mr. and Mrs. Maurice E. Culberg, 53.24

AERATED VIII

Signed and dated: Kurt Schwitters 1942 Aerated VIII.
Oil and collage on canvas, 19½ × 15½ in. (49.7 × 39.5 cm.)
Robert A. Waller Fund, 59.19

HEY VALENTINE!

Signed and dated: Kurt Schwitters 1947 Hey Valentine!
Collage, 9½ × 7¼ in. (24.2 × 18.5 cm.)
Gift of Mr. and Mrs. Maurice E. Culberg, 53.23

Ref: Graphis *11, no. 57: 54, 1955 (ill.)*

SEGNA DE BONAVENTURA ~ *Active 1298. d. before 1331 Siena*

Segna, a follower of Duccio, continued to exert a strong influence on Sienese artists at a time when the more advanced pictorial concepts of Pietro Lorenzetti and Simone Martini had already outdated his style.

MADONNA ENTHRONED WITH SAINTS

Painted early 14th century. Tempera on panel, 17$\frac{1}{16}$ × 11½ in. (43.6 × 29.2 cm.)
Mr. and Mrs. Martin A. Ryerson Collection, 37.1007

Although the Virgin follows the traditional Byzantine type, a new spirit of humanism is evident in the emotinal relationship of the Mother and Child.

Coll: H. Goldschmidt, Paris, 1898

Ref: Breck, J., Art in America *1: 112–5, 1913; Offner, R.,* Italian Primitives at Yale University, *1927, p. 4; Venturi, L.,* Pitture Italiane in America, *1931, no. 22; Chicago. Art Institute,* A Century of Progress Exhibition, *1933, cat. no. 95, pl. 12; Chicago. Art Institute,* Bulletin *32: 2–3, 1938*

SELIGMANN, Kurt ~ *b. 1900 Basle, Switzerland*

Seligmann studied at the School of Applied Arts in Basle, at the Ecole des Beaux-Arts in Geneva, and at the Academy in Florence. He has lived in New York since 1939.

PART OF A GARDEN

Signed and dated: Seligmann 1952. Oil on canvas, $35\frac{3}{16} \times 35\frac{1}{4}$ in. (89.3×89.5 cm.)
Gift of the Society for Contemporary American Art, 53.198

METAMORPHOSIS

Signed and dated: K. Seligmann 59.
Oil and tempera on canvas, 60×72 in. (152.5×182.9 cm.)
Gift of Mr. and Mrs. Earle Ludgin, 59.167

SELLAJO, Jacopo del ~ *1441/42–1493 Florence*

Jacopo, son of a saddler (sellajo) is said to have been apprenticed to Filippo Lippi. An eclectic painter who imitated the styles of his contemporaries, he was most of all influenced by Botticelli. He was adept in grouping figures within the complicated spatial structure of his panels, an arrangement particularly suited to the decorative cassoni fronts in which he specialized.

SUSANNA AND THE ELDERS (two panels)

Painted about 1475–1500. Tempera on panel, each $21\frac{1}{4} \times 51\frac{1}{2}$ in. (54.1×130.9 cm.)
Mr. and Mrs. Martin A. Ryerson Collection, 33.1029, 33.1030

Coll: Trotti, Paris

Ref: Schubring, P., Cassoni, *1915, pp. 301, 302, cat. nos. 351, 352; Van Marle, R.,* The Development of the Italian Schools of Painting, *XII, 1931, p. 409, XIII, p. 234; Berenson, B.,* Pitture Italiane del Rinascimento, *1936, p. 452*

SEPESHY, Zoltan ~ *b. 1898 Kassa, Hungary*

Educated in Budapest, Vienna, and Paris, Sepeshy came to the United States in 1920.

JANUARY

Painted 1939, signed: Z. Sepeshy. Tempera on panel, $22\frac{7}{8} \times 27\frac{1}{4}$ in. (58.2×69.3 cm.)
Art Institute Purchase Fund, 42.52

SEURAT, Georges ~ *1859–1891 Paris*

A pupil of Henri Lehmann and influenced by Puvis de Chavannes and Delacroix, Seurat was early associated with Impressionists and influenced by them. Scientific discoveries of the 19th century, particularly those related to optical color laws, were greatly responsible for his consuming interest in the relationship of color to the human eye. He learned that complementary hues, applied in small contrasting areas, made for the effect of greater luminosity. Seurat called this method Neo-Impressionism. His earlier work, like *La Grande Jatte,* revives the classical tradition of poise and spatial structure, while his later development tended towards a patterned surface related to Symbolism and Art Nouveau.

SUNDAY AFTERNOON ON THE ISLAND OF LA GRANDE JATTE Illus. p. 325
Painted 1884–1886, signed: Seurat. Oil on canvas, 81 × 120⅜ in. (205.7 × 305.8 cm.)
Helen Birch Bartlett Memorial Collection, 26.224

Seurat made innumerable sketches and studies for La Grande Jatte. Retaining a strong interest in volume and form, but using a broken color technique, he designed the painting with classical precision. Here form and depth do not melt in strong light, for Seurat wished to do more than represent sunlight, as the Impressionists had; he wanted to give his composition a feeling of permanence and also make his painting seem a source of light. To this end he employed a new technique, using a complete palette of pure color and applying pigment in dots small enough to blend when seen at a distance—a method known as the optical mixture. The carefully planned and painted border was intended as a transition from picture to frame.

Coll: Mme Seurat, Paris; Lucie Cousturier, Paris

Ref: Apollon *7: 54, 1911; Salmon, A.,* Burlington Magazine *37: 120, 121, 122, 1920; Coquiot, G.,* Les Indépendents, *1884–1920, ca. 1920, pp. 10, 11, 20, 21, 44, 52, 209; Rey, R.,* La Peinture Française à la fin du XIXe siècle, La Renaissance du Sentiment Classique *. . . , 1921, pp. 115–37; Pach, W.,* Georges Seurat, *1923, pp. 22, 26, pl. 6; Pach, W.,* The Arts *3: 165, 168, 169, 171, 1923; Chicago. Art Institute,* Bulletin *18: 90, 91, 93, 94, 1924; Eglington, G.,* International Studio *81: 289–92, 1925; Chicago. Art Institute,* Annual Report, *1926 (ill.); Chicago. Art Institute,* Birch Bartlett Handbook, *1926, pp. 22, 23, 54; Frey, R.,* Transformations, *1926, pp. 188, 193; Roger-Marx, C.,* Gazette des Beaux-Arts *16, per. 5: 314, 1927; Zervos, C.,* Cahiers d'Art *3: 361–75, 1928; Chicago. Art Institute,* Birch Bartlett Handbook, *1929, pp. 30, 31, 60; Jamot, P.,* Bulletin des Musées de France *2: 49–52, 1930; Roger-Marx, C.,* Seurat, *1931, p. 8, pl. 10; Van Deene, J. F.,* Maandblad Voor Beeldende Kunsten *8: 163–76, 1931; Chicago. Art Institute,* A Century of Progress Exhibition, *1933, cat. no. 370; Walter, F.,* Revue de l'Art *63: 165–76, 1933; Chicago. Art Institute,* A Century of Progress Exhibition, *1934, cat. no. 324;* Gazette des Beaux-Arts *11, per. 6: 49–55, 1934; Rich, D. C.,* Seurat and the Evolution of "La Grande Jatte", *Chicago, 1935; Meyer Schapiro,* Columbia Review *17: 9–16, 1935; Tietze, H.,* Meisterwerke Europaeischer Malerei in Amerika, *1935, pl. 304; Hélion, J.,* Burlington Magazine *69: 10, 13, 1936; Wilenski, R. H.,* Modern French Painters, *1940, pp. 74, 75, 87, 93; Goldwater, R. J.,* Art Bulletin *23: 117–30, June 1941; Rewald, J.,* Georges Seurat, *1943, pp. 19–30, 42, 58, 63–8, pls. 63–71; Chicago. Art Institute,* Bulletin *38: 93, 1944; Chicago. Art Institute,* The Birch Bartlett Collection, *1946, pp. 44, 45; Masson, A.,* Magazine of Art *39: 22, 23, 1946; Bazin, G.,* L'Epoque Impressioniste, *1947, pp. 44–7, 80, 81, pl. 77; Kimball, F. and L. Venturi,* Great Paintings in America, *1948, p. 200, pl. 93; Lhote, A.,*

Arts *171: q, June 18, 1948; Gauss, C. E.,* The Aesthetic Theories of French Artists, *1949, pp. 24–7; Venturi, L.,* Impressionists and Symbolists, *London, 1950, pp. 144, 145, 151; Cogniat, R.,* Histoire de la Peinture, *II, 1955, pp. 109, 230*

SEVERINI, Gino ~ *b. 1883 Cortona, Italy*

Severini, a leading Futurist, experimented with the staccato movement of dancers and with café interiors. After giving up Futurism, about 1916, he turned to more formal problems related to Cubism. Later, about 1921, he became interested in a revival of Classicism (true also of Picasso at that time) and published a book on the subject, *Du Cubisme au Classicism.*

STILL LIFE WITH PICTURE

Painted 1916. Oil on canvas, 26¼ × 24 in. (66.7 × 61 cm.)
Alfred Stieglitz Collection, 49.581

STILL LIFE, "BARBARA"

Painted 1918, signed: G. Severini. Oil on panel, 18⅛ × 10⅞ in. (46.2 × 27.6 cm.)
Gift of Mr. and Mrs. Daniel Saidenberg, 55.819

SEYFFERT, Leopold Gould ~ *b. California, Mo. d. 1956 Bound Brook, N.J.*

Seyffert studied with William Merritt Chase and at the Pennsylvania Academy of the Fine Arts.

MYSELF

Signed and dated: Leopold Seyffert 1925. Oil on canvas, 37½ × 29½ in. (95.3 × 75 cm.)
Gift of Percy B. Eckhart, 25.1509

SHAHN, Ben ~ *b. 1898 Kaunas, Lithuania*

MINE DISASTER

Painted 1948, signed: Ben Shahn. Tempera on plywood, 24 × 30 in. (61 × 76.3 cm.)
Gift of the Society for Contemporary American Art, 48.77

SHEE, Sir Martin Archer ~ *b. 1769 Dublin. d. 1850 Brighton, England*

Shee was trained in Dublin, then studied at the Royal Academy in London. He was elected a member of the Academy in 1800, becoming its president in 1830.

JOHN PHILIP KEMBLE (1757–1823)

Painted about 1795. Oil on canvas, 28⅝ × 23½ in. (72.8 × 59.6 cm.)
Gift of Mr. and Mrs. William Owen Goodman, 25.587

Kemble was a member of a well-known family of English actors.

SHEELER, Charles ~ *b. 1883 Philadelphia*

Sheeler studied at the Pennsylvania Museum School of Industrial Art and the School of the Pennsylvania Academy of the Fine Arts. Later he traveled in Europe with William Merritt Chase. In 1912 he turned to photography, and since then has made a reputation both as painter and photographer.

THE ARTIST LOOKS AT NATURE Illus. p. 387

Signed and dated: Sheeler 1943. Oil on canvas, 21×18 in. (53.5×45.8 cm.)
Gift of the Society for Contemporary American Art, 44.32

The artist here has painted a paradox, showing himself on a dining-room chair out-of-doors, drawing with a pencil on a canvas already finished years before the *Interior with Stove.*

Ref: Chicago. Art Institute, Bulletin *39: 6, 1945; Chicago. Art Institute,* Bulletin *41: 36, 1947*

SHINN, Everett ~ *b. 1876 Woodstown, N.J. d. 1953 New York City*

Shinn was one of the New York realists, called The Eight, who were associated with Robert Henri. He had been an illustrator in Philadelphia and was keenly interested in the theatre both as playwright and stage designer.

EARLY MORNING, PARIS

Signed and dated: Everett Shinn 1901. Pastel on paper, 21×29⅛ in. (53.5×74 cm.)
Watson F. Blair Purchase Prize, 39.181

LONDON HIPPODROME

Painted 1902, signed: E. Shinn. Oil on canvas, 26⅜×35¼ in. (67×89.5 cm.)
Friends of American Art Collection, 28.197

SHIRLAW, Walter ~ *b. 1838 Paisley, Scotland. d. 1909 Madrid*

Shirlaw began as a banknote engraver but in 1870 went to Munich to study painting. This was the period when Currier, Chase and Duveneck were among a large group of other Americans studying at the Munich Academy. Shirlaw made murals for the Library of Congress and for the Chicago World's Fair.

TONING THE BELL

Signed and dated: Walter Shirlaw 1874. Oil on canvas, 40×30 in. (101.7×76.6 cm.)
Friends of American Art Collection, 38.1280

SELF PORTRAIT

Signed and dated: W. Shirlaw 1878. Oil on canvas, 27⅝×21⅛ in. (70.3×53.8 cm.)
Gift of Joseph M. Rogers, 87.234

AN ITALIAN BOY

Signed and dated: W. Shirlaw 1878. Oil on canvas, $34\frac{1}{2} \times 42\frac{1}{2}$ in. (87.6×108 cm.)
Gift of Mrs. Cyrus Hall McCormick, 99.47

WASHERWOMEN

Painted about 1880, signed: W. Shirlaw. Oil on canvas, $28\frac{1}{2} \times 17$ in. (72.5×43.3 cm.)
Gift of Emmanuel F. Selz, 40.1128

SIMON, Lucien ~ *1861–1945 Paris*

Simon studied with Jules Didier and at the Académie Julian with Tony Robert-Fleury. The realistic influence of Zola and de Maupassant was important in his development.

SELF PORTRAIT

Painted about 1900, signed: L. Simon. Oil on canvas, $37\frac{9}{16} \times 27\frac{1}{8}$ in. (95.4×69 cm.)
The Stickney Fund, 21.86

Ref: Chicago. Art Institute, Annual Report, *1920*

SISLEY, Alfred ~ *b. 1839 Paris. d. 1899 Moret-sur-Loing*

Born of English parents in Paris, Sisley studied under Gleyre with Monet, Bazille, and Renoir. He was mainly influenced by Corot and Monet, though while in England during 1870 he became familiar with and much impressed by the work of Constable and Turner. Showing first at the Salon of 1866, Sisley later contributed to four of the eight Impressionist exhibitions between 1874 and 1886.

A TURN IN THE ROAD

Signed and dated: Sisley 75. Oil on canvas, $21\frac{1}{2} \times 25\frac{1}{2}$ in. (54.7×64.8 cm.)
Charles H. and Mary F. S. Worcester Collection, 47.112

At the time Sisley painted this scene he, like Pissarro, was working in Louveciennes and its environs.

Coll: Dr. Georges Viau, Paris

Ref: Chicago. Art Institute, The Worcester Collection, *1937, cat. no. 82, pl. 47*

SAND HEAPS Illus. p. 290

Signed and dated: Sisley 75. Oil on canvas, $21\frac{1}{4} \times 28\frac{7}{8}$ in. (54.1×73.4 cm.)
Mr. and Mrs. Martin A. Ryerson Collection, 33.1177

Coll: Dr. Georges Viau, Paris

Ref: Chicago. Art Institute, A Century of Progress Exhibition, *1933, cat. no. 302;* Ibid., *1934, cat. no. 262*

STREET IN MORET

Painted about 1890, signed: Sisley. Oil on canvas, 23⅞×28⅞ in. (60.8×73.4 cm.)
Potter Palmer Collection, 22.441

Bought by Mrs. Potter Palmer in 1894, this canvas was shown at the World's Columbian Exposition in the loan exhibition from private collections.

Coll: Mrs. Potter Palmer (1892–1892); Honoré and Potter Palmer

Ref: Chicago. Art Institute, The Potter Palmer Collection, *1910, cat. no. 52; Chicago. Art Institute,* A Century of Progress Exhibition, *1933, cat. no. 303;* Ibid., *1934, cat. no. 263*

SLOAN, John ~ *b. 1871 Lock Haven, Pa. d. 1951 Hanover, N.H.*

Sloan, one of the most prominent members of The Eight, worked first as an illustrator in Philadelphia. His earlier paintings were devoted to realistic scenes of life in New York. Later he developed a completely different technique of broad cross-hatching applied mostly to nudes and other figure subjects.

RENGANESCHI'S SATURDAY NIGHT

Signed and dated: John Sloan 1912. Oil on canvas, 26¼×32 in. (66.7×81.3 cm.)
Gift of Mary Otis Jenkins, 26.1580

Renganeschi's was a popular Italian restaurant on West 10th Street, New York.

SMIBERT, John ~ *b. 1688 Edinburgh. d. 1751 Boston*

After spending seven years apprenticed to a house painter, Smibert went to London to work as a coach painter. He studied briefly at the early Academy at Great Queen's Street headed by Sir James Thornhill. In 1717 he went to Italy for three years to copy old masters. He came to America in 1728 and settled in Boston a year later, where he was active as a portrait painter for the rest of his life. Smibert painted fluently and somewhat realistically in the late Baroque tradition, as interpreted by English taste.

RICHARD BILL

Painted about 1740. Oil on canvas, 50¼×40¼ in. (127.7×102.2 cm.)
Friends of American Art Collection, 44.28

A Boston merchant who owned a store on Corn Hill under the sign of the Crown and Cross, Richard Bill was also an officer in the Ancient and Honorable Artillery Company.

PORTRAIT OF CAPTAIN JOHN GERRISH

Painted about 1735. Oil on canvas, 29½×24 in. (75×61 cm.)
Anonymous Gift, 59.517

SORGH, Hendrik Martensz ~ *about 1611–1670 Rotterdam*

Sorgh was a pupil of David Teniers the Younger and Willem Buytewech. He specialized in peasant scenes and kitchen interiors.

THE HOUSEWIFE

Signed and dated: H. M. Sorgh 1657. Oil on panel, 18½×25 in. (47.1×63.6 cm.)
Mr. and Mrs. Martin A. Ryerson Collection, 33.1092

SORIA, Martín de, (Follower of)

ALTARPIECE WITH THREE SAINTS

Painted second half of the 15th century. Tempera on panel, center panel 123×33 in. (305.9×83.9 cm.), flanking panels, 63×28½ in. (160.1×72.5 cm.)
Gift of the Antiquarian Society, 11.201

This altarpiece, depicting scenes from the lives of three Spanish saints, was painted by a follower of Martín de Soria. Although his style emulated the Catalan painter Jaime Huguet, the elaborate decorative detail is typically Aragonese.

Ref: Post, C. R., A History of Spanish Painting, *VIII, pt. 1, 1941, pp. 378–80, fig. 169*

SOROLLA Y BASTIDA, Joaquín ~ *b. 1864 Valencia. d. 1923 Cercedilla, Spain*

Sorolla, a pupil at the Valencia Academy of Arts in 1878, later studied the old masters in Spain, France, and Italy. He was visiting instructor at the School of the Art Institute in 1910 and 1911, and became a professor in the Academy at Madrid in 1919.

BATHERS—STUDY FOR THE SAD INHERITANCE

Painted about 1899. Oil on panel, 12½×23¼ in. (31.8×59.1 cm.)
Charles H. and Mary F. S. Worcester Collection, 47.113

Ref: Chicago. Art Institute, Catalogue of Paintings by . . . Sorolla . . . , *1911, pp. 15, 16; Chicago. Art Institute,* The Worcester Collection, *1937, cat. no. 100*

TWO SISTERS, VALENCIA

Signed and dated: J. Sorolla 1909. Oil on canvas, 68½×44 in. (174×111.9 cm.)
Gift of Mrs. William Stanley North in memory of William Stanley North, 11.28

Ref: Doménech, R., Sorolla *(Vol. 1 of Bibliothèque d'Art Espagnol), 1910, pp. 84, 85, 86, fig. 111; Chicago. Art Institute,* Catalogue of Paintings by . . . Sorolla . . . , *1911, cat. no. 7; Chicago. Art Institute,* Bulletin *4: 60, 61, 1911; Gill, R.,* Joaquín Sorolla, *1913, p. 53; Chicago. Art Institute,* A Century of Progress Exhibition, *1933, cat. no. 275; Pantorba, B. de,* La Vida y la Obra de Joaquín Sorolla, *1953, pl. 98, cat. no. 1097, p. 166*

SOUSA-CARDOZO, Amadeo de ~ *b. 1887 Manhufe. d. 1918 Espinho, Portugal*

Sousa-Cardozo worked with the Cubists in Paris and was one of the exhibitors in the famous Armory Show of 1913 in New York.

MARINE: PONT L'ABBE

Signed and dated: A. de S. Cardozo 1909. Oil on canvas, 19¾ × 24¼ in. (50.4 × 61.7 cm.)
Arthur Jerome Eddy Memorial Collection, 31.513

Ref: Eddy, A. J., Cubists and Post-Impressionists, *1919, p. 85; Chicago. Art Institute,* The Eddy Collection, *1922, cat. no. 16*

THE LEAP OF THE RABBIT

Signed and dated: A. de Sousa Cardozo 1911. Oil on canvas, 19⅝ × 24⅛ in. (50 × 61.3 cm.)
Arthur Jerome Eddy Memorial Collection, 31.514

Ref: Eddy, A. J., Cubists and Post-Impressionists, *1914, p. 85; Chicago. Art Institute,* The Eddy Collection, *1922, cat. no. 17*

THE STRONGHOLD

Painted about 1911. Oil on canvas, 36½ × 24 in. (92.8 × 61 cm.)
Arthur Jerome Eddy Memorial Collection, 31.512

Ref: Eddy, A. J., Cubists and Post-Impressionists, *1919, p. 85; Chicago. Art Institute,* The Eddy Collection, *1922, cat. no. 15*

SOUTINE, Chaim ~ *b. 1894 Smilovitschi, Russia. d. 1944 Paris*

Soutine was influenced by Van Gogh. Though he was a close friend of Modigliani, the only similarity in their work is a repeated emphasis on the melancholy of their figures.

LANDSCAPE AT CAGNES

Painted about 1923, signed: Soutine. Oil on canvas, 23⅝ × 28½ in. (60.1 × 72.5 cm.)
Charles H. and Mary F. S. Worcester Collection, 47.114

A small canvas where varying shades of green predominate and the influence of Van Gogh's later style is evident. This landscape is more disciplined than is frequently the case with Soutine. The artist painted several versions of the same scene.

DEAD FOWL

Painted about 1926, signed: Soutine. Oil on canvas, 38⅜ × 24⅞ in. (97.5 × 63.3 cm.)
The Joseph Winterbotham Collection, 37.167

SMALL TOWN SQUARE, VENCE

Painted 1929, signed: Soutine. Oil on canvas, 27⅞ × 18 in. (70.9 × 45.8 cm.)
The Joseph Winterbotham Collection, 31.709

Coll: J. Hessel, Paris

Ref: Chicago. Art Institute, A Century of Progress Exhibition, *1933, cat. no. 741;* Ibid., *1934, cat. no. 363; Chicago. Art Institute,* Catalogue of the Winterbotham Collection, *1947, pp. 39–40; Wheeler, M.,* Soutine, *New York, 1950, pp. 100–1, 102*

LO SPAGNA (Giovanni di Pietro) ~ *b. about 1450 Spain. d. 1528 Spoleto, Italy*

Because of his Spanish origin, this painter was called Lo Spagna. He was a pupil of Perugino, was later influenced by Raphael, and worked in Perugia and, after 1512, in Spoleto.

ST. CATHERINE OF SIENA

Painted about 1516. Oil on panel, 41¼ × 19 in. (104.8 × 48.3 cm.)
Mr. and Mrs. Martin A. Ryerson Collection, 37.1008

Coll: Lord Brownlow, Ashridge Park, England

Ref: Gregory, E. W., Connoisseur *14: 4, 7, 1906; Berenson, B.,* The Central Italian Painters of the Renaissance, *1909, p. 253; Harter, E.,* Rassegna d'Arte *14, no. 3: 58–61, 1914; Berenson, B.,* Italian Pictures of the Renaissance, *1932, p. 544; Chicago. Art Institute,* A Century of Progress Exhibition, *1933, cat. no. 19; Van Marle, R.,* The Development of the Italian Schools of Painting, *XIV, 1933, pp. 459–60; Chicago. Art Institute,* Bulletin *32: 3, 1938*

SPANISH SCHOOL, 14th century

THE AYALA ALTAR

Illus. pp. 92–93

Painted 1393. Tempera on panel, altar 99¾ × 251¾ in. (253.6 × 639.4 cm.), antependium 33½ × 102 in. (85.2 × 259.2 cm.)
Gift of Charles Deering, 28.817

This great altar is one of the oldest and most important monuments of Spanish art to be found outside Spain. Don Pedro López de Ayala, Chancellor of Castile, and author of the portion of Crónicas Espanolas devoted to Castile, dedicated this altarpiece to the convent founded by his father at Quejana in the Province of Ayala. Until sold in 1913, this retable remained in the mortuary chapel of the López family where there still can be seen the sculptured effigies marking the tombs of the chancellor and his wife. The panels of the altarpiece illustrate the life of Christ in this order: Lower row, (1) Annunciation (2) Visitation, (3) Nativity, (4) Three Magi, (5) Purification, and (6) Flight into Egypt. Upper row, (7) Christ Disputing with the Doctors, (8) Marriage at Cana, (9) Resurrection of Christ, (10) Crucifixion, (11) Ascension, (12) Pentecost, and (13) Assumption of the Virgin, including the Donation of the Girdle to St. Thomas. The Frontal, (1) Annunciation, (2) and (3) Nativity and the Three Magi. On the frames are found the López arms, *two wolves passant,* and the Guzman arms, *two kettles.*

EUROPEAN PAINTINGS

SECTION ONE

XXth Century

ILLUSTRATIONS

Picasso, Mother and Child, 1921. Gift of Mary & Leigh Block Charitable Fund, Inc., Mr. & Mrs. Edwin E. Hokin, Maymar Corporation, Mr. & Mrs. Chauncey Mc Cormick, Mrs. Maurice L. Rothschild and the Ada Turnbull Hertle Fund

Picasso, Daniel-Henry Kahnweiler, 1910. Gift of Mrs. Gilbert Chapman

Picasso, Head of the Acrobat's Wife, 1904. Gift of Kate L. Brewster

Picabia, Francis, Edtaonisl, 1913. Gift of Mr. & Mrs. Armand Phillip Bartos

Delaunay, Robert, Champs de Mars, the Red Tower, 1911
The Joseph Winterbotham Collection

Miró, Joan, Portrait of a Woman, 1918. The Joseph Winterbotham Collection

Opposite:
Modigliani, Amedeo, Jacques Lipchitz and His Wife, 1916
Helen Birch Bartlett Memorial Collection

LIPCHITZ
modigliani

Mondrian, Piet, Diagonal Composition, 1921. Gift of Edgar Kaufmann, jr.

Picasso, The Reader, 1953
Gift of Mr. & Mrs. Arnold H. Maremont through the Maremont Foundation

Kandinsky, Wassily, Improvisation No. 30, 1913. Arthur Jerome Eddy Memorial Collection

Leger, Fernand, Follow the Arrow, 1919. Gift of Mrs. Patrick Hill in memory of Rue Winterbotham Carpenter to The Winterbotham Collection

Picasso, The Red Armchair, 1931. Gift of Mr. & Mrs. Daniel Saidenberg

Coll: Chapel of the de Ayala family, Convent of San Juan at Quejana, until 1913

Ref: Bengoa, R. B., Boletín de la Sociedad Española de Excursiones *24: 167–9, 1916; Tormo, E.,* Boletín de la Sociedad Española de Excursiones *24: 152–60, 1916; Von Loga, V.,* Die Malerei in Spanien, *1923, p. 13; Chicago. Art Institute,* Bulletin *20: 95–9, 1926; Post, C. R.,* A History of Spanish Painting, *II, 1930, pp. 126–33 (ill.); Chicago. Art Institute,* A Century of Progress Exhibition, *1933, cat. no. 182;* Ibid., *1934, cat. no. 80; Guidol, J.,* Spanish Painting, *1941, p. 14, cat. no. 11*

SPANISH SCHOOL, 17th century

QUEEN MARGARETA OF SPAIN (1564–1611)

Painted between 1600 and 1608. Oil on canvas, 67½ × 43 in. (171.5 × 109.9 cm.)
Gift of Mrs. Sidney Gorham and Mrs. Walter Kahler, Jr., in Memory of Mr. and Mrs. Eugene McVey, 41.975

The identification of this artist is not certain, but he was probably a follower of Alónzo Sánchez Coello, who was active from 1542 to 1590. Without sufficient evidence, the painting has been attributed to Juan Pantoja de la Cruz (1551–1602), a court painter who followed the style of Coello. An attribution has also been made to Pantoja's successor, Bartolomé Gonzales.

Coll: T. J. Blakeslee, London; Mrs. Arthur Meeker

Ref: Chicago. Art Institute, Bulletin *38: 17–9, 1944*

SPARHAWK-JONES, Elizabeth ~ *b. 1885 Baltimore, Md.*

Elizabeth Sparhawk-Jones studied at the Pennsylvania Academy of the Fine Arts. In her early paintings the influence of both William Merritt Chase and John Singer Sargent is apparent.

THE SHOE SHOP

Painted about 1912, signed: Elizabeth Sparhawk-Jones.
Oil on canvas, 39 × 33 in. (99.2 × 83.9 cm.)
William Owen and Erna Sawyer Goodman Collection, 39.393

SHOP GIRLS

Painted about 1912, signed: Elizabeth Sparhawk-Jones.
Oil on canvas, 38⅛ × 48 in. (96.9 × 122 cm.)
Friends of American Art Collection, 12.1677

SPEICHER, Eugene ~ *b. 1883 Buffalo, N.Y.*

Speicher attended the School of the Albright Art Gallery in Buffalo, then went to New

York in 1907 to study with William Merritt Chase and Robert Henri. His earlier work, dark and somber in the manner of the Munich School, later gave way to a light and more colorful palette.

JEAN BELLOWS

Signed and dated: Eugene Speicher 40. Oil on canvas, 48×41 3/8 in. (122×105.1 cm.)
Friends of American Art Collection, 41.33

The subject is the younger daughter of Speicher's friend, George Bellows. This is the second of two versions painted at Woodstock, N.Y.

SPELT, Adriaen van der ~ *active 1658 Leyden*

Adriaen van der Spelt, a pupil of Wouter Crabeth II, specialized in still life. Very little is known about this artist except that he joined the painters' guild in Leyden in 1658, and spent several years in Berlin as painter to the court of the Elector of Prussia.

FLOWERPIECE

Signed and dated: A. van der Spelt 1658. Oil on panel, 18 1/4×25 5/8 in. (46.5×63.9 cm.)
Wirt D. Walker Fund, 49.585

This is the earliest of the few known paintings by van der Spelt. The picture was formerly at Stafford House in England, where Waagen saw it and described it: "A wreath of flowers in which [van der Spelt] nearly equals [Daniel] Seghers. In the blue curtain he has attained that deceptive truth which Dutch painters frequently delight in." It was customary in 17th century Holland to protect paintings from both light and dirt by curtains like this blue one attached to the still life.

Coll: Duke of Sutherland, England

Ref: Waagen, G. F., Treasures of Art in Great Britain, *II, 1854, p. 71; Von Wurzbach, A.,* Niederlaendisches Kuenstler-Lexikon, *II, 1910, p. 645*

SPENCER, Robert ~ *b. 1879 Harvard, Neb. d. 1931 New Hope, Pa.*

Spencer studied at the National Academy of Design, the New York School of Art, and with William Merritt Chase and Frank V. DuMond.

THE HUCKSTER CART

Signed and dated: Robert Spencer 1913. Oil on canvas, 30×36 in. (76.3×91.5 cm.)
Friends of American Art Collection, 16.440

SPINELLO ARETINO (Spinello de Luca Spinelli) ~ *about 1347–1410 Arezzo*

Spinello may have studied with Agnolo Gaddi. He was also influenced by Nardo and Andrea di Cione. Working in Arezzo, Florence and Pisa, he made his most important murals for St. Francesco in Arezzo and the Palazzo Publico in Siena. Vigorous and simple in his style, Spinello was one of the last and closest followers of Giotto.

ST. FRANCIS AND HIS FOLLOWERS BEFORE POPE INNOCENT III

Painted end of the 14th century. Tempera on panel, 33⅜×24 in. (84.9×61 cm.)
Mr. and Mrs. Martin A. Ryerson Collection, 33.1031

The scene depicts the Pope, accompanied by three cardinals, receiving St. Francis and his followers who offer the rules of their new order for approval. The gilt relief ornaments in the upper angles of the picture are probably modern additions.

Coll: Città di Castello, Italy; H. Morison, Boston

Ref: Perkins, F. M., Rassegna d'Arte *18: 5, 6, 1918; Wyer, R.,* Art in America *8: 211, 1920; Chicago. Art Institute,* A Century of Progress Exhibition, *1933, cat. no. 96;* Ibid., *1934, cat. no. 38; Quintavalle, A. O.,* Bolletino d'Arte *31: 230, 1937*

STEEN, Jan ~ *1626–1679 Leyden*

Steen, a pupil of Nicolas Knupfer of Utrecht, was mainly influenced by Adriaen van Ostade and Jan van Goyen, whose daughter he married.

THE FAMILY CONCERT Illus. p. 187

Signed and dated: J. Steen 1666. Oil on canvas, 34⅛×39¾ in. (86.6×101 cm.)
Gift of T. B. Blackstone, 91.65

Coll: Sir Charles Bagot, 1833; Prince Demidoff, San Donato, Italy

Ref: The Works of Jan Steen *(Masters in Art, VI), 1905, p. 293; Hofstede de Groot,* Catalogue Raisonné of the Works of the Most Eminent Dutch Painters of the Seventeenth Century, *I, 1907, p. 115, no. 442;* Thieme-Becker, *XXXI, 1937, p. 512*

STELLA, Joseph ~ *b. 1880 Muro Lucano, Italy. d. 1946 Astoria, Queens, N.Y.*

Stella played a prominent role in launching modern art in America. After two years of medical studies in Italy he decided to become a painter and joined his older brother in New York. In 1908 he went to Pittsburgh to make studies of steel mills and factories. In 1909 he returned to Europe, staying in Rome and Paris. It was during this period in Italy that he joined the Futurist movement. Coming back to New York in 1913, he found in that city a never-ending theme; he is perhaps best remembered for his many views of Brooklyn Bridge.

FACTORIES

Painted in 1915, signed: Joseph Stella. Oil on canvas, 24×24 in. (61×61 cm.)
Gift of Mr. and Mrs. Noah Goldowsky in memory of Esther Goldowsky, 55.816

STERNE, Hedda ~ *b. 1916 Bucharest*

Hedda Sterne, who studied drawing and sculpture in the Akademie für Bildende Kunst in Vienna and at the University of Bucharest, moved to New York in 1941.

NEW YORK, 1956

Painted 1956, signed: Hedda Sterne. Oil on canvas, $32\frac{1}{8} \times 50$ in. (81.6×127 cm.)
Gift of the Society for Contemporary American Art, 56.62

STERNE, Maurice ~ *b. 1877 Libau, Latvia. d. 1957 Mt. Kisco, N.Y.*

Sterne studied at the National Academy of Design and subsequently traveled all over the world, living for some time in Bali, Italy and New Mexico.

ON THE GANGES, BENARES

Painted 1911/12, signed: Maurice Sterne.
Tempera and oil on cardboard, $8\frac{13}{16} \times 13\frac{5}{16}$ in. (32.3×33.7 cm.)
Mr. and Mrs. Martin A. Ryerson Collection, 37.1041

ON THE ISLE OF BALI: TWO GIRLS GOING TO MARKET

Painted about 1913, signed: Sterne Bali. Oil on canvas, $21 \times 12\frac{1}{2}$ in. (53.5×31.8 cm.)
Mr. and Mrs. Martin A. Ryerson Collection, 33.1218

SEA SAND AND WIND

Signed and dated: Sterne '48. Oil on canvas, $26 \times 32\frac{1}{8}$ in. (66.1×81.6 cm.)
Gift of the Heirs of Mrs. Samuel A. Lewisohn, 54.266

STEVENS, Alfred ~ *b. 1823 Brussels. d. 1906 Paris*

Stevens first studied in Brussels and later at the Ecole des Beaux-Arts in Paris.

HESITATION (Madame Morteaux [?])

Painted about 1860, signed Alfred Stevens. Oil on panel, $22 \times 17\frac{3}{16}$ in. (56×43.7 cm.)
Mr. and Mrs. Martin A. Ryerson Collection, 33.1178

AT THE RAILWAY STATION

Painted about 1874, signed: Stevens. Oil on panel, $26\frac{1}{4} \times 19\frac{1}{4}$ in. (66.7×49 cm.)
A. A. Munger Collection, 01.436

Ref: Chicago. Art Institute, A Century of Progress Exhibition, *1933, cat. no. 260*

STROZZI, Bernardo ~ *b. 1581 Genoa. d. 1644 Venice*

Rubens' stay in Genoa in 1607 probably exerted an influence on Strozzi. In 1630, however, he went to Venice; there, under the spell of the Venetians, especially Veronese, his mature style reached its full development.

AN EPISCOPAL SAINT Illus. p. 50

Painted about 1630. Oil on canvas, $51\frac{1}{4} \times 39\frac{3}{8}$ in. (130.3×100 cm.)
Alexander A. McKay Fund, 58.328

This picture may have been done in Genoa, just before Strozzi's removal to Venice.

Coll: Earl of Wilton; Mrs. H. Daminger, England

Ref: Manchester, Eng., Catalogue of the Art Treasures of the United Kingdom, *1857, p. 36, no. 359*

STUART, Gilbert ~ *b. 1755 North Kingstown, R.I. d. 1828 Boston*

At fourteen Stuart was a pupil of Cosmo Alexander, an itinerant Scotch artist with whom he went to Scotland. He also studied in London in 1775, ultimately becoming a pupil of Benjamin West. After the Revolution he returned to Philadelphia to paint the notables of the new Federal Government, and finally settled in Boston in 1805, where he spent the remainder of his life.

MAJOR GENERAL HENRY DEARBORN

Painted 1811–1812. Oil on canvas, 28$\frac{1}{8}$ × 22$\frac{9}{16}$ in. (71.5 × 57.3 cm.)
Friends of American Art Collection, 13.793

Born in Hampton, N.Y. in 1751 and trained as a doctor, Dearborn practiced a short time before joining the Revolutionary army. Jefferson appointed him Secretary of War for his two terms, during which time (1803–1804) Fort Dearborn, on the site of the future Chicago, was built and named for him. Dearborn then served in the army in the War of 1812 and was later sent to Portugal as Minister, but retired after two years. He died in 1829.

STUART, Gilbert (copy after)

GEORGE WASHINGTON

Painted early 19th century. Oil on canvas, 92 × 57$\frac{1}{2}$ in. (233.8 × 146.1 cm.)
The Gift of the People of Chicago. 24.612

In 1796 William Bingham commissioned Stuart to paint two portraits of Washington, one for himself, to be hung in his Philadelphia house, Lansdowne House (which is now in the Pennsylvania Academy of the Fine Arts), and the other for the Marquis of Lansdowne (now owned by the Earl of Rosebury, Edinburgh, Scotland). Hence Washington in this pose is known as the Lansdowne type. The present picture is a copy after the Philadelphia version.

STUEMPFIG, Walter ~ *b. 1914 Germantown, Pa.*

Stuempfig studied at the Pennsylvania Academy of the Fine Arts.

LANDSCAPE OF LONELINESS

Painted about 1943–1944, signed: Stuempfig. Oil on canvas, 35$\frac{1}{4}$ × 48 in. (89.5 × 122 cm.)
Friends of American Art Collection, 44.29

SULLY, Robert M. ~ *b. 1803 Petersburgh, Va. d. 1855 Buffalo, N.Y.*

Sully studied painting with his uncle, Thomas Sully, in Philadelphia. He went to London in 1824, returning to Virginia a few years later.

JUNIUS BRUTUS BOOTH

Painted about 1830, signed: R. M. Sully. Oil on canvas, 29½ × 24¼ in. (75 × 62.4 cm.)
Gift of Mr. and Mrs. William Owen Goodman, 23.384

SULLY, Thomas ~ *b. 1783 Horncastle, England. d. 1872 Philadelphia*

Sully came to Charleston, S.C. at the age of nine. His older brother Lawrence, a miniature painter, was his principal instructor. Sully worked in Richmond, Norfolk, and New York, and finally settled in Philadelphia in 1808.

DR. JOSEPH KLAPP

Painted 1814. Oil on canvas, 36 × 28 in. (91.5 × 71.2 cm.)
Gift of Annie Swan Coburn to the Mr. and Mrs. Lewis L. Coburn Memorial Collection, 50.1363

MRS. JOSEPH KLAPP (Anna B. Milnor) Illus. p. 370

Painted 1814. Oil on canvas, 36¼ × 28⅛ in. (92.1 × 71.5 cm.)
Gift of Annie Swan Coburn to the Mr. and Mrs. Lewis L. Coburn Memorial Collection, 50.1362

MRS. GEORGE LINGEN (Maria Oldmixon)

Painted 1842. Oil on canvas, 27 × 24 in. (oval) (68.7 × 61 cm.)
Friends of American Art Collection, 17.264

SYMONS, George Gardner ~ *b. 1863 Chicago. d. 1930 Hillside, N.J.*

Symons studied at The Art Institute of Chicago and in Paris, London, and Munich.

THE WINTER SUN

Painted about 1910, signed: Gardner Symons.
Oil on canvas, 47¼ × 71½ in. (120 × 181.7 cm.)
Friends of American Art Collection, 10.313

TADDEO DI BARTOLO ~ *1362/63 to about 1422 Siena*

Probably a pupil of Bartolo di Fredi, Taddeo was trained in the tradition of Simone Martini and the Lorenzetti. He also worked in Pisa, Genoa and Perugia.

CRUCIFIXION

Painted probably early 15th century. Tempera on panel, 12⅞ × 26⅝ in. (32.6 × 67.7 cm.)
Mr. and Mrs. Martin A. Ryerson Collection, 33.1033

Coll: Lord Northwick, England; Rev. Canon A. F .Sutton, Brant-Broughton, Lincs., England; Martin A. Ryerson, Chicago, 1924

Ref: Berenson, B., Central Italian Painters of the Renaissance, *1909, p. 256; Berenson, B.,* Italian Painters of the Renaissance, *1932, p. 551; Chicago. Art Institute,* A Century of Progress Exhibition, *1933, cat. no. 98*

TAMAYO, Rufino ~ *b. 1899 Oaxaca, Mexico*

Mainly self-taught, Tamayo depends on his own Indian background for theme material. In 1936 he and Siqueiros went to New York as delegates to the Congress of Revolutionary Artists, and since then he has divided his time between Mexico and the United States.

MARIA IZQUIERDO

Painted early 1930s, signed: Tamayo. Oil on canvas, 29½×25½ in. (75×64.8 cm.)
Gift of Mrs. Frances A. Elkins, 46.340

Ref: Villaurrutia, J., Mexican Folkways *7, no. 3: 138–42, 1932; Venturi, L.,* Commentari, *Anno I, pt. 2, 1950, pp. 112, 113, fig. 131, pl. 50*

WOMAN WITH A BIRD CAGE

Signed and dated: Tamayo 41. Oil on canvas, 43¼×33¼ in. (109.9×84.5 cm.)
The Joseph Winterbotham Collection, 42.57

Ref: Chicago. Art Institute, Bulletin *37: 33–5, 1943; Chicago. Art Institute,* The Winterbotham Collection, *1947, pp. 41–2; Goldwater, R.,* Rufino Tamayo, *1947, p. 81, pl. 37;* Drawings by Tamayo, *Mexico, 1950, p. 25*

TANGUY, Yves ~ *b. 1900 Paris. d. 1955 Waterbury, Conn.*

Tanguy did not become actively interested in art until 1923, when he started to experiment with Surrealist drawings. In 1939 he came to the United States.

THE RAPIDITY OF SLEEP

Signed and dated: Yves Tanguy 45. Oil on canvas, 50×40 in. (127×101.7 cm.)
The Joseph Winterbotham Collection, 46.46

TANNER, Henry Ossawa ~ *b. 1859 Pittsburgh, Pa. d. 1937 Paris*

Tanner studied with Thomas Eakins and for a time taught art himself. Later he went to Paris as a pupil of Jean-Paul Laurens and Benjamin Constant at the Académie Julian.

THE TWO DISCIPLES AT THE TOMB

Painted 1906, signed: H. O. Tanner. Oil on canvas, 51×41⅞ in. (129.6×106.4 cm.)
Robert A. Waller Fund, 06.300

TENIERS, David the Younger ~ *b. 1610 Antwerp. d. 1690 Brussels*

Teniers was a pupil of his father, David Teniers the Elder, and was also influenced by Adriaen Brouwer. Later his lighter, more colorful palette showed his admiration of

Rubens. During his later years in Brussels he was in charge of the art gallery owned by the Archduke Leopold Wilhelm of Hapsburg. There he made small oil copies from which engravings were taken for a catalogue of the collection published in 1660.

THE FLAGEOLET PLAYER

Painted about 1635–1640, signed: D. Teniers.
Oil on panel, $8\frac{3}{4} \times 6\frac{1}{4}$ in. (22.3×15.8 cm.)
Mr. and Mrs. Martin A. Ryerson Collection, 33.1095

Coll: M. R. Papin, 1873

Ref: Smith, John, A Catalogue Raisonné of the Works of the Most Eminent Dutch, Flemish and French Painters . . . , *III, 1831, pp. 415, 416, cat. no. 583; subject was engraved by Le Bas as "Le Fluteur"*

THE GUARDHOUSE

Painted between 1640 and 1650, signed: D. Teniers.
Oil on canvas, $28\frac{1}{2} \times 21\frac{3}{4}$ in. (72.5×55.4 cm.)
Gift of Mrs. George N. Culver, 94.1029

Coll: Prince A. Demidoff, San Donato; Prince Demidoff, Pratolino

Ref: Chicago. Art Institute, A Century of Progress Exhibition, *1934, cat. no. 111*

ABRAHAM'S SACRIFICE OF ISAAC (copy after Veronese)

Painted about 1650. Oil on panel, $8\frac{1}{4} \times 12\frac{1}{8}$ in. (21×30.8 cm.)
Gift of Charles L. Hutchinson, 36.123

This and the following two pictures are copies of paintings in the Archduke Leopold's collection. The original, a late picture by Paolo Veronese, was cut down in the early 18th century to fit into the Stallburg Museum in Vienna.

Ref: Stampart and Prenner, Prodomus, *1735 (reprod. in* Jahrbuch der Kunsthistorischen Sammlungen des Allerhöchsten Kaiserhauses *7: book II, pl. 12, 1888)*

RAPE OF EUROPA (copy after Titian)

Painted about 1650. Oil on panel, $8\frac{1}{2} \times 12\frac{1}{4}$ in. (21.7×31.2 cm.)
Gift of Mrs. Charles L. Hutchinson, 36.124

This is a copy of a lost picture by Titian presumably painted between 1562 and 1565.

Ref: Stampart and Prenner, op. cit., *pl. 24; Suida, W.,* Art in America *29: 12–3, 1941*

RAPE OF EUROPA (copy after Giorgione)

Painted about 1650. Oil on panel, $8\frac{1}{2} \times 12\frac{1}{4}$ in. (21.7×31.2 cm.)
Gift of Mrs. Charles L. Hutchinson, 36.125

This is supposedly a copy from a lost painting by Giorgione.

Ref: Stampart and Prenner, op. cit., *pl. 12; Richter, G. M.,* Giorgio da Castelfranco, called Giorgione, *1937, p. 260; Suida, W.,* Art in America *29: 12–3, 1941; Richter, G. M.,* Art in America *30: 217–8, 1942*

TERBORCH, Gerard ~ *b. 1617 Zwolle. d. 1681 Deventer, Holland*

Terborch was influenced by a group of Amsterdam artists, Duyster, Duck and de Codde, who specialized in military subjects. Around 1634 he became a pupil of the Haarlem portrait painter Pieter Molijn. Later he went to England, Italy and Spain where he was much impressed by the work of Van Dyck, Hals, and Velasquez.

PORTRAIT OF A GENTLEMAN

Painted about 1660. Oil on canvas, 28⅜×19⅝ in. (59.4×50 cm.)
Mr. and Mrs. Martin A. Ryerson Collection, 33.1096

Ref: Hofstede de Groot, A Catalogue Raisonné of the Works of the Most Eminent Dutch Painters of the Seventeenth Century, *V, 1913, p. 102, no. 329*

PORTRAIT OF A LADY

Painted about 1660. Oil on canvas, 29½×20⅜ in. (75×51.8 cm.)
Mr. and Mrs. Martin A. Ryerson Collection, 33.1907

A companion to the preceeding picture.

Ref: Hofstede de Groot, op. cit., *V, 1913, p. 124, cat. no. 406*

THE MUSIC LESSON

Painted about 1660, signed with monogram.
Oil on canvas, 25×19⅝ in. (63.6×50 cm.)
Gift of Charles T. Yerkes, 91.9

A similar version of *The Music Lesson* can be found in the Gardner Museum, Boston.

Coll: Gabriel François Joseph; Chevalier Verhulst, Brussels, 1779; Prince Galitzin, Paris, 1825; John Fairlie, London, 1830; Prince A. Demidoff, San Donato; Prince P. Demidoff, Pratolino, 1890

Ref: Masters in Art, *II, 1901, p. 40; Hellens, F.,* Gerard Terborch, *1911, p. 127; Hofstede de Groot, V, 1913, pp. 47, 48, cat. no. 130; Chicago. Art Institute,* A Century of Progress Exhibition, *1933, cat. no. 79;* Ibid., *1934, cat. no. 113; Hannema, F.,* Gerard Terborch, *1943, pp. 105, 106, pl. 197*

PORTRAIT OF A LADY

Painted 1672–1675. Oil on canvas, 33½×28 in. (85.2×71.2 cm.)

Max and Leola Epstein Collection, 54.300

A companion piece to this picture, representing a young man, is owned by the Landes Museum Ferdinandeum in Innsbruck.

Coll: De la Bouderie, Luzerne

Ref: Innsbruck. Landesmuseum Ferdinandeum, Catalogue of Paintings, *1928, cat. no. 608; Amsterdam. Rijksmuseum,* Drie Eeuwen Portret in Nederland, *June/October 1952, cat. no. 19*

THAYER, Abbott H. ~ *b. 1849 Boston. d. 1921 Dublin, N.Y.*

Thayer studied at the National Academy and the Brooklyn Academy of Design and then went to Paris. There he studied with Auguste Bonheur, with Jean Léon Gérôme, and was further influenced by Jules Bastein-Lepage.

WINGED FIGURE

Signed and dated: Abbott H. Thayer 1899.
Oil on canvas, $51\frac{1}{2} \times 37\frac{3}{4}$ in. (130.9 × 95.9 cm.)
Simeon B. Williams Fund, 47.32

SKETCH OF A BOY

Painted between 1903 and 1905, signed: Abbott H. Thayer.
Oil on canvas, $25\frac{7}{16} \times 19\frac{1}{4}$ in. (64.5 × 49 cm.)
Friends of American Art Collection, 23.977

A sketch of Thayer's nephew. The Metropolitan Museum owns the finished picture, which is dated 1903–1905.

TIEPOLO, Giovanni Battista ~ *b. 1696 Venice. d. 1770 Madrid*

Tiepolo was apprenticed to Gregorio Lazzarini, and was influenced by Veronese, Piazzetta, and Sebastiano Ricci. He worked in and around Venice, Milan, Würzburg, and Madrid. His work, unrivaled for its atmospheric effects and decorative brilliance, made Tiepolo a decisive force in the development of European painting during the following century.

ST. JEROME

Painted 1732–1733. Oil on canvas, $13\frac{5}{8} \times 9\frac{13}{16}$ in. (34.7 × 24.8 cm.)
Charles H. and Mary F. S. Worcester Collection, 29.917
This very early painting by Tiepolo is reminiscent of Magnasco's night subjects and also brings to mind Ricci's broad brushwork. A drawing for this painting is owned by the Print Room of the State Museum in Berlin, and there is a related drawing in the Museo Civico of Bassano.

Coll: G. Palumbo, Rome

Ref: Voss, H., Kunst und Künstler *20: 431, 432, 1922; Chicago. Art Institute,* Annual Report, *1929, p. 20; Chicago. Art Institute,* Bulletin *23: 37, 43, 1929; Chicago. Art Institute,*

A Century of Progress Exhibition, *1933, cat. no. 160; Chicago. Art Institute,* The Worcester Collection, *1937, cat. no. 23, pl. 17; Chicago. Art Institute,* Tiepolo, *1938, cat. no. 1; Stechow, W.,* Art in America *26: 84, April 1938*

THE INSTITUTION OF THE ROSARY

Probably painted about 1737. Oil on canvas, 38 × 19 in. (96.5 × 48.3 cm.)
Mr. and Mrs. Martin A. Ryerson Collection, 33.1098

A Venetian order of Dominicans commissioned Tiepolo to paint this scene on the ceiling of their church in Venice, Santa Maria del Rosario. The *modeletti* for the fresco of the *Institution of the Rosary* are in the Dahlem Museum, Berlin, and in the Crespi Collection, Milan. Although this painting has been attributed to Giovanni Battista Tiepolo, it is more likely to be a studio replica of an early sketch by the master.

Ref: Chicago. Art Institute, Bulletin *20: 8, 1926; Rich, D. C.,* Art News *28, pt. 1: 9–10, March 1930; Chicago. Art Institute,* A Century of Progress Exhibition, *1933, cat. no. 154; Daley, C. M.,* Liturgical Arts *3, nos. 3–4; 140, 1934, cat. no. 22; Chicago. Art Institute,* Tiepolo, *1938, cat. no. 5; Chicago. Art Institute,* Bulletin *32: 26, 1938; Stechow, W.,* Art in America *26: 84, April 1938; Chicago. Art Institute,* Bulletin *34: 54–7, 1940*

FOUR EPISODES FROM THE STORY OF RINALDO AND ARMIDA Illus. pp. 44–45

Painted about 1755. Oil on canvas, (a) and (d), 73½ × 84½ in. (186.9 × 214.7 cm.); (b) and (c), 73 × 102⅛ in. (186.8 × 259.9 cm.)
Gift of James Deering, 25.699, 25.700, 25.701, 25.702

(a) Rinaldo Enchanted by Armida (Tasso , *Gerusalemme Liberata,* Canto 14).
(b) Rinaldo and Armida in the Garden Surprised by Ubaldo and Guelfo (*Ibid.,* Canto 16).
(c) Armida Abandoned by Rinaldo (*Ibid.,* Canto 16).
(d) Rinaldo and the Hermit (*Ibid.,* Canto 17).

It has been stated, without proof, that these panels were originally owned by the Serbelloni family of Milan. Tiepolo painted the same series for the Castle at Würzburg (1751–52) and for the Villa Valmarana at Vicenza (1757). There also exist several studies on the same theme.

Coll: Counts Serbelloni (of Milan), Venice; G. Cartier, Genoa

Ref: Malaguzzi-Valeri, F., Rassegna d'Art *8: 179, 1908; Sack, E.,* Giambattista and Domenico Tiepolo, *1910, p. 236, nos. 622–5; Molmenti, P.,* Tiepolo, *1911, pp. 188, 189; Ojetti, U.,* Emporium *36: 64–9, 1912; Chicago. Art Institute,* Annual Report, *1925, (ill.); Chicago. Art Institute,* Bulletin *20: 5–9, 1926;* Arno Art Studies, *I, 211, 1930; Venturi, L.,* Pitture Italiane in America, *1931, pls. 422–5; Chicago. Art Institute,* A Century of Progress Exhibition, *1933, cat. nos. 156–9;* Ibid., *1934, cat. nos. 334–7; Chicago. Art Institute,* Tiepolo, *1938, cat. nos. 6–9; Stechow, W.,* Art in America *26: 84, April 1938; Middeldorf, U. A.,* Pantheon *21: 17–8, May 1938; Lee, R. W.,* Art Bulletin *22: 242–50, December*

1940; Pallucchini, R., Gli Affreschi di Giambattista e Giandomenico Tiepolo alla Villa Valmarana di Vicenza, *1945, p. 34; Mazzariol, F. and T. Pignatti,* Itinerario Tiepolesco, *1951, p. 68; Morassi, A.,* G. B. Tiepolo, *London, 1955, p. 148, nos. 69, 72*

MADONNA AND CHILD WITH SS. DOMINIC AND HYACINTH

Painted between 1740 and 1750. Oil on canvas, 108×54 in. (274.4×137.2 cm.)
Mr. and Mrs. Martin A. Ryerson Collection, 33.1099

Coll: Morselli, Florence; Ladiskaus Bloch, Vienna; Hugh Lane, Dublin

Ref: Sack, E., Giambattista und Domenico Tiepolo, *1910, pp. 86, 88, 89; Molmenti, P.,* Tiepolo, *1911, p. 201, pl. 205; Chicago. Art Institute,* Bulletin *7: 45, 1917; 20: 8, 1926; Chicago. Art Institute,* A Century of Progress Exhibition, *1933, cat. no. 155; Daley, C. M.,* Liturgical Arts *3, nos. 3–4: 139, 140, 1934, no. 23; Chicago. Art Institute,* Tiepolo, *1938, cat. no. 12; Middeldorf, U. A.,* Pantheon *21: 17–8, May 1938; Stechow, W.,* Art in America *26: 84, April 1938; Chicago. Art Institute,* Bulletin *37: 97, 1943*

TIEPOLO, Giovanni Domenico (attributed to)

HEAD OF A PATRIARCH Illus. p. 53

Painted about 1750–1775. Oil on canvas, 23¾×18 in. (60.5×45.8 cm.)
Gift of Mrs. Richard E. Danielson and Mrs. Chauncey McCormick, 45.175

In the series of thirty heads etched by Giovanni Domenico Tiepolo and published in 1770, there is one of a patriarch, Number 7, of the same type as this picture.

Ref: Sack, E., Giambattista und Domenico Tiepolo, *1910, p. 211, no. 450b, p. 339, no. 128*

TINTORETTO, Jacopo Robusti, called il Tintoretto ~ *1518–1594 Venice*

Tintoretto, according to his earliest biographer, Carlo Ridolfi, was apprenticed to Titian (who allowed him to stay but ten days) and later worked with Andrea Schiavone and Bonifazio de'Pitati. His style was founded on the work of these men with compelling influences derived from Michelangelo and, to a lesser degree, Parmigianino. More than any other *cinquecento* Venetian, his *oeuvre* is tied to Venice, and his greatest autograph works are still there. He had a large and productive shop with various specialists for different tasks. It is essential to differentiate between his own sure autographs and the many works (of varying quality) executed by the firm, more or less under his supervision. Save for the work of his son Domenico (his immediate successor in the firm), attempts to identify the other hands at work in the shop are not yet persuasive.

TARQUIN AND LUCRETIA Illus. p. 42

Painted probably after 1560. Oil on canvas, 69×59¾ in. (175.3×151.8 cm.)
Art Institute Purchase Fund, 49.203

This is a condensed version of the picture in the Prado, and it is not clear whether the Chicago picture also was once much wider. The condition of neither painting is satisfactory. It perhaps represents a design by Tintoretto himself, but the execution is surely from the workshop, possibly by Domenico.

Coll: Cardinal de Bernis, Rome (before 1794); Richard Goetz, New York

Ref: von der Bercken, E., Die Gemaelde des Jacopo Tintoretto, *1942, pp. 42, 119; Tietze, H.,* Tintoretto, *1948, p. 357; Chicago. Art Institute,* Bulletin *44: 22–3, 1950*

SCENE FROM THE INVENTION OF THE HOLY CROSS

Painted after 1561. Oil on canvas, 8⅜ × 19⅛ in. (21.4 × 48.6 cm.)
Gift of Boehler and Steinmeyer, 32.44

This picture was surely painted by an imitator (perhaps by an immediate follower) not before the end of the 16th century.

Coll: Sir Thomas Andrós de la Rue; Philip Lydig, New York; Rita Lydig, New York; Hess, Berlin

Ref: Berlin, Hess Collection sale, 1931, cat. no. 4, pl. III; Chicago. Art Institute, Bulletin *26: 80, 1932*

VENUS AND MARS IN A LANDSCAPE WITH THREE GRACES

Probably painted after 1580. Oil on canvas, 41¾ × 56 in. (106 × 142.3 cm.)
Charles H. and Mary F. S. Worcester Collection, 29.914

This picture seems to have been executed in the shop, perhaps by a northern follower whose style is close to Domenico Robusti's yet different from it. There is a pendant, *Diana and Endymion,* sometime in the London market (cf. E. von der Bercken, *Die Gemälde des J.T.,* Munich, 1942, pp. 193, 194).

Coll: H. M. Clark, London

Ref: Chicago. Art Institute, Annual Report, *1928, p. 15; Chicago. Art Institute,* Bulletin *22: 102–3, 1928; Venturi, L.,* Pitture Italiane in America, *1931, pl. 409; Berenson, B.,* Italian Pictures of the Renaissance, *1932, p. 558; Chicago. Art Institute,* A Century of Progress Exhibition, *1933, cat. no. 137; Venturi, L.,* Italian Paintings in America, *III, 1933, pl. 551; Chicago. Art Institute,* A Century of Progress Exhibition, *1934, cat. no. 55; Berenson, B.,* Pitture Italiane del Rinascimento, *1936, p. 480; Chicago. Art Institute,* The Worcester Collection, *1937, cat. no. 11, pl. 10; von der Bercken, E.,* Die Gemälde des Jacopo Tintoretto, *1942, pp. 70, 107*

ANTONIO ZANTANI

Inscribed: Antonius Zantani, Comes et. Eques.
Oil on panel, 12¼ × 9¾ in. (31.8 × 24.8 cm.)
Charles H. and Mary F. S. Worcester Collection, 47.115

An old inscription identifies the sitter as Antonio Zantani (1514–1576), a Senator and Knight of Venice who was known for his literary and philanthropic interests. It is likely that the inscription was added later, since the sitter was probably an admiral, as indicated by the three knobs he wears on his shoulder. Hans Tietze pointed out this fact and also the unlikely possibility that the portrait might represent Jacopo Soranzo the Younger (1518–1587) who held the rank of quartermaster in the Venetian navy at the time of the Battle of Lepanto in 1571. The execution is either by the workshop or else, more probably, is the work of an untalented imitator of the master.

Coll: Rushton Hall, Kettering, Northants, England; L. Breitmeyer, London

Ref: Chicago. Art Institute, The Worcester Collection, *1937, cat. no. 10, pl. 9; Comstock, H.,* Connoisseur *121: 46, March 1948*

TITIAN (Tiziano Vecelli) ~ *1477/89–1576 Venice*

Titian was first trained as a mosaic worker and later worked with both Gentile and Giovanni Bellini, and with Giorgione. His relationship to the younger Bellini seems to have been that of shop foreman and principal assistant, while his precise relationship to Giorgione is still debated. He was the major figure in Venice between the death of Giorgione in 1510 and his own. During his life his style evolved from that of Giorgione and the late manner of Bellini through a ripe, Venetian version of Mannerism, to a kind of proto-Baroque done in his own kind of broken color.

GIULIA GONZAGA

Painted c. 1530–1540. Oil on canvas, 25½×30⅜ in. (63.9×51.8 cm.)
Max and Leola Epstein Collection, 54.301

The attribution of this picture, like that of most female portraits by Titian, is inconclusive. It is related to the Pitti *Bella* and the Vienna *Girl in a Fur.*

GIOVANNI FRANCESCO LEONI

Painted c. 1545–1550. Oil on canvas, 35×28 in. (89.9×71.2 cm.)
Gift of Chester D. Tripp, 54.195

The identification of the subject is not certain. The picture relates stylistically to the *Bearded Man* in Berlin, the *Barbaro* in Ottawa, and the *Anselmi* once in Lugano. The picture also relates to a certain period of Lotto. The condition makes the attribution inconclusive at present, but the evidence suggests that it probably is an autograph work of the 1545 to 1550 period.

TOBEY, Mark ~ *b. 1890 Centerville, Wisconsin*

Tobey was influenced by the calligraphy and brushwork of the Orient, where he traveled widely.

ABOVE THE EARTH Illus. p. 389

Signed and dated: Tobey 53.
Gouache on cardboard, 39¼×29¾ in. (100.3×76.5 cm.)
Gift of Mr. and Mrs. Sigmund Kunstadter, 53.340

Tobey remarks that this picture was inspired by memories of violent electrical storms in the Middle West.

TORREY, Elliot B. ~ *b. 1867 East Hardwicke, Vt. d. 1949 San Diego, Calif.*
Torrey studied in Paris and Florence.

ORVIETO

Painted between 1908 and 1911, signed: Elliot Torrey.
Oil on canvas, 40×50 in. (101.7×127 cm.)
Friends of American Art Collection, 15.267

TOULOUSE-LAUTREC, Henri de ~ *b. 1864 Albi. d. 1901 Malromé*
Toulouse-Lautrec's first teacher was René Princeteau; he then passed through the studios of Bonnet and Cormon to discover that his great passion was for drawing and his real masters were Goya, Degas, and the Japanese. Around 1885, eager for the subject matter which could be found in the excitements of its cafés, he went to Montmarte. For fifteen years, he lived with his subject matter, constantly designing, on paper or canvas, with terrific energy and undiminished power.

BALLET DANCERS

Painted 1885. Oil on plaster transferred to canvas, 60½×60 in. (153.7×152.5 cm.)
Helen Birch Bartlett Memorial Collection, 31.571

The canvas is one of four which Lautrec painted to decorate the Ancelin Inn at Villiers-sur-Morin near Paris. It has more the quality of a wall decoration than a finished painting.

Coll: Tetzen-Lund, Copenhagen; L. C. Hodebert, Paris

Ref: Duret, T., Lautrec, *1920, pp. 119, 120;* Gazette des Beaux-Arts *10: 18, January 1932; Chicago. Art Institute,* Bulletin *26: 2–3, 1932; Chicago. Art Institute,* A Century of Progress Exhibition, *1934, cat. no. 326; Chicago. Art Institute,* The Birch Bartlett Collection, *1946, pp. 48, 49*

MADAME LILI GRENIER

Painted 1885–1888, signed with monogram.
Oil on cardboard, 17×12½ in. (43.3×31.8 cm.)
Gift of Mr. and Mrs. Carter H. Harrison, 35.309

Mme Grenier was the wife of the landscape painter Claude Jules Grenier, whose studio Toulouse-Lautrec shared for a short time. The picture is sketched on composition board with a landscape by Grenier on the back.

Coll: Mme Grenier, Paris; Henri Cottereau, Paris

Ref: Chicago. Art Institute, The Harrison Collection, *1929, cat. no. 16; Chicago. Art Institute,* Toulouse-Lautrec, *1930/31, cat. no. 1*

WOMAN WITH A PINK BOW Illus. p. 286

Painted 1886, signed HT-Lautrec. Oil on canvas, 32 × 23¼ in. (81.3 × 59.1 cm.)
Gift of Annie Swan Coburn to the Mr. and Mrs. Lewis L. Coburn Memorial Collection, 41.824

Coll: M. A. Huc, Toulouse; Pierre Decourcelle, Paris; Jérome Stoneborough, Paris

Ref: Joyant, M., Henri de Toulouse-Lautrec, Peintre, *1926, p. 261; Coquiot, G.,* La Renaissance d'Art Français . . . *9: 273, 276, May 1926; Chicago. Art Institute,* Bulletin *36: 49–51, 1942*

IN THE CIRCUS FERNANDO: THE RINGMASTER Illus. p. 329

Painted 1888, signed: HT-Lautrec. Oil on canvas, 39½ × 63½ in. (100.3 × 161.3 cm.)
The Joseph Winterbotham Collection, 25.523

Coll: Oller, Paris; Baron Lafaurie, Paris

Ref: Chicago. Art Institute, Bulletin *19: 94, 95, 1925; Joyant, M.,* Henri de Toulouse-Lautrec, Peintre, *1926, pp. 162, 265; Joyant, M.,* L'Art et les Artistes, *N.S. 14: 164, 168, 1927; Chicago. Art Institute,* Toulouse-Lautrec, *1930/31, cat. no. 7; Chicago. Art Institute,* A Century of Progress Exhibition, *1933, cat. no. 373;* Ibid., *1934, cat. no. 328; Orlan, P. M.,* Lautrec, Le Peintre, *Paris, 1934, p. 132; Mack, G.,* Toulouse-Lautrec, *1938, pp. 215, 220; Chicago. Art Institute,* The Winterbotham Collection, *1947, pp. 44–45;* Art Digest *23: 10, 30, July 1949; Coquiot, G.,* Toulouse-Lautrec, *n.d., p. 57*

MOULIN DE LA GALETTE

Painted 1889, signed: HT-Lautrec. Oil on canvas, 35 × 39⅞ in. (88.9 × 101.3 cm.)
Mr. and Mrs. Lewis L. Coburn Memorial Collection, 33.458

Coll: Gallinard, Paris; Mme Montandon, Paris

Ref: Alexandre, A., Les Arts *13: 10, August 1914; Duret, T.,* Lautrec, *1920, p. 18; Coquiot, G.,* Lautrec, *Paris, 1921, p. 207; Joyant, M.,* Henri de Toulouse-Lautrec, Peintre, *1926, pp. 125, 126, 266, 267; Joyant, M.,* L'Art et les Artistes, *N.S. 14: 156, 170, 1927; de Lapparent, P.,* Toulouse-Lautrec, *1928, pp. 27, 28; Chicago. Art Institute,* Toulouse-Lautrec, *1930/31, cat. no. 9; Chicago. Art Institute,* The Coburn Collection, *1932, cat. no. 37; Chicago. Art Institute,* A Century of Progress Exhibition, *1933, cat. no. 372;* Ibid., *1934, cat. no. 327; Mack, G.,* Toulouse-Lautrec, *1938, pp. 119–24; Lassaigne, J.,* Toulouse-Lautrec, *1939, p. 165, no. 74; Rinaldini, J.,* Toulouse-Lautrec, *1942, p. 16; Borgese, L.,* Toulouse-Lautrec, *Milan, 1945, pl. 10; Coquiot, G.,* Lautrec, *n.d., p. 55*

MAY MILTON

Painted 1895, signed: HT-Lautrec.
Oil and pastel on cardboard, 26×19⅜ in. (66.1×49.4 cm.)
Gift of Kate L. Brewster, 49.263

Coll: E. Duplan, Paris; Th. Duret, Paris; J. Allard, Paris

Ref: Duret, T., Lautrec, *1920, pl. 13; Joyant, M.,* Henri de Toulouse-Lautrec, Peintre, *1926, p. 288; Joyant, M.,* Henri de Toulouse-Lautrec, Dessins-Estampes-Affiches, *1927, p. 198; Joyant, M.,* L'Art et les Artistes, *N.S. 14: 153, 170, 1927; Chicago. Art Institute,* Toulouse-Lautrec, *1930/31, cat. no. 26; Chicago. Art Institute,* A Century of Progress Exhibition, *1933, cat. no. 374*

AT THE MOULIN ROUGE Illus. p. 334

Painted 1892, signed with monogram. Oil on canvas, 48⅜×55¼ in. (122.9×140.4 cm.)
Helen Birch Bartlett Memorial Collection, 28.610

Here some of Toulouse-Lautrec's friends are seen seated around a table at the Moulin Rouge. The critic Edouard Dujardin, editor of the *Revue Indépendent,* with his whiskers and fedora, is talking to La Macarona, a dancer. Next to her is Paul Sescau, the photographer, beside whom is seated Maurice Guibert. The identity of the lady seen from the rear is not known. The woman whose face looms so brilliantly in the foreground is called only Nelly C. In the background, arranging her hair, is La Goulue. Topping the group is the lean figure of Gabriel Tapié de Céleyran, Toulouse-Lautrec's cousin and devoted friend, accompanied by the painter. The painting was originally smaller, but the artist added to both the bottom and the right side.

Coll: Manzi-Joyant, Paris; Jean Laroche, Paris, 1926

Ref: Alexandre, A., Le Figaro Illustré *22: 21, April 1902; Geffroy, G.,* Gazette des Beaux-Arts *12, per. 4: 100, 1916; Duret, T.,* Lautrec, *1920, pp. 15–22; Joyant, M.,* Henri de Toulouse-Lautrec, Peintre, *1926, pp. 137, 138, 275; Joyant, M.,* L'Art et les Artistes, *N.S. 14: 159, 160, 1927; Chicago. Art Institute,* Annual Report, *1928; de Lapparent, P.,* Toulouse-Lautrec, *1928, pp. 27–9; Chicago. Art Institute,* Bulletin *23: 14–5, 1929; Chicago. Art Institute,* The Birch Bartlett Collection, *1929, cat. no. 37; Chicago. Art Institute,* Toulouse-Lautrec, *1930/31, cat. no. 19 (ill.); Tériade, E.,* Cahiers d'Art *6, no. 1: 21, 1931; Chicago. Art Institute,* A Century of Progress Exhibition, *1933, cat. no. 371;* Ibid., *1934, cat. no. 325; Mack, G.,* Toulouse-Lautrec, *1938, pp. 125–34; Chicago. Art Institute,* Bulletin *33: 98, 99, 1939; Lassaigne, J.,* Toulouse-Lautrec, *1939, p. 166, no. 87; Chicago. Art Institute,* The Birch Bartlett Collection, *1946, pp. 46–7; Paris. Galerie de L'Orangerie,* De David a Toulouse-Lautrec . . . , *1955, cat. no. 54, pl. 84*

TREBILCOCK, Paul ~ *b. 1902 Chicago*

Trebilcock studied at the University of Illinois and at the School of the Art Institute of Chicago.

PORTRAIT OF A PAINTER (Self Portrait)

Painted about 1927, signed: Paul Trebilcock.
Oil on canvas, $43\frac{3}{8} \times 33\frac{3}{4}$ in. (110.3×85.8 cm.)
Mr. and Mrs. Frank G. Logan Purchase Prize, 28.228

TREIMAN, Joyce Wahl ~ *b. 1922 Evanston, Ill.*

The artist studied at the University of Iowa with Philip Guston.

ESCAPE

Painted 1950, signed: Treiman. Oil on canvas, $44\frac{1}{8} \times 36\frac{1}{8}$ in. (112.1×91.8 cm.)
Mr. and Mrs. Frank G. Logan Purchase Prize, 51.130

TROYON, Constant ~ *b. 1810 Sèvres. d. 1865 Paris*

Troyon's father was a painter-craftsman working with porcelain as were also the fathers of Diaz and Dupré, two artists who were Troyon's colleagues in the Barbizon School. Much impressed by the Dutch painter Paulus Potter, Troyon, like the Dutch master, specialized on landscapes with cattle.

UNFINISHED STUDY OF SHEEP

Painted about 1850, signed C T. Oil on canvas, $18 \times 14\frac{7}{8}$ in. (45.8×37.8 cm.)
Henry Field Memorial Collection, 94.1071

PASTURE IN NORMANDY

Signed and dated: C. Troyon 1852. Oil on panel, $15\frac{1}{8} \times 21\frac{5}{8}$ in. (35.5×55 cm.)
Henry Field Memorial Collection, 94.1069

Coll: Laurent Richard, 1886; E. Secrétan

Ref: Muther, R., The History of Modern Painting, *II, 1896, p. 440; Soullié, L.,* Constant Troyon, *1900, p. 58; Gensel, W.,* Corot und Troyon, *1906, p. 97*

THE ROAD TO MARKET

Painted about 1858–1859, signed: C. Troyon.
Oil on canvas, $36\frac{1}{4} \times 28\frac{7}{8}$ in. (92.1×73.4 cm.)
Henry Field Memorial Collection, 94.1068

Coll: E. Gaillard, Paris; B. Narischkin

Ref: Soullié, L., Constant Troyon, *1900, p. 146*

A CLUMP OF TREES

Painted about 1860. Oil on canvas, $13 \times 9\frac{7}{8}$ in. (33×25.1 cm.)
Henry Field Memorial Collection, 94.1070

This painting, sold with Troyon's estate in 1866, was left unfinished.

TRUMBULL, John ~ *b. 1756 Lebanon, Conn. d. 1843 New York City*

A meeting with Copley in 1773 stimulated Trumbull to take up painting, but before he began his career he served as Washington's aide-de-camp in the Revolutionary War. In 1780 Trumbull gave up his commission and went to London to become a pupil of Benjamin West. In 1815 he returned and settled permanently in the United States, receiving an important commission to paint four historical panels for the Rotunda of the Capitol in Washington.

WILLIAM BROWN

Probably painted 1804–1806. Oil on canvas, 36¼ × 28 in. (92.1 × 71.2 cm.)
Friends of American Art Collection, 23.920

William Brown was a merchant engaged in the East India trade. A similar portrait is owned by the Addison Gallery in Andover, Mass.

TURNER, Joseph Mallord William ~ *b. 1775 London. d. 1851 Chelsea*

Turner, together with Constable, was one of the two great figures in English landscape painting. He studied at the Royal Academy, but the two strongest influences on his work came from Claude Lorrain and Richard Wilson. In his later work, Turner gave way completely to visionary impressions of color, light, and atmosphere.

DUTCH FISHING BOATS

Painted 1837/38, signed: J. M. W. Turner.
Oil on canvas, 68⅝ × 78¼ in. (174.4 × 198.8 cm.)
Mr. and Mrs. W. W. Kimball Collection, 22.4472

Coll: J. Naylor, Leighton Hall

Ref: Armstrong, W., Turner, *1902, p. 229; Chicago. Art Institute,* Bulletin *14: 71, 77, 1920; Chicago. Art Institute,* Annual Report, *1922 (ill.); Chicago. Art Institute,* A Century of Progress Exhibition, *1933, cat. no. 205;* Ibid., *1934, cat. no. 153*

VALLEY OF AOSTA—SNOWSTORM, AVALANCHE AND THUNDERSTORM Illus. p. 236

Painted 1836/37. Oil on canvas, 36 × 48¼ in. (91.5 × 122.6 cm.)
Frederick T. Haskell Collection, 47.513

On his second trip to Italy in 1836, Turner visited the Italian Alps, making a number of sketches and watercolors which he later used in his London studio as a basis for oil paintings.

Coll: Munro-Novar; Earl of Warncliffe; James Price, Paignton, England; Sir Donald Currie, 1902; Mrs. Craven, Haselmere

Ref: Thornbury, W., Turner, *1877, pp. 104, 578, 597; Bell, C.,* Exhibited Works by Turner, *1901, pp. 132–3; Armstrong, W.,* Turner, *II, 1902, pp. 172, 218; London. Royal Academy,* Commemorative Catalogue of the Exhibition of British Art, *January/March 1934, cat. no. 370; Chicago. Art Institute,* Bulletin *42: 20–2, 1948*

TWACHTMAN, John Henry ~ *b. 1853 Cincinnati, Ohio. d. 1902 Gloucester, Mass.*
Twachtman studied under Duveneck, whom he accompanied in 1876 to Munich. After 1883 Impressionism became a major influence in his work. On returning to the United States in 1885 he was a member of the American Impressionist group which founded the Ten American Painters. Original members were Benson, DeCamp, Dewing, Hassam, Metcalf, Reid, Simmons, Tarbell, Weir, and Twachtman.

SNOWBOUND
Signed and dated: J. H. Twachtman 1885. Oil on canvas, 25¼ × 30⅛ in. (64.2 × 76.6 cm.)
Friends of American Art Collection, 17.200

FROM THE UPPER TERRACE
Painted about 1890, signed: J. H. Twachtman.
Oil on canvas, 25 × 30 in. (63.6 × 76.3 cm.)
Friends of American Art Collection, 19.2

THE WHITE BRIDGE
Painted about 1895, signed: J. H. Twachtman. Oil on canvas, 29½ × 29½ in. (75 × 75 cm.)
Mr. and Mrs. Martin A. Ryerson Collection, 37.1042

GLOUCESTER
Painted about 1895, signed: J. H. Twachtman.
Oil on canvas, 25 × 30 in. (63.6 × 76.3 cm.)
Walter H. Schulze Memorial Collection, 24.916

UFER, Walter ~ *b. 1876 Louisville, Ky. d. 1936 Taos, N.M.*
Ufer went to Germany as an apprentice to a lithographer and subsequently attended the academies in Dresden and Munich. Returning to America about 1913, he continued his studies at the Art Institute.

THE SOLEMN PLEDGE, TAOS INDIANS
Painted about 1915, signed: W. Ufer. Oil on canvas, 40½ × 36½ in. (102.9 × 92.8 cm.)
Friends of American Art Collection, 16.441

UTRILLO, Maurice ~ *b. 1883 Paris. d. 1955 Dax, France*
Utrillo was trained by his mother, Suzanne Valadeon. Through her, he came to know Renoir and Degas. By 1907, Utrillo found his style, specializing in the streets and architecture of Montmartre, the churches and squares of Paris and its environs.

RUE SAINT VINCENT, PARIS
Signed and dated: Maurice Utrillo V., 20 Juin 1913.
Oil on canvas, 25¼ × 39⅞ in. (64.2 × 101.3 cm.)
Mr. and Mrs. Martin A. Ryerson Collection, 33.1179

Coll: Georges Bernheim, Paris

Ref: Chicago. Art Institute, A Century of Progress Exhibition, *1933, cat. no. 713*

STREET IN PARIS

Signed and dated: Maurice Utrillo V. 1914.
Oil on canvas, $25\frac{5}{8} \times 31\frac{15}{16}$ in. (65.2×81 cm.)
Helen Birch Bartlett Collection, 26.226

Ref: Chicago. Art Institute, The Helen Birch Bartlett Memorial, *1926, pp. 40, 41; Einstein, C.,* Die Kunst des 20. Jahrhunderts, *1926, p. 253; Chicago. Art Institute,* A Century of Progress Exhibition, *1933, cat. no. 714*

THE TAVERN LA BELLE GABRIELLE

Painted about 1915, signed: Maurice Utrillo V.
Oil on canvas, $17\frac{1}{2} \times 21\frac{1}{4}$ in. (44.5×54.1 cm.)
Gift of Mr. and Mrs. Carter H. Harrison, 35.310

Ref: Chicago. Art Institute, Exhibition of Paintings from the Collection of Carter H. Harrison, *1929, cat. no. 17;* Die Kunst, *75, 1937, p. 335*

VALLOTTON, Félix ~ *b. 1865 Lausanne. d. 1925 Paris*

Valloton studied at the Académie Julian in Paris with Bonnard, Vuillard and Denis.

NUDE

Signed and dated: F. Vallotton '11. Oil on canvas, 35×46 in. (88.9×116.9 cm.)
Gift of Mr. and Mrs. Chester Dale, 45.18

Ref: Hahnloser-Buehler, H., Felix Vallotton et Ses Amis, *1936, p. 297, no. 788; Fegdal, C.,* L'Amour de l'Art *14: 94–6, April 1933*

VEDDER, Elihu ~ *b. 1836 New York City. d. 1923 Rome*

Vedder studied in New York and in Paris with François Picot, a pupil of David. He was largely influenced by the late Renaissance masters as well as William Black and Gustave Doré. Along with John La Farge and William Morris Hunt, Vedder took part in the movement to create a school of mural painting in America.

STORM IN UMBRIA

Signed and dated: Elihu Vedder, Rome 1875.
Oil on canvas, 13×45 in. (33×114.4 cm.)
The Nickerson Collection, 00.605

This painting was bought directly from the artist in 1875 by the Chicago collector, S. M. Nickerson.

FATES GATHERING IN THE STARS

Signed and dated: Elihu Vedder, Rome, 1887.
Oil on canvas, 45×23¼ in. (114.4×59.1 cm.)
Friends of American Art Collection, 19.1

Among Vedder's most important works were the fifty-six illustrations for Edward Fitzgerald's translation of the Rubáiyát of Omar Khayyám, published in 1884. This canvas is related to these illustrations.

VELAZQUEZ, Diego Rodriquez de Silva y ~ *b. 1599 Seville. d. 1660 Madrid*

Velázquez was a pupil of Francisco Herrerra the Elder and Francisco Pacheco. In 1629 he went to Italy, but even before he arrived there, his imagination had been fired by the new naturalism of Caravaggio. Depending on accents of color to lighten his adeptly painted greys and blacks, Velázquez, a master portrait painter, used a rapid technique punctuated by frequent highlights.

JOB

Painted about 1618. Oil on canvas, 47×36½ in. (119.4×92.8 cm.)
Gift of Mr. and Mrs. Chauncey McCormick, 36.355

Showing the influence of Caravaggio, this early painting is harder and more realistic than later work by Velázquez. The attribution to Velázquez was proposed by Mayer who discovered the painting on the London art market in 1922 as a work of the "School of Ribera." Mayer believed this to be an early work by the master when he was still working in Pacheco's studio. The painting is believed to be identical with a picture listed as "Zurbaran" in the catalogue of the Spanish painting collection of King Louis-Philippe of France, and was exhibited at the Louvre between 1838 to 1848. The Art Institute painting may have been cut, a possibility pointed out by Soria. The picture perhaps is by a still unidentified painter of Seville.

Coll: Charles Deering

Ref: A. L. Mayer, Diego Velázquez, *1924, pp. 40, 41; Cortissoz, R.,* Personalities in Art, *1925, pp. 128–32; Wolter, F.,* Der Junge Velázquez, *1929, p. 5; Mayer, A. L.,* Velázquez, A Catalogue Raisonné of the Pictures and Drawings, *London, 1936, cat. no. 3; Mayer, A. L.,* Burlington Magazine, *40, 1922, pp. 3–9; De Pantorba, B.,* La Vida y la Obra del Velázquez, *1955, p. 214, cat. no. 127*

THE SERVANT Illus. p. 99

Painted between 1618 and 1622. Oil on canvas, 21⅞×41⅛ in. (55.7×104.5 cm.)
Robert A. Waller Fund, 35.380

A variation on this same subject can be found in the collection of Sir Alfred Beit. The Beit version includes a small scene showing Christ at Emmaus in the left background.

Coll: Private collection, Zürich; Dr. L. von Buerkel, Munich

Ref: Justi, K., Diego Velázquez and His Time, *1889, pp. 138, 160; Mayer, A. L.,* Cicerone; *19, pt. 2, 1927, pp. 562, 563; Justi, K.,* Diego Velázquez und sein Jahrhundert, *1933, p. 143, Mayer, A. L.,* Velázquez, A Catalogue Raisonné of the Pictures and Drawings, *1936, cat. no. 105; Chicago. Art Institute,* Bulletin, *31, 1937, pp. 2–5; Lafuente, E.,* Velázquez, *1943, no. 3; du Gué Trapier, E.,* Velázquez, *1948, pp. 54–81; pp. 72, 73; Soria, M. S.,* Burlington Magazine, *91, 1949, pp. 124, 126, 127, 128; De Pantorba, B.,* La Vida y la Obra del Velázquez, *1955, p. 65, cat. no. 5*

SAINT JOHN THE BAPTIST Illus. p. 98

Painted about 1619–1620. Oil on canvas, 69×60 in. (175.3×152.5 cm.)
Gift of Mrs. Richard E. Danielson, 57.563

The naturalistic treatment of this canvas, painted before Velázquez' appointment to the court in 1623, is reminiscent of Caravaggio. Pentimenti can be seen in the upper left corner where clouds have been painted over the foliage.

Coll: Consul Julian Williams; F. H. Standish, London; Anthony . . . , London (1853); R. P. Nichols; Hugh Blaker, Isleworth; Charles Deering; Mr. Richard E.. Danielson

Ref: Stirling, Velázquez, *n.d., p. 192; Standish, F. H.,* Seville and Vicinity, *1840, p. 186; Mayer, A. L.,* Velázquez, *1924, pp. 50, 52; Mayer, A. L.,* Velázquez . . . , *1936, cat. no. 34; Lafuente, E.,* Velázquez, *1943, no. 11; E. du Gué Trapier,* Velázquez, *1948, pp. 126–35; Mayer, A. L.,* Burlington Magazine *40: 4, 9, 1922*

QUEEN ISABELLA OF SPAIN Illus. p. 94

Painted about 1632. Oil on canvas, 49¾×40 in. (126.4×101.7 cm.)
Max and Leola Epstein Collection, 54.302

This portrait was discovered in 1927 and has created much discussion among scholars. Mayer and Lafuente attribute it to Velázquez himself. De Pantorba and Iñiquez believe it to be a studio replica after the original. Crombie, in his recent study of this group of portraits, corroborates the latter opinion. As the official portrait was sent from Madrid to the Viennese court in 1632, this canvas may have been painted shortly thereafter during the period following Velázquez' first trip to Italy.

VELDE, Adriaen van de ~ *1636–1672 Amsterdam*

FIGURES AND CATTLE

Signed and dated: A. v. Velde f. 1664. Oil on canvas, 26⅝×30¾ in. (67.7×78.1 cm.)
Sidney A. Kent Fund, 94.1024

Coll: Van Loon, Amsterdam, 1834; Prince Anatole Demidoff, San Donato

Ref: Hofstede de Groot, A Catalogue Raisonné of the Works of the Most Eminent Dutch Painters of the Seventeenth Century, *vol. 4, 1912, pp. 511, 512, no. 185*

VERGE-SARRAT, Henri ~ *b. 1880 Anderlecht, Belgium*

Vergé-Sarrat studied at the Ecole des Beaux-Arts in Paris. Before 1918 he worked chiefly as a graphic artist, but devoted himself to painting.

QUAY AT CALVI, CORSICA

Signed and dated: Vergé-Sarratt 1936. Oil on canvas, $23\frac{3}{4} \times 28\frac{1}{4}$ in. (60.5×71.7 cm.)
Gift of Mr. and Mrs. Carter H. Harrison, 36.13

Ref: Chicago. Art Institute, Exhibition of Paintings from the Collection of Carter H. Harrison, *1929, cat. no. 19*

TERRACE AT CALENZANA, CORSICA

Painted 1936, signed: Vergé-Sarrat. Oil on canvas, $25\frac{5}{8} \times 28\frac{1}{4}$ in. (65.2×71.7 cm.)
Gift of Mr. and Mrs. Carter H. Harrison, 37.388

Ref: Chicago. Art Institute, Exhibition of Paintings from the Collection of Carter H. Harrison, *1929, cat. no. 20*

VERNET, Claude Joseph ~ *b. 1714 Avignon. d. 1789 Paris*

After an apprenticeship to his father, Antoine, Claude Vernet went to Rome in 1752 to study with Bernardino Fergioni, a painter of seascapes. Influenced by Claude Lorrain, Vernet produced romantic paintings of sea, tempests and moonlight. In 1753 he was recalled to Paris to execute commissions for Louis XV.

THE MORNING

Signed and dated: J. Vernet f. 1760. Oil on canvas, 25×38 in. (63.6×96.5 cm.)
Mr. and Mrs. Martin A. Ryerson Collection, 33.1101

Coll: Edmond Noel

Ref: Ingersoll-Smouse, F., Joseph Vernet, *1926, nos. 732–5*

VERONESE, Paolo (Paolo Caliari) ~ *b. 1528 Verona. d. 1588 Venice*

Paolo Caliari, called Veronese (after his native town), was influenced by Titian and Parmigianino. He settled in Venice in 1554 after having first worked in Verona and Mantua.

SAINT JEROME

Painted about 1561. Oil on canvas, $53\frac{1}{4} \times 69\frac{1}{2}$ in. (135.3×176.6 cm.)
Charles H. and Mary F. S. Worcester Collection, 47.117

The picture may in part be shop-work.

Coll: Earl of Stafford, Wrotham Park, Barnet. England

Ref: Chicago. Art Institute, Bulletin *41: 63, 1947*

CREATION OF EVE — Illus. p. 38

Painted about 1570. Oil on canvas, 31⅞ × 40¼ in. (81 × 102.2 cm.)
Charles H. and Mary F. S. Worcester Collection, 30.286

Ref: Berenson, Italian Pictures of the Renaissance, *1932, p. 420; Venturi, L.,* Italian Paintings in America, *1933, pt. 3, pl. 575; Berenson,* Pitture Italiane del Rinascimento, *1936, p. 361; Pallucchini, R.,* Veronese, *1943, pl. 125; Rich, D. C.,* Pantheon *7: 20–23, 1931; Friedlaender, W.,* Art in America *26: 131, 1938;* Art News *36: 10, April 16, 1938; Chicago. Art Institute,* Catalogue of the Worcester Collection, *1937, cat. no. 13; Chicago. Art Institute,* A Century of Progress Exhibition, *1933, cat. no. 141;* Ibid., *1934, cat. no. 59*

VIGEE-LEBRUN, Elisabeth-Louise, School of

PORTRAIT OF A LADY IN A STRAW HAT

Painted about 1795. Oil on canvas, 32 × 25 in. (81.3 × 63.6 cm.)
Gift of John Wentworth, 42.308

VILLON, Jacques (Gaston Duchamp) ~ *b. 1875 Damville, France*

Villon started as an engraver and newspaper illustrator. In 1911 he turned to painting, becoming one of the organizers of La Section d'Or, a group of young artists who held their first major exhibition in 1912.

MUSICAL INSTRUMENTS

Signed and dated: Jacques Villon 12. Oil on panel, 42 × 31⅝ in. (106.7 × 80.5 cm.)
Gift of Mr. and Mrs. Francis Steegmuller, 42.305

Ref: Lassaigne, J., Jacques Villon, *1950, p. 8*

VLAMINCK, Maurice de ~ *1876–1958 Paris*

Vlaminck's early influences were Cézanne and Van Gogh. In 1905 he exhibited with the Fauves, in the company of his friends Derain and Matisse.

HOUSES AT CHATOU

Painted 1903, signed: Vlaminck. Oil on canvas, 32 × 39⅝ in. (81.3 × 101.3 cm.)
Gift of Mr. and Mrs. Maurice E. Culberg, 51.19

Ref: Huyghe, R., L'Amour de l'Art, *14, 1933, pp. 130, 133*

VILLAGE (RUEIL)

Painted about 1912, signed: Vlaminck. Oil on canvas, 29 × 36¼ in. (73.7 × 92.1 cm.)
Arthur Jerome Eddy Memorial Collection, 31.517

Coll: Arthur Jerome Eddy

EUROPEAN PAINTINGS

SECTION TWO

XXth Century

ILLUSTRATIONS

Leger, Fernand, Divers on Yellow Background, 1941. Gift of Mr. & Mrs. Maurice E. Culberg

Matisse, Henri, Apples, 1916. Gift of Mr. & Mrs. Samuel A. Marx

Braque, Georges, Still Life, 1919. The Joseph Winterbotham Collection

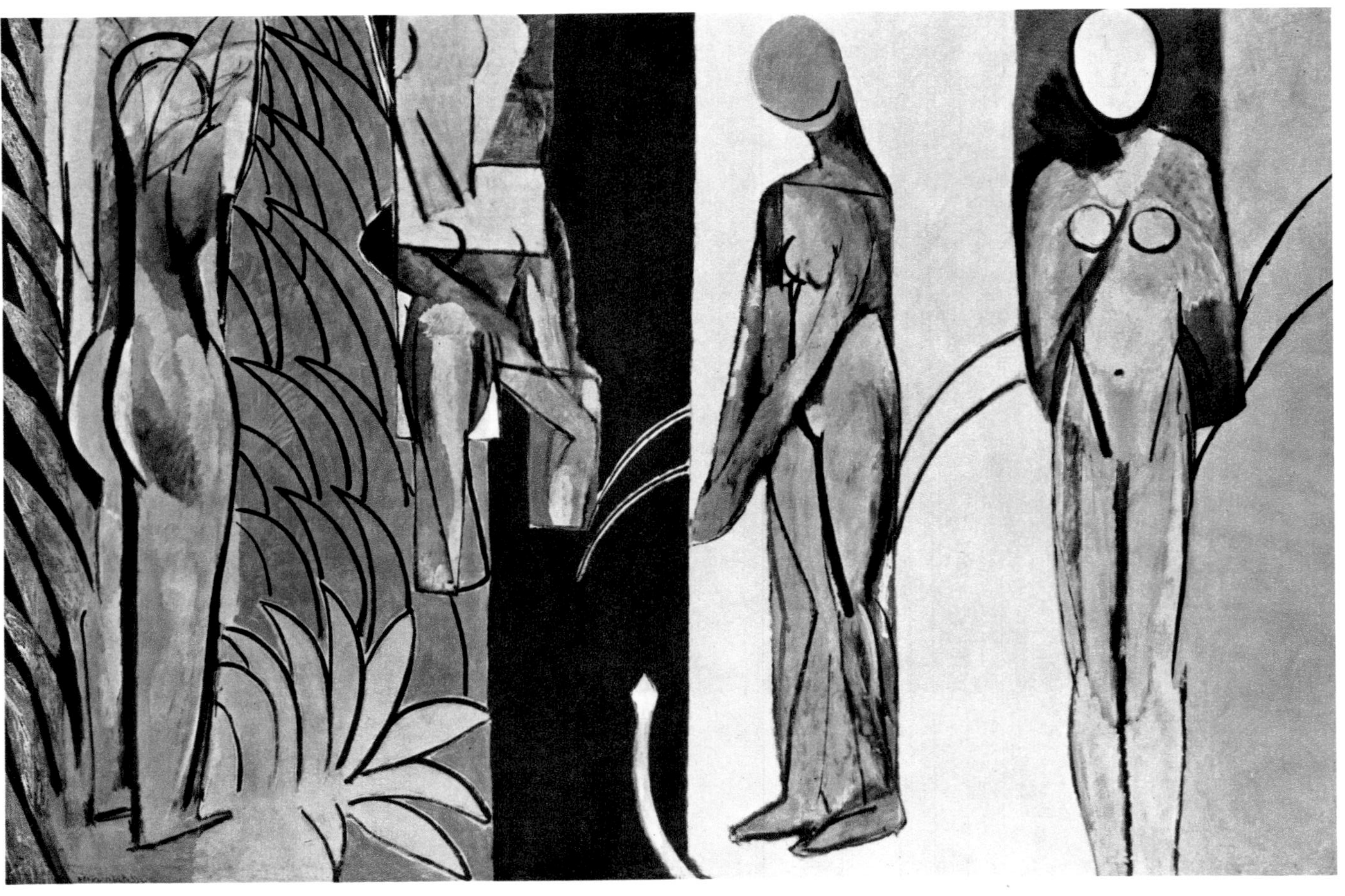

Matisse, Henri, Bathers by a River, 1916/17. Charles H. & Mary F. S. Worcester Collection

Chagall, Marc, The Praying Jew, 1914. The Joseph Winterbotham Collection

Gris, Joan, The Checkerboard, 1915
Gift of Mrs. Leigh B. Block with a contribution from the Ada Turnbull Hertle Fund

De Chirico, Giorgio, The Philosopher's Conquest, 1914. The Joseph Winterbotham Collection

Orozco, José, Zapata, 1930. The Joseph Winterbotham Collection

Beckmann, Max, Self Portrait, 1937
Gift of Mr. & Mrs. Philip Ringer

Rouault, Georges, The Academician, 1913–15
Gift of Mrs. Leigh B. Block in memory of her father, Albert D. Lasker

Matisse, Henri, Woman Before an Aquarium, 1921. Helen Birch Bartlett Memorial Collection

Opposite: Rousseau, Henri, The Waterfall, 1910
Helen Birch Bartlett Memorial Collection

Ref: Eddy, A. J., Cubists and Post-Impressionism, *1914, p. 136; Chicago. Art Institute,* The Arthur Jerome Eddy Collection of Modern Paintings and Sculpture, *1922, cat. no. 65*

NEAR PONTOISE

Painted about 1918–1920, signed: Vlaminck.
Oil on canvas, $31\frac{3}{16} \times 39\frac{1}{4}$ in. (79.2×99.8 cm.)
Gift of Mr. and Mrs. Carter H. Harrison, 35.311

Ref: Chicago. Art Institute, Exhibition of Paintings from the Collection of Carter H. Harrison, *1935–1936, cat. no. 9*

BOUQUET IN GRAY VASE

Painted about 1930, signed: Vlaminck. Oil on canvas, $12\frac{1}{2} \times 9\frac{1}{4}$ in. (31.8×23.5 cm.)
Gift of Kate L. Brewster, 50.135

VUILLARD, Edouard ~ *b. 1868 Cuiseaux. d. 1940 La Baule, France*

Vuillard was a pupil of Bouguereau and Gérôme. In 1892, he joined the Nabis, a group of artists who drew inspiration from Gauguin and the Symbolists.

CHILD IN A ROOM

Painted about 1900, signed: E. Vuillard. Oil on cardboard, $17\frac{1}{4} \times 22\frac{3}{4}$ in. (43.9×57.9 cm.)
Mr. and Mrs. Martin A. Ryerson Collection, 33.1110

Coll: Mme Blanche Marchesi

Ref: Colour *5: 119, 1916; Chicago. Art Institute,* A Century of Progress Exhibition, *1933, cat. no. 718;* Ibid., *1934, cat. no. 288; Ritchie, Andrew C.,* Edouard Vuillard *(Museum of Modern Art), 1954, pp. 74, 102*

INTERIOR WITH SEATED WOMAN

Painted 1904/05, signed: E. Vuillard. Oil on canvas, $17\frac{3}{8} \times 15$ in. (44.2×38.2 cm.)
Charles H. and Mary F. S. Worcester Collection, 47.118

Ref: Chicago. Art Institute, A Century of Progress Exhibition, *1933, cat. no. 117;* Ibid., *1934, cat. no. 289; Chicago. Art Institute,* Bonnard-Vuillard, *1938–1939, cat. no. 32; CAI,* Bulletin *27: 117, 1933; CAI,* Catalogue of the Worcester Collection, *1937, cat. no. 96*

WOMAN SEATED ON A SOFA

Painted about 1906, signed: E. Vuillard.
Oil on composition board, $19\frac{1}{2} \times 24\frac{3}{4}$ in. (49.7×63 cm.)
Charles H. and Mary F. S. Worcester Collection, 47.119

STILL LIFE

Signed and dated: E. Vuillard 1905. Oil on board, $28\frac{3}{4} \times 24\frac{1}{2}$ in. (76×62.4 cm.)
Gift of Mr. and Mrs. Sterling Morton, 59.4

WOMAN IN INTERIOR

Painted 1932, signed: E. Vuillard. Pastel and gouache, 29¾×37¼ in. (75.6×94.7 cm.)
Gift of Mrs. George L. Simmonds, 59.508

WALDO, Samuel Lovett ~ *b. 1783 Windham, Conn. d. 1861 New York City*

Waldo studied with Joseph Steward, a painter and minister of Hartford, Conn. After a short stay in Charleston, S.C., he went to London in 1806, where he studied with West and Copley. On his return to America in 1809, he settled in New York. In 1822, he took his pupil, William Jewett, into a partnership; they became popular portrait painters of the period.

MR. J. F. MACKIE

Probably painted between 1835 and 1840. Oil on canvas, 35½×29 in. (90.2×73.7 cm.)
Friends of American Art Collection, 21.99

MRS. J. F. MACKIE

Probably painted between 1835 and 1840. Oil on canvas, 36⅛×28⅞ in. (91.8×73.4 cm.)
Friends of American Art Collection, 21.98

WALDO and JEWETT

In 1812, William S. Jewett (b. 1795 East Haddam, Conn., d. 1873 Bayonne, N.J.) became a pupil of Waldo, who in 1822 made him a partner in the firm.

HARRIET WHITE

Painted probably between 1835 and 1840. Oil on panel, 48⅝×35⅛ in. (123.5×89.3 cm.)
Gift of Joseph Winterbotham, Jr., 37.1100

WATTEAU, Antoine ~ *b. 1684 Valenciennes, Belgium. d. 1721 Nogent-sur-Marne*

Watteau, who studied in Paris with Claude Gillot and Claude Audran, was also influenced by Rubens and Veronese.

PORTRAIT OF JEAN-FRANÇOIS PATER

Painted about 1720. Oil on canvas, 31⅞×25⅝ in. (81×65.2 cm.)
Max and Leola Epstein Collection, 54.303

This portrait was attributed to Watteau by Jules Féral, and is said to represent the young sculptor, Jean-François Pater, brother of the painter. Earlier, Watteau did a portrait of their father, Antoine-Joseph Pater, who was also a sculptor.

WATTS, George Frederic ~ *b. 1817 London. d. 1904 Compton, England*

Watts was mainly self-taught. He first exhibited at the Royal Academy in 1837, and in 1843 won a prize in a competition for the decoration of the Houses of Parliament.

TIME, DEATH AND JUDGMENT

Painted about 1866. Oil on canvas, 35½×27½ in. (90.2×70 cm.)
Gift of Charles L. Hutchinson, 25.724

A LAMPLIGHT STUDY: HERR JOACHIM

Signed and dated: G. F. Watts 1868. Oil on canvas, 37×23 in. (94×58.6 cm.)
Gift of Charles L. Hutchinson, 25.725

This portrait of the great violinist is a replica made by Watts in 1868 for his friend C. H. Rickards of Manchester. The original is in the Watts Gallery at Compton.

WAUGH, Frederick Judd ~ *b. 1861 Bordentown, N.J. d. 1940 Provincetown*

Waugh studied at the Pennsylvania Academy of the Fine Arts in Philadelphia, and at the Académie Julian in Paris.

SURF AND FOG, MONHEGAN, MAINE

Painted about 1910, signed: Waugh. Oil on canvas, 52¼×66½ in. (132.8×169 cm.)
Friends of American Art Collection, 12.1813

WEBER, Max ~ *b. 1881 Bialistok, Russia*

Weber was one of the first students of Matisse. It was the Cubist movement, however, that exerted the strongest influence on his work.

STILL LIFE

Signed and dated: Max Weber '44. Oil on canvas, 31×40 in. (78.8×101.7 cm.)
Friends of American Art Collection, 45.189

WEIR, J. Alden ~ *b. 1852 West Point. d. 1919 New York City*

The painter received his first training from his father, who was instructor in drawing at West Point. In 1873, he went to Paris to study at the Ecole des Beaux-Arts. When Weir returned to the United States in 1883, he joined The Ten. In 1893, he was one of the painters commissioned to paint murals at the Columbian Exposition.

THE TWO SISTERS

Painted between 1890 and 1899, signed: J. Alden Weir.
Oil on canvas, 51×39⅜ in. (129.6×100 cm.)
Gift of Mrs. Albert J. Beveridge in memory of Abby Louise Spencer Eddy, 38.19

A portrait of the Spencer sisters, Delia Spencer Caton (later Mrs. Marshall Field), and Abby Louise Spencer Eddy.

THE GRAY BODICE

Signed and dated: J. Alden Weir 1898. Oil on canvas, 30¼×25¼ in. (76.9×64.2 cm.)
Friends of American Art Collection, 11.536

A DAY IN JUNE

Painted between 1900 and 1909, signed: J. Alden Weir.
Oil on canvas, $23\frac{3}{8} \times 31\frac{3}{4}$ in. (59.4×80.8 cm.)
Walter H. Schulze Memorial Collection, 41.1106

AN AMERICAN GIRL

Painted during the winter of 1911/12, signed, J. Alden Weir.
Oil on canvas, $36 \times 28\frac{1}{4}$ in. (91.5×71.7 cm.)
Gift of Mr. William T. Cresmer, 51.221

THE LUTE PLAYER

Painted between 1910 and 1919, signed: J. Alden Weir.
Oil on canvas, $33\frac{1}{2} \times 23$ in. (85.2×58.6 cm.)
Walter H. Schulze Memorial Collection, 24.917

WEISENBORN, Rudolph ~ *b. 1881 Chicago*

Weisenborn studied painting in Denver between 1905 and 1910.

PROVINCETOWN NO. 4

Signed and dated: Weisenborn—50. Tempera on panel, $30 \times 24\frac{1}{8}$ in. (76.3×61.3 cm.)
Cyrus McCormick Fund, 51.57

WEST, Benjamin ~ *b. 1738 Springfield, Pa. d. 1820 London*

When he was only eighteen, West had already established himself as a portrait painter in Philadelphia. In 1760, he went abroad, where he spent three years in Italy, and then settled in London. There he was one of the founders of the Royal Academy, and became its President in 1792, after the death of Reynolds.

CEPHALUS AND PROCRIS

Signed and dated: B. West 1770. Oil on panel, $13\frac{3}{8} \times 16\frac{7}{8}$ in. (34×42.9 cm.)
Gift of William O. Cole, 00.445

PORTRAIT OF A GENTLEMAN

Signed and dated: Benjamin West 1794. Oil on canvas, $50\frac{1}{2} \times 40$ in. (128.3×101.7 cm.)
Gift of the Family of Byron L. Smith, 16.209

HE THAT IS WITHOUT SIN

Painted about 1800. Oil on canvas, $51 \times 29\frac{1}{2}$ in. (129.6×75 cm.)
Friends of American Art Collection, 15.488

WEYDEN, Rogier van der ~ *b. 1399/1400 Tournai. d. 1464 Brussels*

In the generation following the van Eycks, Rogier became the leading artist of the Flemish School. His teacher in Tournai was Robert Campin, and, in addition, he was influenced by the Van Eycks. Rogier settled in Brussels about 1435. In 1450, he visited Italy, going to Rome and, possibly, Ferrara.

MADONNA AND CHILD

Painted probably between 1450 and 1460. Oil on panel, $15\frac{1}{8} \times 11\frac{1}{8}$ in. (38.5×28.3 cm.)
Mr. and Mrs. Martin A. Ryerson Collection, 33.1052

Coll: V. Steyaert, Bruges (1867); Mathys, Brussels

Ref: Hymans, H., Gazette des Beaux-Arts, *ser. 3, July/December 1902, p. 194; Le Brun, G.,* Rassegna d'Arte, *October 1902, pp. 146, 147; Friedlaender, M. J.,* Meisterwerke der Niederlaendischen Malerei des XV und XVI Jahrhunderts auf der Ausstellung zu Bruegge, *1902, p. 6; Voll, K.,* Altniederlaendische Malerei von Van Eyck bis Memling, *1906, p. 292; Fierens-Gevaert,* La Peinture en Belgique . . . Les Primitifs Flamands, *1908, vol. 1, p. 50; Lafond, P.,* Roger van der Weyden, *1912, p. 86; Winkler, F.,* Der Meister von Flémalle und Rogier van der Weyden, *1913, p. 175; Conway, M.,* The Van Eycks and Their Followers, *1921, p. 150; Friedlaender, M. J.,* Die Altniederlaendische Malerei, *vol. 2, 1924, pp. 34, 101;* Early Flemish Paintings in the Renders Collection at Bruges *(Burlington House), January 1927, p. 62;* Fierens-Gevaert, Histoire de la Peinture Flamande . . ., *1928, vol. 2, p. 60; Destrée, J.,* Roger de la Pasture van der Weyden, *1930, vol. 1, p. 119; Beenken, H.,* Rogier van der Weyden, *1951, pp. 77, 78; Richardson, E. P.,* The Journal of the Walters Art Gallery *2: 41, 1939; Chicago. Art Institute,* Bulletin *27: 114, 1933; Chicago. Art Institute,* A Century of Progress Exhibition, *1933, cat. no. 56;* Ibid., *1934, cat. no. 129*

JEAN DE GROS Illus. p. 147

Painted between 1450 and 1460. Oil and tempera on panel, $15\frac{3}{16} \times 11\frac{1}{4}$ in. (38.5×28.6 cm.)
Mr. and Mrs. Martin A. Ryerson Collection, 33.1051

This is the right wing of a devotional diptych. The left wing, a Virgin and Child, is in the Renders Collection in Bruges. The donor, a member of the great de Gros family of Burgundy, was undoubtedly the same Jean de Gros who held high rank at the court of Charles the Bold, ruler of Flanders and Burgundy. Charles' successor and son-in-law, the Archduke Maximilian of Hapsburg, made Jean treasurer of the Order of the Golden Fleece, and gave him membership in his privy council. Jean de Gros died in 1484 and was buried in Dijon. The reverse of the panel bears arms of the sitter.

Coll: Dr. August de Meyer, Bruges; Rodolphe Kann, Paris; Duveen Brothers, N.Y. (1909); Kleinberger Galleries, Paris (1913)

Ref: Michel, E., Gazette des Beaux-Arts, *per. 3, January/June 1901, p. 498; Marguillier, A.,* Les Arts *2: 3, 1903; Laban, F.,* Zeitschrift für Bildende Kunst *19: 58, 1907; Ricci, S.,* Gazette des Beaux-Arts, *per. 3, vol. 38, July/December, 1907, pp. 187, 188;* Catalogue of the Rodolphe Kann Collection, *1907, vol. 2, p. 15, cat. no. 110; W. von Bode,* La Galerie de Tableaux de M. Rodolphe Kann à Paris, *n.d., pl. 84; Winkler, F.,* Der Meister von Flémalle und Rogier van der Weyden, *1913, p. 174; Friedlaender, M.,* Die Altniederlaendische Malerei, *vol. 2, 1924, pp. 37, 101, cat. no. 28;* Early Flemish Paintings in the Renders Collection at Bruges, *1927 (Burlington House), pp. 59–62; Fierens-Gevaert,*

Histoire de la Peinture Flamande . . . , *1928, vol. 2, pp. 60, 64; Destrée, J.,* Roger de la Pasture van der Weyden, *1930, vol. 1, p. 117, pl. 38; Beenken, H.,* Rogier van der Weyden, *1951, pp. 70, 71; Friedlaender, M. J.,* Art in America *9: 62, 1921; de Loo, H.,* Burlington Magazine *43: 53, 54, 1923; Stein, W.,* Jahrbuch der Preussischen Kunstsammlungen *47: 31 (note 2), 32, 1926; Tovell, R. M.,* Rogier van der Weyden and the Flémalle Enigma, *1955, pl. 54; Chicago. Art Institute,* A Century of Progress Exhibition, *1933, cat. no. 55;* Ibid., *1934, cat. no. 128*

WHISTLER, James Abbott McNeill ~ *b. 1834 Lowell, Mass. d. 1903 London*

While a cadet at West Point, Whistler received his first lessons in drawing under Robert E. Weir. Later, he worked as an etcher for the United States Coast and Geodetic Survey. In 1855 he went to Paris, where he was influenced by the work of Fantin-Latour and the Impressionists. In 1859, Whistler settled in London.

GRAY AND SILVER: BATTERSEA REACH

Signed and dated: Whistler 63. Oil on canvas, 20×27⅛ in. (50.9×69 cm.)
Potter Palmer Collection, 22.449

GRAY AND GREEN: THE SILVER SEA

Painted about 1864, signed: Whistler. Oil on canvas, 20¼×30¼ in. (51.5×76.9 cm.)
Potter Palmer Collection, 22.448

THE ARTIST IN HIS STUDIO Illus. p. 375

Painted about 1864, signed with the butterfly. Oil on panel, 24¾×18¾ in. (63×47.7 cm.)
Friends of American Art Collection, 12.141

This is one of two studies for a larger composition that was never executed. The other version is in the City of Dublin Art Gallery. Whistler described to Fantin-Latour his plans for a large group picture like the one Fantin had done in honor of Delacroix. He planned to include Fantin, Albert Moore, the White Girl (Jo), La Japonaise, and himself.

STUDY FOR THE PORTRAIT OF THOMAS CARLYLE

Painted 1872, signed with the butterfly. Oil on canvas, 10×10⅞ in. (25.5×27.6 cm.)
Gift of Emily Crane Chadbourne, 56.763

This is the preliminary sketch for the large portrait of Carlyle in the Glasgow Art Gallery.

COAST SCENE—BATHERS

Painted about 1875, signed with the butterfly. Oil on panel, 5×8½ in. (12.7×21.7 cm.)
Gift of Walter S. Brewster, 33.208

NOCTURNE, SOUTHAMPTON WATERS
(Nocturne black and gold, entrance to Southampton Waters)

Painted 1880–1882, signed with the butterfly. Oil on canvas, 20×30 in. (50.9×76.3 cm.)
The Stickney Fund, 00.52

PORTRAIT OF A YOUNG GIRL

Painted mid-1890s. Oil on panel, $5\frac{7}{8} \times 3\frac{1}{4}$ in. (14.9×8.3 cm.)
Gift of Walter S. Brewster, 33.212

ARTHUR JEROME EDDY

Painted 1894, signed with the butterfly. Oil on canvas, $82\frac{3}{4} \times 36\frac{3}{4}$ in. (209.1×93.4 cm.)
Arthur Jerome Eddy Memorial Collection, 31.501

SEASCAPE: VIOLET AND SILVER, THE DEEP SEA

Painted about 1892. Oil on canvas, $19\frac{1}{2} \times 28\frac{3}{4}$ in. (49.7×73 cm.)
Gift of Clara Lynch, 55.743

WIGGINS, J. Carleton ~ *b. 1848 Turner, N.Y. d. 1932 Old Lyme, Conn.*

Wiggins studied at the National Academy of Design in New York, and with George Inness.

LAKE AND MOUNTAINS

Signed and dated: J. C. Wiggins '71. Oil on canvas, $16\frac{1}{8} \times 28\frac{1}{8}$ in. (41.1×71.7 cm.)
Gift of George H. Glover, 12.1831

WIGGINS, Guy Carleton ~ *b. 1883 Brooklyn, N.Y.*

Wiggins first studied with his father, J. Carleton Wiggins, and later at the National Academy of Design in New York.

SNOW-CROWNED HILLS

Painted before 1913, signed: Guy C. Wiggins.
Oil on canvas, $33\frac{1}{4} \times 39\frac{1}{2}$ in. (84.5×100.3 cm.)
Walter H. Schulze Memorial Collection, 24.918

LIGHTLY FALLING SNOW

Painted before 1917, signed: Guy C. Wiggins.
Oil on canvas, 34×40 in. (86.3×101.7 cm.)
Walter H. Schulze Memorial Collection, 17.267

WILLIAMS, George Alfred ~ *b. 1875 Newark, N.J. d. 1932 Kennebunkport, Me.*

Williams studied at the Art Students League and with William Merritt Chase. He began his career in 1899 as an illustrator for magazines and books.

THE DRAMA OF LIFE—THE MARGINAL WAY

Signed and dated: George Alfred Williams, 1913.
Oil on canvas, 22×30 in. (56×76.3 cm.)
Friends of American Art Collection, 14.182

WILSON, Richard ~ *b. 1714 Penegoss, England. d. Colomondie, Wales*

Wilson was a pupil of Thomas Wright. He began his career as a portrait painter, but is best known for his landscapes. While living in Italy from 1749 to 1755, he was influenced by Claude, Claude Joseph Vernet, and Francesco Zuccarelli.

ITALIAN LANDSCAPE

Painted probably between 1750 and 1760. Oil on canvas, 20×24 in. (50.9×61 cm.)
Mr. and Mrs. W. W. Kimball Collection, 22.4474

Ref: Chicago. Art Institute, A Century of Progress Exhibition, *1933, cat. no. 207*

WINTER, Fritz ~ *b. 1905 Westphalia, Germany*

Fritz Winter studied at the Bauhaus in Dessau under Kandinsky and Klee.

RED RUNNING THROUGHOUT

Signed and dated: F. Winter—53. Oil on paper, 19¾×27⅝ in. (50.4×70.3 cm.)
Harriott A. Fox Fund, 54.192

WITTE, Emanuel de ~ *b. ca. 1617 Alkmaar, Holland. d. 1692 Amsterdam*

De Witte, a pupil of Evert van Aelst, was later influenced by Carel Fabritius and Rembrandt.

CHURCH INTERIOR Illus. p. 190

Painted about 1670, signed: E de Witte. Oil on panel, 24⅜×19 5/16 in. (62×49.2 cm.)
Charles H. and Mary F. S. Worcester Collection, 41.1038

Ref: Chicago. Art Institute, Catalogue of the Worcester Collection, *1937, cat. no. 47; Siple, E. S.,* Burlington Magazine *82: 25, 1942*

WOLLASTON, John ~ *b. 1710 [?] London. d. ca. 1769 Bath*

Wollaston came to New York about 1751 and painted portraits. After 1760 he spent some time in Charleston, and then returned to England.

MRS. REBECCA BEEKMAN STEWARD SPRY

Painted about 1749. Oil on canvas, 52¼×42 3/16 in. (132.8×107 cm.)
Friends of American Art Collection, Goodman Fund, 53.462

MASTER STEWARD

Painted about 1749. Oil on canvas, 52¼×42¼ in. (132.8×107.4 cm.)
Friends of American Art Collection, Goodman Fund, 53.463

WOOD, Grant ~ *b. 1892 Anamosa, Ia. d. 1942 Iowa City, Ia.*

Grant Wood studied at the Minneapolis Handicraft Guild and at The Art Institute of Chicago. In 1920, he went to Paris, and in 1928, to Munich.

AMERICAN GOTHIC Illus. p. 382

Signed and dated: Grant Wood 1930. Oil on beaver board, 29⅞ × 24⅞ in. (76 × 63.3 cm.)
Friends of American Art Collection, 30.934

WORCESTER, Charles Henry ~ *b. 1864 Detroit. d. 1956 Chicago*

Charles H. Worcester served as a Trustee and Vice-President of the Art Institute, and in 1938 became Honorary President. Mr. Worcester, together with his wife, gave a large collection of paintings to the Institute.

LADY AT THE WINDOW

Painted probably about 1923. Oil on masonite, 16 × 20 in. (40.8 × 50.9 cm.)
Charles H. and Mary F. S. Worcester Collection, 47.120

WYANT, Alexander H. ~ *b. 1836 Port Washington, Ohio. d. 1892 New York*

Wyant was self-taught, but sought guidance from Inness. In 1865 he settled in New York, painting mostly in the Adirondacks and the Catskills.

LANDSCAPE

Painted about 1880, signed: A. H. Wyant. Oil on canvas, 18⅛ × 30 in. (46.2 × 76.3 cm.)
Cyrus Hall McCormick Fund, 47.26

YOUNG, Stark ~ *b. 1881 Como, Missouri*

APPARITION OF FLOWERS

Painted about 1944, signed: Stark Young. Oil on canvas, 24⅛ × 30⅛ in. (61.3 × 76.6 cm.)
Gift of Mr. and Mrs. J. B. Robertson, 47.34

ZAK, Eugène ~ *b. 1884 Mogilno, Russia. d. 1926 Paris*

Zak went to Paris in 1901, where he studied at the Ecole des Beaux-Arts.

THE SHEPHERD

Painted about 1910, signed: Eug. Zak. Oil on canvas, 46 × 32⅛ in. (116.9 × 81.6 cm.)
Arthur Jerome Eddy Memorial Collection, 31.519

Ref: New York, International Exhibition of Modern Art *(Armory Show), 1913, cat. no. 233; Chicago. Art Institute,* Catalogue of the Eddy Collection, *1922, cat. no. 67; Hartford, Conn., Wadsworth Atheneum,* An Exhibition of Literature and Poetry in Painting since 1850, *1933, cat. no. 76; Chicago. Art Institute,* A Century of Progress Exhibition, *1933, cat. no. 743*

ZAO, Wou-Ki ~ *b. 1920 Peiping*

The artist studied at the National School of Fine Arts in Hangchow. He has been in Paris since 1948.

THE WORLD AND THE DEER

Painted 1951–1952, signed: Zao Wou-Ki. Oil on canvas, 34¼×45 in. (87×114.4 cm.)
Gift of James W. Alsdorf, 54.1203

ZEEMAN, Reinier (Nooms) ~ *ca. 1623–1667 Amsterdam*

Zeeman worked most of his life in Amsterdam, and followed in the tradition of the great 17th century seascape painters.

COAST SCENE WITH SHIPPING

Painted probably mid-17th century. Oil on canvas, 21⅛×19⅛ in. (53.8×48.6 cm.)
Gift of Byron L. Smith, 90.40

The painting was attributed to Zeeman when a Van de Velde signature proved spurious.

Coll: Demidoff

ZEHETMAYR, Thomas ~ *1550–1623 Munich*

Very little is known of this artist, except that he established himself as a master painter in Munich in 1573, and that he was probably associated with Hans Mielich.

DOROTHEA HAFFNERIN

Painted 1575, inscribed: Dorothea Haffnerin, IERES ALTERS L. JAR ANO MDLXXV, and coat of arms, *griffin rampant dexter*. Oil on panel, 30⅜×24¼ in. (77.2×61.7 cm.)
Charles H. and Mary F. S. Worcester Collection, 44.427

Coll: Flerscheim (Frankfurt a. Main)

Ref: Chicago. Art Institute, Catalogue of the Worcester Collection, *1937, cat. no. 43*

ZOFFANY, Johann ~ *b. 1734 Frankfurt. d. 1810 London*

Zoffany came to London about 1761, where he painted portraits and conversation pieces.

FAMILY IN A ROOM

Painted about 1765. Oil on canvas, 28¼×36 in. (71.7×91.5 cm.)
Gift of Emily Crane Chadbourne, 51.205

The painting was attributed to Zoffany by William G. Constable.

ZOPPO, Marco ~ *b. 1433 Cento. d. 1478 Venice* (attributed to)

PIETA

Painted in the second half of the 15th century.
Tempera on panel, 28¼×21¾ in. (71.7×55.4 cm.)
Mr. and Mrs. Martin A. Ryerson Collection, 33.1037

This painting is a free copy after Tura's *Pietà* in the Museo Correr in Venice. It bears certain stylistic characteristics of Marco Zoppo.

Coll: Delaroff, Leningrad

Ref: Chicago. Art Institute, Bulletin *20: 55–6, 1926; Chicago. Art Institute,* A Century of Progress Exhibition, *1933, cat. no. 101;* Ibid., *1934, cat. no. 40; Van Marle,* Apollo *21: 12–3, 1935*

ZORN, Anders Leonard ~ *1850–1920 Mora, Sweden*

In 1893, the artist was sent to Chicago as a commissioner for Sweden to the World's Columbian Exposition. Here he became acquainted with Chicago society and particularly with Charles Deering, who made an important collection of Zorn's prints, which he later bequeathed to the Art Institute.

MRS. POTTER PALMER

Signed and dated: Zorn, Chicago, 1893. Oil on canvas, 101⅜×55¾ in. (257.6×141.6 cm.)
Potter Palmer Collection, 22.450

Mrs. Potter Palmer is painted in the gown and jewels she wore when she officially opened the Columbian Exposition.

Ref: Asplund, K., Zorn, *1921, p. 42; Boethius, G.,* Zorn, *1949, fig. 156*

MRS. JONATHAN YOUNG SCAMMON

Signed and dated: Zorn 1895. Oil on canvas, 32×25¾ in. (81.3×65.5 cm.)
Gift of Mrs. Jonathan Y. Scammon, 02.39

Mrs. Scammon (born Maria Sheldon) established the Scammon Lectures in 1901, with a bequest of a fund to the Art Institute to be used for lectures on the history of art.

Ref: Asplund, K., Zorn, *1921, p. 42; Boethius,* Zorn, *1949, p. 547*

NUDE GIRL IN DOORWAY

Painted about 1900, signed: Zorn. Oil on canvas, 20⅛×13½ in. (51.2×34.4 cm.)
Gift of Mrs. Richard E. Danielson and Mrs. Chauncey McCormick, 45.176

Ref: Boethius, G., Zorn, *1949, p. 549*

INTERIOR WITH NUDES

Signed and dated: Zorn 1905. Oil on canvas, 41½×32 in. (105.4×81.3 cm.)
Gift of Woodruff J. Parkers, 26.429

Ref: Chicago. Art Institute, A Century of Progress Exhibition, *1933, cat. no. 276; Boethius, G.,* Zorn, *1949, p. 551*

PORTRAIT OF A MAN

Signed and dated: Zorn 1901. Oil on canvas, 30×25 in. (76.3×63.6 cm.)
Anonymous Gift, 51.316

ZULOAGA, Ignacio ~ *b. 1870 Eibar, Spain. d. 1945 Madrid*

Though Zuloaga was self-taught, he carefully observed the work of the great Spanish painters of the past. He first exhibited at the Paris Salon of 1890.

THE ACTRESS CONSUELO

Painted in the early 1920s, signed: I. Zuloaga.
Oil on canvas, 81×57½ in. (205.7×146.1 cm.)
Wirt D. Walker Fund, 25.918

Ref: Chicago. Art Institute, A Century of Progress Exhibition, *1933, cat. no. 278*

ZURBARAN, Francisco de ~ *b. 1598 Fuente de Cantos. d. 1664 Madrid*

Zurbarán was influenced by a number of Spanish artists: in his early realistic period by Sanchéz-Cotán and Herrera; later by Velásquez and Ribera. Toward the end of his life, he admired the gentler style of Murillo.

CRUCIFIXION Illus. p. 104

Signed: Franco de Zurba fat 1627. Oil on canvas, 114½×65¼ in. (291×165.8 cm.)
Robert Alexander Waller Fund, 54.15 (Soria no. 225)

Coll: San Pablo (now the church of S. Magdalena), Seville

Ref: Cean Bermudez, Diccionario Historico de las mas illustres profesores de las bellas artes en España, *1800, pp. 47–50; Kehrer, H.,* Francisco de Zurbarán, *1918, p. 18; Soria, M. S.,* Gazette des Beaux-Arts, *ser. 6, vol. 25, March 1944, pp. 40, 41; Guinard, P.,* Archivo Español de Arte, *vol. 20, nos. 77–80, 1947, pp. 193, 194, 198, 199; Milicua, J.,* Archivo Español de Arte, *vol. 26, no. 103, July/September 1953, pp. 177–86;* Emporium, *vol. 122, August 1955, pp. 88–9; Soria, M. S.,* The Paintings of Zurbarán, *1955, p. 189, no. 225*

SAN ROMAN Illus. p. 101

Dated: 1638. Oil on canvas, 97×63 in. (246.5×185.4 cm.)
Gift of Mrs. Richard E. Danielson and Mrs. Chauncey McCormick, 47.793 (Soria no. 148)

In the painting appear San Román, Deacon of Caeserea, and the boy Barulas, both of whom were martyred at Antioch in A.D. 303. The canvas was once owned by the church of San Román in Seville; it was looted by Napoleon's general, Maréchal Soult, and was sold at a sale of his pictures in 1867.

Coll: San Román, Seville; Maréchal Soult (sale: cat. 1853, no. 28; cat. 1867, no. 6); Stchoukine, Moscow; Carvallo, Paris; Charles Deering

Ref: Ortiz de Zúñiga, Annales eclesiásticos, *Madrid, 1677, p. 73; Bermúdez,* Diccionario historico, *Madrid, 1800, p. 48; Kehrer, H.,* Zurbarán, *1918, pp. 82, 138, no. 40, 145; Guinard, P.,* Archivo Español de Arte *18: 263, 1946; Soria, M. S.,* Gazette des Beaux-Arts, *ser. 6, vol. 25, 1944, p. 155; Soria, M. S.,* The Paintings of Zurbarán, *1955, p. 169, no. 148*

ZURBARAN, Francisco de (attributed to) Illus. p. 97

STILL LIFE: FLOWERS AND FRUIT

Probably painted between 1633 and 1644. Oil on canvas, 32½×42¾ in. (82.6×108.6 cm.)
Wirt D. Walker Fund, 47.511 (Soria no. 178)

This composition is reminiscent of Zurbarán's only signed still life in the Bonacossi-Contini collection.

Coll: Madrazo; Marquis of Salamanca, Madrid

Ref: Chicago. Art Institute, Bulletin *42: 17, 1948; Soria, M. S.,* Gazette des Beaux-Arts, *ser. 6, vol. 25, March 1944, p. 164; Soria, M. S.,* Art in America *32: 128, 129, 1944; Seckel, H. P. G.,* Gazette des Beaux-Arts, *ser. 6, vol. 30, October/December 1946, pp. 288ff.;* Ibid., *ser. 6, vol. 31, January/February 1947, p. 62; Soria. M. S.,* The Paintings of Zurbarán, *1955, p. 177, no. 178*

ZURBARAN, Francisco de, Follower of

CHESTNUTS IN A BASKET

Painted about 1640. Oil on canvas, 25⅞×29⅞ in. (65.8×76 cm.)
A. A. Munger Collection, 34.389

This provincial still life shows the influence of Zurbarán in its careful design and rendering of surface textures.

Ref: Canton, S., Archivo Español *15: no. 52, July 1942, p. 232; Seckel, H. P. G., see* supra; *Sanchez-Canton, F. J.,* La Sensibilidad de Zurbaran, *1944, pp. 13, 14, pl. 2*

This book was designed by Suzette Morton Zurcher,
set in Bembo types, printed by Joh. Enschedé en Zonen, Haarlem
and bound by J. Brandt & Zn, Amsterdam, The Netherlands